SO-BAL-662

REVIEWING

PHYSICS

THE PHYSICAL SETTING

WITH SAMPLE EXAMINATIONS

SECOND EDITION

Judah Landa
Member New York State Regents Physics Committee
Coordinator of Physics
Midwood High School, Brooklyn, New York

David R. Kiefer
Former Assistant Principal for Physical Science
Midwood High School, Brooklyn, New York
Science Supervisor, Indian Hills High School
Oakland, New Jersey

AMSCO

Amsco School Publications, Inc.
315 Hudson Street / New York, N.Y. 10013

The publisher wishes to thank the following teachers who acted as reviewers:

Harold Kozak
Science Teacher
Fort Hamilton High School
Brooklyn, New York

Dr. Duncan Rogers Lee II
Science Teacher
Nyack High School
Upper Nyack, New York

Timothy M. Williamson
Science Teacher
Grand Island High School
Grand Island, New York

Text and Cover Design: Howard S. Leiderman
Composition and Art: Nesbitt Graphics, Inc.

Reading Comprehension Questions and *Science, Technology, and Society* features written by Christine Caputo.

Please visit our Web site at: *www.amscopub.com*

When ordering this book, please specify:
either **R 731 P** *or* REVIEWING PHYSICS: THE PHYSICAL SETTING, SECOND EDITION

ISBN: 0-87720-184-6

Copyright © 2002 by Amsco School Publications, Inc.

No part of this book may be reproduced in any form without written permission from the publisher.

Printed in the United States of America

2 3 4 5 6 7 8 9 10   08 07 06 05 04 03

Note to the Teacher

The newly revised, second edition books of this series—*Reviewing Biology: The Living Environment, Reviewing Earth Science: The Physical Setting, Reviewing Chemistry: The Physical Setting*, and *Reviewing Physics: the Physical Setting*—offer an innovative format that reviews the new, National Science Standards-based Core Curriculum. The chemistry and physics books also offer in the enrichment sections material that is covered in a college-preparatory science course. Each book is readily correlated with the standard textbooks for this level. The series is specifically geared to the needs of students who want to refresh their memory and review the material in preparation for final exams.

The text begins with a review of *Measurement and Mathematical Skills* that are useful to physics students. The remainder of the material in *Reviewing Physics: The Physical Setting, Second Edition* is divided into five chapters, each of which is subdivided into major topic sections followed by an enrichment section. The book is abundantly illustrated with clearly labeled drawings and diagrams that illuminate and reinforce the subject matter. Important science terms are **bold-faced** and defined in the text. Other terms that may be unfamiliar to students are *italicized* for emphasis. In addition, the large work-text format and open design make *Reviewing Physics: The Physical Setting, Second Edition* easy for students to read.

Within each chapter are several sets of multiple-choice questions, open-ended or constructed-response questions, and a reading comprehension question that test the student's knowledge and reasoning while provoking thought. Diagrams that aid in reviewing and testing the material often accompany questions. The more than 1,000 questions found in the text can be used for topic review throughout the year, as well as for exams and homework assignments. The tests at the back of the book can be used for final exams or practice for the final exam.

A section called *Laboratory Skills* follows the five chapters. This special section reviews the skills that all students should master in the course of completing one year of physics instruction at this level. *Reviewing Physics: The Physical Setting, Second Edition* also contains the latest edition of *Reference Tables and Charts*. There is a full Glossary, where students can find concise definitions of significant scientific terms. The extensive Index should be used by students to locate fuller text discussion of these and other physics terms.

Also included in this edition of *Reviewing Physics: The Physical Setting, Second Edition* are seven new *Science, Technology, and Society* features that explore current, controversial issues in physical science, technology, and society. Reading comprehension, constructed-response, and research questions presented at the end of each feature encourage students to evaluate the issues and to make their own decisions about the impact of science and technology on society, the environment, and their lives.

Contents

Measurement and Mathematical Skills

MEASUREMENT

Science is built upon observation and measurement. Measurement involves a comparison of an unknown quantity with known, standard units. Measurements are always inexact because they are subject to error.

Errors in Measurement

Factors that affect the accuracy of measurements include flaws in the method used to obtain the measurement, fluctuations in the environment, limitations of the instruments used, and human error. Measurement errors fall into two basic groups—systematic and random.

Systematic errors tend to be in one direction, either too high or too low. For example, if a thermometer reads 5°C instead of 0°C in an ice and water mixture, then all of its readings will be too high by 5°C. Systematic error can be reduced by checking the method used and adjusting, or calibrating, all instruments.

Random errors tend to produce readings that fluctuate; some readings are too high, some are too low. Such fluctuations are always present in measurements. For example, repeated measurements of temperature of a liquid might produce readings of 56.4°C, 56.5°C, and 56.2°C. Random error can be reduced by taking the average of a large number of measurements and by controlling environmental fluctuations.

Precision

Precision refers to the smallest decimal place obtained by a measurement. Units are always specified when giving the precision of a measurement.

Table M1

Measurement	Precision
143 m	1 m (the units place in meters)
4.8 g	0.1 g (the tenths place in grams)
24.962 s	0.001 s (the thousandths place in seconds)

The scale markings on an instrument determine the possible precision of measurements made with that instrument. A measurement may be *estimated* to one-tenth of the smallest interval printed on the scale. Thus, the last recorded digit in a number obtained by a measurement is usually an estimate based on a reading between the smallest intervals marked on the scale. For example, the smallest printed interval on a 10-cm ruler is 1 mm, or 0.1 cm (Figure M-1). The possible precision when using this ruler is one-tenth of 1 mm, or 0.01 cm. Such a ruler could be used to obtain a reading of 7.68 cm, with the last digit (8) as an estimate. A reading of 7.683 cm would be beyond the possible precision of a measurement with this ruler.

Significant Figures

Significant figures are those digits that are obtained properly and directly from an instrument,

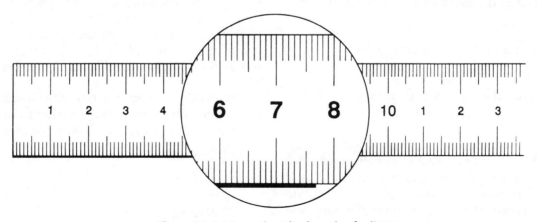

Figure M-1. Measuring the length of a line.

Rule	Example	Number of Significant Figures
1. Zeros located at the end of a number and to the right of a decimal point are significant. They indicate the precision possible with the instrument used.	3.0 g 12.3000 km 1.000 s 5.20 N	2 6 4 3
2. Zeros located between significant digits are significant.	30.9 V 402.06007 mm 1.030 ml	3 8 4 (rules 1 & 2)
3. Leading zeros are not significant. They may be included for clarity of format or to "hold place," but they are not the result of a measurement.	.042 kg 0.042 J 0.00000009 m 0.160 A 0.106 W 0.016 m/s 0.0010100 s	2 2 1 3 (rules 1 & 3) 3 (rules 2 & 3) 2 5 (rules 1, 2, & 3)
4. Zeros located at the end of a number and to the left of a decimal point are significant.	40. °C 3000. K 250,600. g	2 4 6 (rules 2 & 4)
5. Zeros located at the end of a number are not significant if they are not followed by a decimal point.	40 °C 3000 K 250,600 m	1 1 4 (rules 2 & 5)

including the final, estimated digit. In determining the significant figures in a measurement, keep in mind that any digit from 1 to 9 is always significant. The only digit that may not be significant is 0 since zeros are sometime used to "hold place." Table M2 gives rules for determining which zeros in a measurement are significant and which are not significant.

Accuracy

The **accuracy** of a measurement refers to the agreement, or closeness, of its value to the true or accepted value. Accuracy may be expressed in terms of **absolute error** or **percent error.** In both cases, the absolute value of the difference between the measured and accepted values (indicated by vertical lines) is used to obtain a positive answer.

Absolute error

$$= |\text{Measured value} - \text{Accepted value}|$$

Percent error

$$= \frac{|\text{Measured value} - \text{Accepted value}| \times 100\%}{\text{Accepted value}}$$

Sample Problem

1. The average of several measurements of the mass of an object is 48.60 g. Find the absolute error and percent error of this measurement if the actual mass of the object is 48.75 g.

Solution:

Absolute error $= |48.60\,\text{g} - 48.75\,\text{g}| = 0.15\,\text{g}$

Percent error $= \dfrac{|48.60\,\text{g} - 48.75\,\text{g}| \times 100\%}{48.75\,\text{g}}$

$= 0.31\%$

Rounding Off in Calculations

A chain is only as strong as its weakest link. Similarly, a calculated answer can only be as precise as the least precise measurement involved in the calculation. As a result, calculated answers must often be rounded off. If the digit to be dropped is less than 5, the digit to the left of it remains unchanged. For example, if 27.23 is rounded off to three significant figures, it becomes 27.2. If the digit to be dropped is 5 or more, the digit to the left of it is increased by 1; for example, 27.46 rounded off to three significant figures becomes 27.5.

In addition and subtraction, the answer must be rounded off to the same precision as the *least* precise number in the calculation. For example:

Addition:

```
   6.12  g
  18.3   g
+  0.044 g
  24.464 g = 24.5 g
```

In this calculation, 18.3 g is the least precise number—to the tenths place.

Subtraction:

$$48.3639 \text{ m}$$
$$- \underline{13.21 \quad \text{ m}}$$
$$35.1539 \text{ m} = 35.15 \text{ m}$$

Here, 13.21 m is the least precise number—to the hundredths place.

In multiplication and division, the answer must be rounded off to contain the same number of significant figures as the measurement with the *least* number of significant figures. For example:

Multiplication:

$$9.78 \text{ m}$$
$$\times \underline{1.4 \quad \text{ m}}$$
$$13.692 \text{ m}^2 = 14 \text{ m}^2$$

In this calculation, 1.4 m has the least number of significant digits—2.

Division:

$$\frac{180 \text{ g}}{5020.00 \text{ ml}} = 0.0358565 \text{ g/ml} = 0.036 \text{ g/ml}$$

Here, 180 g has the least number of significant digits—2.

Sample Problem

Sample Problem

2. Find the perimeter and area of the rectangle in Figure M-2.

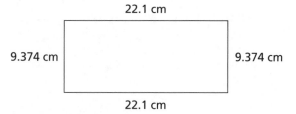

Figure M-2.

Solution:

Perimeter: The perimeter of a rectangle is equal to the sum of the lengths of the sides.

22.1 cm	(tenths)
9.374 cm	(thousandths)
22.1 cm	
+ 9.374 cm	

$$62.948 \text{ cm} = 62.9 \text{ cm} \text{ (rounded to tenths place)}$$

Area: The area of a rectangle is equal to its length multiplied by its width.

$$9.374 \text{ cm} \quad \text{(4 significant figures)}$$
$$\times \underline{22.1 \text{ cm}} \quad \text{(3 significant figures)}$$
$$207.1654 \text{ cm}^2 = 207 \text{ cm}^2$$
$$\text{(3 significant figures)}$$

Scientific Notation

In **scientific notation,** numbers are expressed in the form $A \times 10^n$, where the coefficient A is any number equal to or greater than 1 but less than 10 and the exponent n is an integer. Scientific notation is used to facilitate mathematical operations with very large and very small numbers and to indicate the number of significant figures in a measurement. All of the digits in the coefficient are significant. The value of n is determined by counting the number of decimal places that the decimal point in the original number must be moved to form A. If the decimal point of the original number is moved to the left, n is positive; if the decimal point is moved to the right, n is negative. For example:

93,000,000 m becomes 9.3×10^7 m

(The decimal point is moved 7 places to the left.)

0.0002040 g becomes 2.040×10^{-4} g

(The decimal point is moved 4 places to the right.)

If 93,000,000 m represented a measurement that is precise to the thousands place, only the first five digits are significant. This cannot be expressed in decimal form, but in scientific notation it is possible to indicate *any* desired number of significant figures. The number can be written as 9.3000×10^7 m.

When adding or subtracting numbers in scientific notation, the value of n for each number in the calculation must be made identical before the coefficients are added or subtracted. The resulting number must be adjusted for correct precision and form. For example:

Addition:

$$(3.2 \times 10^4) + (4.9 \times 10^3)$$
$$= (3.2 \times 10^4) + (0.49 \times 10^4)$$
$$= 3.69 \times 10^4 = 3.7 \times 10^4$$

Subtraction:

$$(1.254 \times 10^{-1}) - (8.5 \times 10^{-2})$$
$$= (1.254 \times 10^{-1}) - (0.85 \times 10^{-1})$$
$$= 0.404 \times 10^{-1}$$
$$= 0.40 \times 10^{-1} = 4.0 \times 10^{-2}$$

When multiplying numbers in scientific notation, multiply the coefficient and add the exponents. The product of the coefficients should then be rounded off to the correct number of significant figures. For example:

$$(8.12 \times 10^2) \times (2.13 \times 10^5)$$

$$= 17.2956 \times 10^7$$

$$= 17.3 \times 10^7 = 1.73 \times 10^8$$

When dividing numbers in scientific notation, divide the coefficient of the numerator by the coefficient of the denominator and subtract the exponent of the denominator from the exponent of the numerator. For example:

$$\frac{(6 \times 10^9)}{(8.75 \times 10^{12})} = 0.6857143 \times 10^{-3}$$

$$= 0.7 \times 10^{-3} = 7 \times 10^{-4}$$

Units and Equations

In mathematical calculations, units are treated like algebraic quantities. Units must appear in every step of a calculation, including the answer. For example:

$$2\,m^2 + 3\,m^2 = 5\,m^2$$

$$1.0\,km \times 3.0\,km \times 4.0\,km = 12\,km^3$$

$$8.0\,kg \times (3.0\,m/s)^2 = 8.0\,kg \times 9.0\,m^2/s^2$$

$$= 72\,kg \cdot m^2/s^2$$

$$\sqrt{\frac{64\,m}{32\,m/s^2}} = \sqrt{2.0\,s^2} = 1.4\,s$$

In a formula, the units on either side of the equal side must be equivalent. In some cases, it is necessary to convert some units to others before this equivalence can be demonstrated. When this is the case, three steps should be used:

1. Obtain needed relationships between units.
2. Substitute units with their equivalences.
3. Simplify.

Sample Problem

3. Given that d is the distance in meters, t is the time in seconds, v is the speed in meters/second, and a is the acceleration in meters/second^2, demonstrate that the formula $d = vt + \frac{1}{2}at^2$ is balanced as far as the units are concerned.

Solution:

$$d = vt + \tfrac{1}{2}at^2$$

$$\text{meters} = \left(\frac{\text{meters}}{\text{seconds}}\right)(\text{seconds})$$

$$+ \left(\frac{\text{meters}}{\text{seconds}^2}\right)(\text{seconds})^2$$

$$\text{meters} = \text{meters} + \text{meters}$$

$$\text{meters} = \text{meters}$$

CHAPTER 1

Mechanics

The branch of physics known as **mechanics** deals with motion and forces. Within this branch are **kinematics**, the study of motion; **statics**, the study of forces on stationary objects; and **dynamics**, the study of the relationship between forces and motion.

Units of Measurement

Physicists use **SI (International System)** units, and extension of the **metric system,** for standards of measurement. Three physical quantities are basic to the study of mechanics: length, time, and mass. The **fundamental units** for these quantities are the **meter** (m), the **second** (s), and the **kilogram** (kg), respectively. Units that consist of combinations of the fundamental units are called **derived units.** For example, the unit of force, the newton, is a derived unit which is equivalent to a kilogram meter per second squared (kg · m/s^2).

Scalar and Vector Quantities

Most of the quantities that we measure in daily life are **scalar quantities,** such as 9.3 seconds, 16°C, and 15 meters. A scalar quantity can be expressed by a number and an appropriate unit. It has magnitude but no direction.

Other physical quantities, called **vector quantities,** have a specific direction as well as magnitude. For example, we may need to specify that a car has traveled 50 km due south, that a plane is located 75 m southeast of the runway, or that a force of 20 newtons acts to the right rather than to the left. Such quantities are represented by **vectors.**

Vector quantities can be distinguished from scalar quantities either by placing an arrow over the symbol for the vector quantity or by printing it in **bold** type. In this book, vector quantities are represented by bold letters. When a symbol represents only the magnitude of the vector, it is not bold. Vector quantities are represented geometrically by arrows. The length of the arrow represents the magnitude of the vector quantity (based on a specified scale), and the direction of the arrow is the direction of the vector quantity. For example, Figure 1-1 represents a displacement of 5 meters (using the

given conversion scale) that is directed 40° from the horizontal. Such arrows are called **vectors.**

Figure 1-1. Representation of a vector.

Vector Addition

The sum of two or more vectors is not the sum of their magnitudes. Instead, the sum of two or more vectors is another vector called the **resultant.** Like all vectors, the resultant has a magnitude and a direction. There are several methods for determining a resultant.

The Head-to-Tail Method

In the **head-to-tail method** of vector addition, a diagram is drawn in which the vectors are positioned in series—that is, the tail of one vector is placed at the head of the other vector. Figure 1-2 shows a head-to-tail diagram of two vectors **A** and **B.** The resultant of these two vectors, labeled **C,** is obtained by drawing a new vector from the tail of the first vector to the head of the last. The magnitude of **C** is found by measuring the length of **C** and using the given conversion scale. The direction of **C** can be found with a protractor.

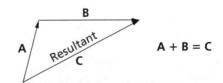

Figure 1-2. The head-to-tail method of vector addition.

The Parallelogram Method

To use the **parallelogram method** of vector addition, begin by drawing a diagram in which the tails of the two vectors to be added (**A** and **B**) are placed at a common point. Then a parallelogram is constructed with the two vectors as adjacent sides (Figure 1-3). The resultant vector **C** is the diagonal of the parallelogram drawn from the point where the tails meet. As with the head-to-tail method, the most direct way of finding the magnitude and direction of the resultant is with a ruler and protractor. Using the specified conversion scale—such as 1 cm = 1 newton (in the case of force vectors), or 1 cm = 1 m/s (in the case of velocity vectors)—the magnitude of the resultant is found by measuring its length, and its direction is found by measuring the angle between the resultant and any chosen direction.

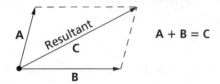

Figure 1-3. The parallelogram method of vector addition.

Mathematical methods of vector addition are particularly convenient for cases involving 0°, 180°, and 90° angles between the vectors to be added. Consider two vectors, one with a magnitude of 5 m and the other with a magnitude of 2 m, and find their resultant at these angles.

At 0°. The simplest case of vector addition occurs when the two vectors to be added point in the same direction (Figure 1-4). In this case, the head-to-tail method must be used. The magnitude of the resultant is simply the sum of the magnitudes of the two vectors (2 m + 5 m, or 7 m), and the direction of the resultant is the same as the direction of the two vectors.

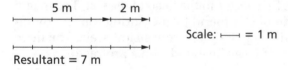

Figure 1-4. Vectors added at 0°.

At 180°. In this case the vectors are pointing in opposite directions and again, the head-to-tail method must be used. Suppose the vector with a magnitude of 5 m points to the right, and the vector with a magnitude of 2 m points to the left. Using the head-to-tail method, we find that the magnitude of the resultant is equal to the difference of the magnitudes of the two vectors (5 m − 2 m, or 3 m), and the direction of the resultant is the direction of the larger vector—in this case to the right (Figure 1-5).

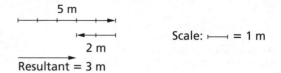

Figure 1-5. Vectors added at 180°.

At 90°. If the vectors are at a 90° angle from one to another, the resultant can be found by using either the head-to-tail method or the parallelogram method. Once the resultant has been drawn using one of these methods, its magnitude can be calculated by using the **Pythagorean theorem,** since the two vectors to be added and their resultant form a right triangle (Figure 1-6). The resultant is the hypotenuse of the triangle. The Pythagorean theorem states that the square of the hypotenuse of a right triangle is equal to the sum of the squares of the other two sides. In our case we can write

$$R^2 = (5 \text{ m})^2 + (2 \text{ m})^2 = 29 \text{ m}^2$$
$$R = \sqrt{29 \text{ m}^2} = 5.4 \text{ m}$$

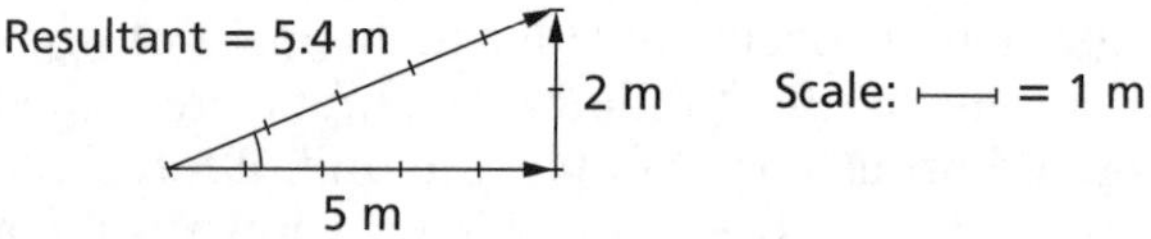

Resultant = 5.4 m   2 m   Scale: ⊢——⊣ = 1 m

5 m

Figure 1-6. Vectors added at 90°.

The direction of the resultant can be found with a protractor or by using certain trigonometric operations. If the vector with a magnitude of 5 m points due east and the vector with a magnitude of 2 m points due north, the direction of the resultant is approximately 22° north of east.

The magnitude of the resultant of any two vectors is a maximum when the vectors point in the same direction—that is, with a 0° angle between them. It is a minimum when the vectors point in opposite directions—with a 180° angle between them. For vectors at angles between 0° and 180°, the magnitude of the resultant lies between the maximum and minimum values. As the angle between two vectors increases from 0° to 180°, their resultant decreases from its maximum to its minimum value.

Resolution of Vectors

In the previous section we learned how two or more vectors can be added to obtain the resultant. The **resolution of vectors** is the reverse procedure: a single vector is regarded as the resultant of two or more vectors, called the **component**

vectors, which must be determined. A vector can be resolved into an infinite number of components. Figure 1-7 shows a vector **R** resolved into four components, **A, B, C,** and **D.**

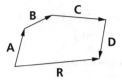

Figure 1-7. Resolution for vector **R** into four components: **A** + **B** + **C** + **D** = **R.**

It is often useful to resolve a vector into two perpendicular components. Consider a force vector with a magnitude of 60. N, directed 30° from the horizontal. Let us resolve this vector into two components—one horizontal and the other vertical. The first step is to draw the 60.-N vector, making sure, with a ruler and protractor and using the appropriate conversion scale, that the length of the vector represents 60. N and its direction is 30° from the horizontal (Figure 1-8).

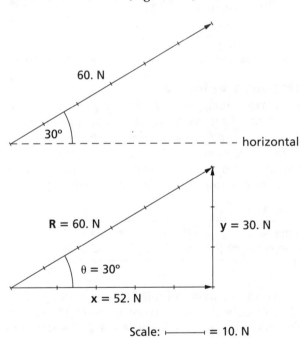

Scale: ⊢————⊣ = 10. N

Figure 1-8. Resolution of vector **R** into two perpendicular components.

The next step is to draw a vertical line through the head of the vector and a horizontal line through the tail of the vector, forming a right triangle. The 60.-N vector to be resolved is now the hypotenuse, and its vertical and horizontal components are the legs of the triangle.

Finally, we measure the legs of the triangle and, using the specified scale, determine the magnitudes of the vertical and horizontal components. In this case, the horizontal component has a magnitude of 52 N and the vertical component has a magnitude of 30. N.

Another way to determine the magnitude of the vertical and horizontal components is by using trigonometry. We know from trigonometry that cos θ is equal to the magnitude of the adjacent leg divided by the magnitude of the hypotenuse. Therefore, the magnitude of the horizontal component can be found by using the formula

$$\cos \theta = \frac{x}{R}$$

where x is the magnitude of the horizontal component, R is the magnitude of the resultant and θ is the angle between them. In the example, the horizontal component becomes

$$\cos 30° = \frac{x}{60. \text{ N}}$$
$$x = (60. \text{ N})(0.866) = 52 \text{ N}$$

Similarly, sin θ is equal to the magnitude of the opposite leg divided by the hypotenuse. Thus, the magnitude of the vertical component can be found by using the formula

$$\sin \theta = \frac{y}{R}$$

where **y** is the magnitude of the vertical component. In the example, the vertical component becomes

$$\sin 30° = \frac{y}{60. \text{ N}}$$
$$y = (60. \text{ N})(0.500) = 30. \text{ N}$$

Displacement

Displacement is a vector quantity, symbolized by **d,** indicating a change of position in a particular direction. An object's displacement vector is always a straight line drawn from the object's initial position to the object's final position no matter what the object's actual path was between these two points (Figure 1-9). The magnitude of the displacement vector represents the shortest distance between the two points. The actual distance the object has traveled is a scalar quantity that represents the length of its path. For example, a boomerang may be thrown a distance of several meters. If it returns to its original starting point, however, the magnitude of its displacement is zero. If the path of an object consists of several displacement vectors, its total displacement vector is the resultant of all the various displacement vectors.

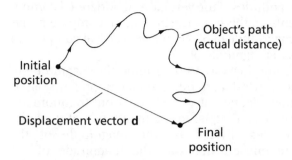

Figure 1-9. Displacement.

1. A bird flies 6 km east, then 4 km west. Find the total distance traveled and displacement after this flight.

Solution: The scalar distance traveled is 6 km + 4 km, or 10 km. To determine the displacement the head-to-tail method of vector addition must be used (see Figure 1-10). The total displacement vector is 2 km east. It is the resultant of the two displacement vectors.

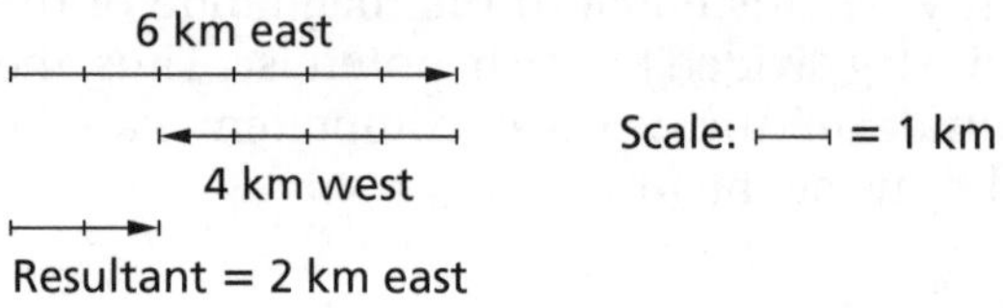

6 km east

4 km west

Scale: ⊢——⊣ = 1 km

Resultant = 2 km east

Figure 1-10.

KINEMATICS

Displacement vectors are the basis of two other important vector quantities, velocity and acceleration. Together, these three vectors are used to describe the motion of an object in space.

Velocity and Speed

Velocity is a vector quantity defined as the change in displacement per unit time. This is stated mathematically as

$$v = \frac{\Delta d}{\Delta t}$$

where Δd is the change in displacement that occurs during the time interval Δt. **Speed** is a scalar quantity equal to the magnitude of the velocity vector. **Average speed** is defined as the distance traveled per unit time and is symbolized by $\bar{v}$.

$$\bar{v} = \frac{\text{total distance}}{\text{total time}}$$

The units for velocity, speed, and average speed are meters per second (m/s).

2. A car travels 2.1 km south in 7.0 minutes. Find its velocity in meters/second.
   Solution:

   $\Delta d = 2.1 \text{ km} \times 1000 \text{ m/km} = 2100 \text{ m south}$

   $\Delta t = 7.0 \text{ min} \times 60 \text{ s/min} = 420 \text{ s}$

   $v = \frac{\Delta d}{\Delta t} = \frac{2100 \text{ m}}{420 \text{ s}} = 5.0 \text{ m/s south}$

3. A car travels 600. m one way with a speed of 40. m/s and then travels 600. m in another way at 20. m/s. What is the car's average speed? (Caution: The answer is not 30. m/s.)
   Solution:

   $$\bar{v} = \frac{\text{total distance}}{\text{total time}} = \frac{1200. \text{ m}}{\Delta t}$$

   The time for trip one is

   $$\Delta t_1 = \frac{600. \text{ m}}{40. \text{ m/s}} = 15 \text{ s}$$

   The time for trip two is

   $$\Delta t_2 = \frac{600. \text{ m}}{20. \text{ m/s}} = 30. \text{ s}$$

   $$\bar{v} = \frac{1200. \text{ m}}{45 \text{ s}} = 27 \text{ m/s}$$

Uniform Velocity

Uniform velocity occurs when the speed and the direction of a moving object are constant. Table 1-1 lists the displacements from the starting point at various times for an object moving with uniform velocity. Note that for every second that passes, there is an equal change in the displacement.

Table 1-1

Time (s)	0	1	2	3	4	5	6	7
Displacement (m)	0	3	6	9	12	15	18	21

Using the data in Table 1-1, the velocity of the object can be found from any of its d and t values. For instance, at $t = 0$ s and $t = 4$ s, $d = 0$ m and $d = 12$ m, respectively. Plugging these values into the equation for velocity, we obtain

$$v = \frac{\Delta d}{\Delta t} = \frac{d_f - d_i}{t_f - t_i} = \frac{12 \text{ m} - 0 \text{ m}}{4 \text{ s} - 0 \text{ s}} = 3 \text{ m/s}$$

The same velocity will be found using any of the other pairs of data. For instance, at $t = 1$ and $t = 6$, $d = 3$ m and $d = 18$ m, respectively. Thus,

$$v = \frac{\Delta d}{\Delta t} = \frac{d_f - d_i}{t_f - t_i} = \frac{18 \text{ m} - 3 \text{ m}}{6 \text{ s} - 1 \text{ s}}$$

$$= \frac{15 \text{ m}}{5 \text{ s}} = 3 \text{ m/s}$$

When all the data pairs are graphed, we obtain the typical displacement-time or *d-t* graph for an object moving at uniform velocity—a straight line with a constant slope Figure 1-11. The slope of the line is equal to the magnitude of the object's velocity.

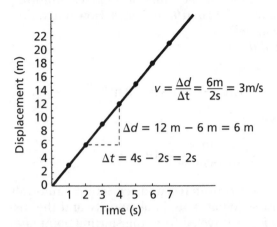

Figure 1-11. Slope equals velocity;

$$\frac{\Delta d}{\Delta t} = \frac{6\ m}{2\ s} = 3\ m/s.$$

Interpreting *d-t* Graphs

The *d-t* graph representing the motion of an object moving with uniform velocity is always a straight line.

Figure 1-12 is the *d-t* graph for an object at rest. As time changes there is no change in the object's position. An object at rest is represented by a line whose slope equals zero.

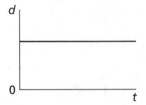

Figure 1-12.

Figure 1-13 represents two objects moving at different uniform velocities. Since the slope of *d-t* graph is equal to the velocity, the faster object is represented by the line with the steeper slope.

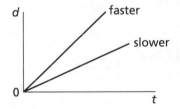

Figure 1-13.

Figure 1-14 represents uniform velocity, but the slope of the line is negative. This means that **d**

is decreasing with time and the object is moving toward (rather than away from) the starting point.

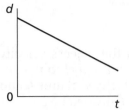

Figure 1-14.

The *d-t* graph in Figure 1-15 is not a straight line and represents nonuniform velocity. The slope increases with time, indicating that the object's speed is increasing as time goes by.

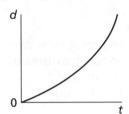

Figure 1-15.

These graphs may be combined to describe the entire journey of an object. For example, in Figure 1-16 an object is initially at rest and remains motionless until time t_1. The object then accelerates until time t_2, after which its velocity is uniform until t_3. Its velocity then jumps to a higher value, and remains constant until time t_4. The object then decelerates (the slope decreases) to a stop and remains at rest between times t_5 and t_6. Finally, the object reverses direction and returns to its starting point with uniform velocity.

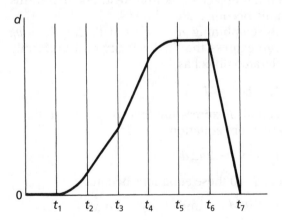

Figure 1-16.

Acceleration

Acceleration is a vector quantity defined as the time-rate of change of velocity. Acceleration is denoted by **a** and is expressed mathematically as

$$a = \frac{\Delta v}{\Delta t} = \frac{v_f - v_i}{t_f - t_i}$$

where $\Delta \mathbf{v}$ is the change in the object's velocity during the time interval Δt. It is equal to the difference between the final velocity $\mathbf{v_f}$ at time t_f and the initial velocity $\mathbf{v_i}$ at time t_i divided by Δt.

The unit for acceleration is m/s/s (meters per second per second). This indicates that acceleration is the change in velocity (in m/s) per unit time (in s). The standard practice is to combine the time units and report acceleration in m/s² (meters per second squared).

Uniform Acceleration

An object whose velocity is changing by a fixed amount per second is said to be **accelerating uniformly.** The average velocity $\overline{v}$ of an object undergoing uniform acceleration can be found from the formula

$$\overline{v} = \frac{v_i + v_f}{2}$$

This expression provides a formula for finding the total distance traveled by an object during uniformly accelerated motion:

$$\Delta d = \overline{v} \Delta t$$

This distance can also be expressed as a function of initial velocity, acceleration, and time.

$$\Delta d = v_i \Delta t + \tfrac{1}{2}a(\Delta t)^2.$$

When the object starts from rest, $v_i = 0$ and this formula becomes $\Delta d = \tfrac{1}{2}a(\Delta t)^2$.

By combining $a = \Delta v/\Delta t$ with $\Delta v = v_f - v_i$, we can express the final velocity of a uniformly accelerated object as

$$v_f = v_i + a\Delta t$$

We can also express the final velocity as a time-independent equation:

$$v_f^2 = v_i^2 + 2a\Delta d$$

When $v_i = 0$ these equations become

$$v_f = a\,\Delta t \quad \text{and} \quad v_f^2 = 2a\,\Delta d$$

Sample Problems

4. A racing car increases its speed at a uniform rate from 30 m/s to 40 m/s in 5 s. Find its acceleration.

Solution:

$$\Delta v = v_f - v_i = 40 \text{ m/s} - 30 \text{ m/s} = 10 \text{ m/s}$$

$$a = \frac{\Delta v}{\Delta t} = \frac{10 \text{ m/s}}{5 \text{ s}} = 2 \text{ m/s}^2$$

5. A cart moving at 9 m/s decelerates uniformly at the rate of 0.16 m/s² to 6 m/s. How much time has elapsed?

Solution:

$$\Delta v = v_f - v_i$$
$$= 6 \text{ m/s} - 9 \text{ m/s} = -3 \text{ m/s}$$

$$\Delta t = \frac{\Delta v}{a}$$

$$= \frac{-3 \text{ m/s}}{-0.16 \text{ m/s}^2} = 19 \text{ s}$$

6. A jet starts from rest and accelerates uniformly at 3 m/s². What is its final velocity and the distance it has traveled from the starting point after 20 s?

Solution:

$$v_f = a\,\Delta t$$
$$= (3 \text{ m/s}^2)(20 \text{ s}) = 60 \text{ m/s}$$

$$\Delta d = \tfrac{1}{2}a(\Delta t)^2$$
$$= \tfrac{1}{2}(3 \text{ m/s}^2)(20 \text{ s})^2 = 600 \text{ m}$$

7. A plane must achieve a speed of 95 m/s to take off. If the runway is 350 m long, what acceleration is required?

Solution:

$$v_f^2 = 2a\,\Delta d$$
$$(95 \text{ m/s})^2 = 2a(350 \text{ m})$$

$$a = \frac{9025 \text{ m}^2/\text{s}^2}{700 \text{ m}} = 13 \text{ m/s}^2$$

8. An object accelerates uniformly from 12 m/s to 40 m/s in 7.0 s. How far has it traveled during this interval?

Solution:

Method I
Find a, then find Δd

$$a = \frac{\Delta v}{\Delta t}$$

$$= \frac{40. \text{ m/s} - 12 \text{ m/s}}{7.0 \text{ s}} = 4.0 \text{ m/s}^2$$

$$\Delta d = v_i \Delta t + \tfrac{1}{2}a(\Delta t)^2$$

$$= (12 \text{ m/s})(7.0 \text{ s}) + \tfrac{1}{2}(4.0 \text{ m/s}^2)(7.0 \text{ s})^2$$

$$= 84 \text{ m} + 98 \text{ m} = 180 \text{ m}$$

Method II
Find $\bar{v}$, then find Δd

$$\bar{v} = \frac{v_i + v_f}{2}$$

$$= \frac{12 \text{ m/s} + 40. \text{ m/s}}{2} = 26 \text{ m/s}$$

$$\Delta d = \bar{v}t$$

$$= (26 \text{ m/s})(7.0 \text{ s}) = 180 \text{ m}$$

Accelerated Motion Graphs

The velocity-time data in Table 1-2 for an object accelerating uniformly from rest show that there are equal increments in velocity for equal increments of time.

Table 1-2

Time (s)	0	1.0	2.0	3.0	4.0	5.0	6.0	7.0
Velocity (m/s)	0	1.5	3.0	4.5	6.0	7.5	9.0	10.5

The object's acceleration can be obtained by dividing the change in velocity Δv between any two points in time by the corresponding change in time Δt. Thus

$$a = \frac{\Delta v}{\Delta t} = \frac{(9.0 \text{ m/s} - 3.0 \text{ m/s})}{(6.0 \text{ s} - 2.0 \text{ s})} = 1.5 \text{ m/s}^2$$

When all the data pairs are graphed, we obtain the typical *v-t* graph for an object undergoing uniform acceleration: a straight line with a constant slope equal to the acceleration (Figure 1-17).

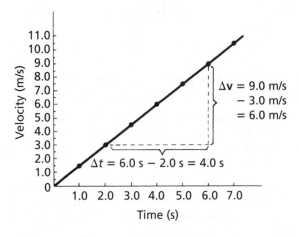

Figure 1-17. Slope equals acceleration;

$$a = \frac{\Delta v}{\Delta t} = \frac{6.0 \text{ m/s}}{4.0 \text{ s}} = 1.5 \text{ m/s}^2$$

The *d-t* (displacement-time) data for this object can be calculated by using the formula $\Delta d = v_i \Delta t + \frac{1}{2}a(\Delta t)^2$ with $v_i = 0$ and $a = 1.5 \text{ m/s}^2$. When these data are graphed, we obtain the typi-

cal *d-t* graph for an object undergoing uniform acceleration: a parabola (Figure 1-18). The slope of a line tangent to the **d**-*t* graph at any point is equal to the **instantaneous velocity** at that point.

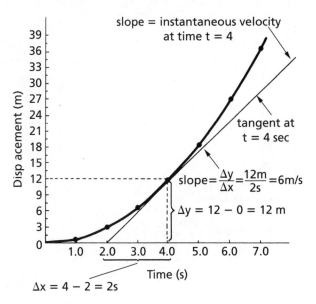

Figure 1-18.

Figure 1-19 represents an object traveling with uniform velocity. The slope of the *v-t* graph is equal to zero, indicating no acceleration.

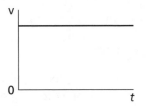

Figure 1-19.

In Figure 1-20, the straight line has a negative slope, indicating that the object is decelerating uniformly.

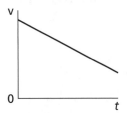

Figure 1-20.

In Figure 1-21, an object decelerates uniformly, until it comes to a stop upon reaching the x-axis, when $v = 0$. Then it reverses direction (v is negative) and travels at ever increasing speed.

The area under a *v-t* graph represents the distance an object has traveled. Figure 1-22 illus-

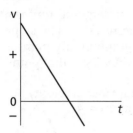

Figure 1-21.

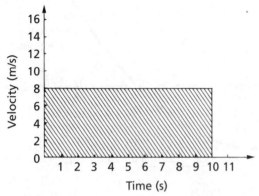

Figure 1-22.

trates the simplest case in which the velocity is constant throughout the given time interval.

$$\begin{aligned}
\text{area} &= (\text{base})(\text{height}) \\
&= (\text{time})(\text{velocity}) \\
&= \text{distance} \\
&= (8 \text{ s})(10 \text{ m/s}) = 80 \text{ m}
\end{aligned}$$

QUESTIONS

1. The average speed of a runner in a 400.-meter race is 8.0 meters per second. How long did it take the runner to complete the race?   (1) 80. s   (2) 50. s   (3) 40. s   (4) 32. s

2. Which graph best represents the relationship between velocity and time for an object that accelerates uniformly for 2 seconds, then moves at a constant velocity for 1 second, and finally decelerates for 3 seconds?

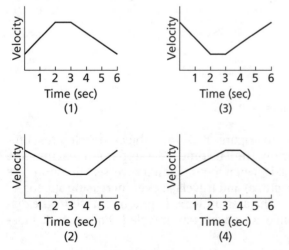

3. The graph below represents the motion of an object traveling in a straight line as a function of time. What is the average speed of the object during the first 4 seconds?   (1) 1 m/s   (2) 2 m/s   (3) 0.5 m/s   (4) 0 m/s

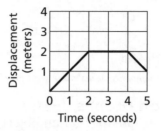

4. Which statement about the movement of an object with zero acceleration is true?   (1) The object must be at rest.   (2) The object must be slowing down.   (3) The object may be speeding up.   (4) The object may be in motion.

5. Which graph represents an object moving at a constant speed for the entire time interval?

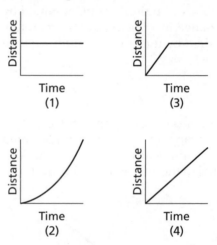

6. Which term represents a fundamental unit? (1) watt   (2) newton   (3) joule   (4) meter

7. An object travels for 8.00 seconds with an average speed of 160. meters per second. The distance traveled by the object is   (1) 20.0 m   (2) 200. m (3) 1,280 m   (4) 2,460 m

8. An object is displaced 12 meters to the right and then 16 meters upward. The magnitude of the resultant displacement is   (1) 1.3 m   (2) 4.0 m (3) 20 m   (4) 28 m

9. An object moves a distance of 10 meters in 5 seconds. The average speed of the object is (1) 0.5 m/s   (2) 2.0 m/s   (3) 40 m/s   (4) 50 m/s

10. The graph following represents the relationship between velocity and time for an object moving in a straight line. What is the acceleration of the object?   (1) 0 m/s^2 (2) 5 m/s^2 (3) 3 m/s^2 (4) 15 m/s^2

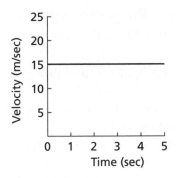

11. Acceleration is a vector quantity that represents the time-rate of change in (1) momentum (2) velocity (3) distance (4) energy

12. A moving body must undergo a change of (1) velocity (2) acceleration (3) position (4) direction

13. The graph shows the relationship between speed and time for two objects, *A* and *B*. Compared with the acceleration of object *B*, the acceleration of object *A* is (1) one-third as great (2) twice as great (3) three times as great (4) the same

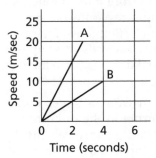

Base your answers to questions 14 through 19 on the graph below, which represents the relationship between speed and time for an object in motion along a straight line.

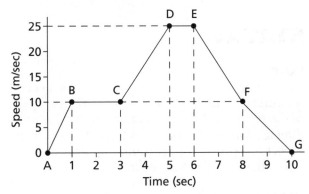

14. What is the acceleration of the object during the time interval $t = 3$ s to $t = 5$ s? (1) 5.0 m/s² (2) 7.5 m/s² (3) 12.5 m/s² (4) 17.5 m/s²

15. What is the average speed of the object during the time interval $t = 6$ s to $t = 8$ s (1) 7.5 m/s (2) 10 m/s (3) 15 m/s (4) 17.5 m/s

16. What is the total distance traveled by the object during the first 3 seconds? (1) 15 m (2) 20 m (3) 25 m (4) 30 m

17. During which interval is the object's acceleration the greatest? (1) *AB* (2) *CD* (3) *DE* (4) *EF*

18. During the interval $t = 8$ s to $t = 10$ s, the speed of the object is (1) zero (2) increasing (3) decreasing (4) constant, but not zero

19. What is the maximum speed reached by the object during the 10 seconds of travel? (1) 10 m/s (2) 25 m/s (3) 150 m/s (4) 250 m/s

Base your answers to questions 20 through 24 on the accompanying graph, which represents the motions of four cars on a straight road.

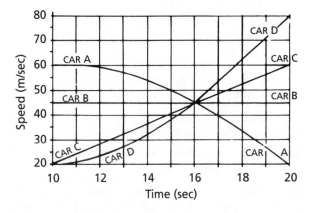

20. The speed of car *C* at time $t = 20$ s is closest to (1) 60 m/s (2) 45 m/s (3) 3.0 m/s (4) 600 m/s

21. Which car has zero acceleration? (1) *A* (2) *B* (3) *C* (4) *D*

22. Which car is decelerating? (1) *A* (2) *B* (3) *C* (4) *D*

23. Which car moves the greatest distance in the time interval $t = 10$ s to $t = 16$ s? (1) *A* (2) *B* (3) *C* (4) *D*

24. Which graph best represents the relationship between distance and time for car *C*?

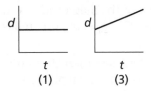

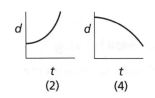

Base your answers to questions 25 through 29 on the four graphs below, which represent the relationship between speed and time of four different objects, *A*, *B*, *C*, and *D*.

25. Which object was slowing down?   (1) *A*   (2) *B*   (3) *C*   (4) *D*

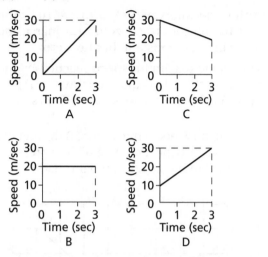

26. Which object was neither accelerating nor decelerating?   (1) *A*   (2) *B*   (3) *C*   (4) *D*

27. Which object traveled the greatest distance in the 3.0-second interval?   (1) *A*   (2) *B*   (3) *C*   (4) *D*

28. Which object had the greatest acceleration?   (1) *A*   (2) *B*   (3) *C*   (4) *D*

29. Compared with the average velocity of object *A*, the average velocity of object *D* is   (1) less   (2) greater   (3) the same

30. What is the magnitude of the vertical component of the velocity vector shown below?

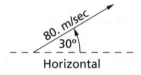

(1) 10. m/s   (2) 69 m/s   (3) 30. m/s   (4) 40. m/s

31. The maximum number of components that a single force may be resolved into is   (1) one   (2) two   (3) three   (4) unlimited

32. Which quantity has both magnitude and direction?   (1) distance   (2) speed   (3) mass   (4) velocity

33. If a man walks 17 meters east then 17 meters south, the magnitude of the man's displacement is   (1) 17 m   (2) 24 m   (3) 30. m   (4) 34 m

Thinking and Analyzing

34. How do fundamental units of measurement differ from derived units?

35. What is a scalar quantity? Give an example.

36. How do vector quantities differ from scalar quantities?

37. Explain how the resultant is found using the head-to-tail method of vector addition.

38. How is the resultant of two vectors found using the parallelogram method?

39. How is the resolution of vectors different from vector addition?

40. What is a displacement vector?

41. Describe the relationship between speed and velocity.

42. What are the characteristics of uniform velocity?

43. A cyclist's distance from an intersection is provided by the relationship $d = 4t + 10$, where d is the distance in meters and t is the time in seconds. Construct a table consisting of two columns, time and distance. Then provide five different distance-time pairs of data for the cyclist.

44. You are located 40. m from a telephone pole when you begin running away from the pole at the uniform rate of 5.0 m/s. Plot a distance-time graph for the first twenty seconds of your run. Base the graph on the *d-t* data you obtain for each even-numbered second.

45. A car located 150 m from a street corner moves away from the corner at the uniform rate of 30. m/s. After maintaining this velocity for 10. s, it decelerates to a stop in 5.0 s. It then rests for another 5.0 s, then accelerates away from the corner at the rate of 2.0 m/s² for 10. s. Construct a velocity-time graph representing the motion of the car for the entire trip.

STATICS

Force

Force is defined as a push or a pull. It is a vector quantity with magnitude and direction. We speak of the downward force of gravity, or the upwardly directed force of buoyancy. A force may act on an object at a distance, without physical contact. The unit of force is the **newton** (N).

Addition of Concurrent Forces

When more than one force acts upon an object at the same time and at the same point, the forces are said to be **concurrent**. The effect on the object is the same as if it were acted upon by the resultant of the concurrent forces. Vector addition must be used to find the resultant, or **net force**.

If two tractors pull on a tree, each with 5000. N of force and with an angle of 60° between their ropes (Figure 1-23), the tree experiences an applied force equal to the resultant of these two forces. Since concurrent forces share a common vertex, it is easiest to find the resultant by using the parallelogram method of vector addition. The resultant of the forces applied by the tractors on the tree has a magnitude of 8660.N (not 5000. N + 5000. N), and its direction is 30° from either of the force vectors.

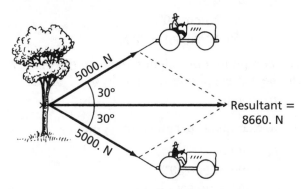

Figure 1-23. Addition of concurrent forces.

From the previous discussion of vector addition, we know that if the angle between the forces is 0°, the resultant is a maximum. If the tractors were pulling in the same direction, the tree would experience an applied force of 5000 + 5000 N, or 10,000 N. Conversely, if the angle between the forces is 180°, the force is a minimum. In this case, if the tractors were pulling in opposite directions, the resultant force on the tree would be zero.

Equilibrium

An object is in **equilibrium** when the vector sum of the concurrent forces acting on the object is zero. When there is no net force on an object at rest, it will remain at rest, or in **static equilibrium.** When there is no net force on an object already in motion, the object maintains a constant velocity and is said to be in **dynamic equilibrium.**

If the resultant of the concurrent forces on an object is not equal to zero, the object is not in a state of equilibrium. In order for equilibrium to be maintained, a force equal in magnitude and opposite in direction to the resultant must be applied to the object. The balancing force that creates equilibrium is called the **equilibrant.**

9. A sign is suspended from a horizontal pole by two wires (Figure 1-24). Each wire is at a 45° angle from the horizontal and pulls on the sign with a force of 28.3 N. (a) Find the resultant force on the

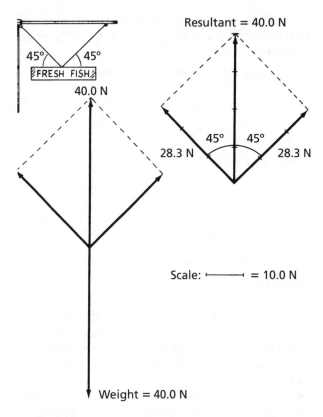

Figure 1-24.

sign due to the forces exerted by the two wires. (b) Find the weight of the sign.

Solution: Using the parallelogram method of vector addition and the given scale, we find that the resultant force has a magnitude of 40.0 N and pulls the sign directly upward.

Since the sign is in static equilibrium, the weight of the sign (acting vertically downward) is the equilibrant of the resultant of the two forces exerted by the wires. What must this weight be? The object's weight must therefore be equal in magnitude to the upward force of the resultant. Thus, the object must weight 40.0 N. If we now add the three forces acting on the sign, the resultant is zero.

Resolution of Forces

Like all vectors, forces can be resolved into an unlimited number of components. In many situations, the effect of a force on an object can best be ascertained by resolving the force into two perpendicular components.

For example, in Figure 1-25 someone is pulling a sled by a rope with a force of 35.0 N in a direction 30° from the horizontal. The horizontal component of the force acts to pull the sled in the horizontal direction while the vertical component of the force acts to lift the sled vertically upward. To determine the magnitude of the force in each of these directions, we must resolve the 35.0-N force into its horizontal and vertical components.

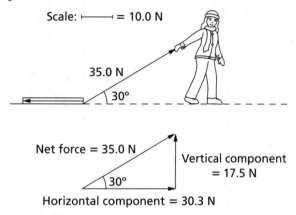

Figure 1-25.

By drawing a vector diagram and using either a ruler and protractor or trigonometry, we find that the vertical component has a magnitude of 17.5 N and the horizontal component has a magnitude of 30.3 N.

In some cases it is useful to resolve a vector into perpendicular components in directions other than horizontal and vertical. For example, consider a 90.-N box at rest on an inclined plane at a 30° angle from the horizontal (Figure 1-26). The weight of the box acts vertically downward. We would like to determine the magnitude of the force that acts to push the box down the incline, and the magnitude of the force that acts to press the box against the surface of the plane. We must

resolve the weight vector **w** into a component parallel to the surface and a component perpendicular to the surface. A vector diagram enables us to calculate the magnitude of these components. The magnitude of the perpendicular component $F_\perp$ can be expressed mathematically as

$$F_\perp = w \cos \theta$$

where θ is the angle between the inclined plane and the horizontal. In the example, $F_\perp$ becomes

$$\begin{aligned} F_\perp &= w \cos \theta \\ &= (90.\,\text{N})(\cos 30°) \\ &= (90.\,\text{N})(0.866) = 78 \text{ N} \end{aligned}$$

The component of weight parallel to the plane $F_\parallel$ can be expressed mathematically as

$$F_\parallel = w \sin \theta$$

In the example $F_\parallel$ becomes

$$\begin{aligned} F_\parallel &= w \sin \theta \\ &= (90.\,\text{N})(\sin 30°) \\ &= (90.\,\text{N})(0.500) = 45 \text{ N} \end{aligned}$$

Sample Problem

10. In Figure 1-27 a person is pushing the handle of a lawn mower with a force of 200. N in a direction 45° from the horizontal. How much force acts to push the lawn mower in the horizontal direction, and how much force acts to push the lawn mower downward into the ground?

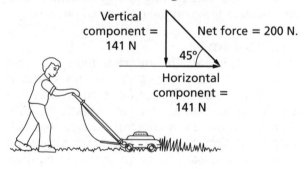

Scale: ⊢———⊣ = 100. N

Figure 1.27.

Solution: Drawing a vector diagram and using trigonometry we find

$$\begin{aligned} \text{vertical component} &= (200.\,\text{N})(\sin 45°) \\ &= (200.\,\text{N})(0.707) \\ &= 141 \text{ N} \end{aligned}$$

$$\begin{aligned} \text{horizontal component} &= (200.\,\text{N})(\cos 45°) \\ &= (200.\,\text{N})(0.707) \\ &= 141 \text{ N} \end{aligned}$$

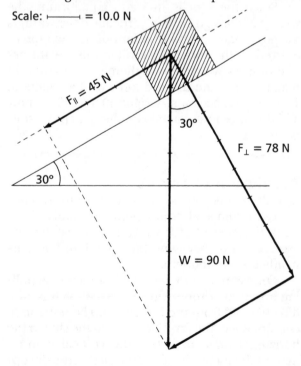

Figure 1-26.

QUESTIONS

46. Two 10.0-newton forces act concurrently on a point at an angle of 180° to each other. The magnitude of the resultant of the two forces is (1) 0.00 N (2) 10.0 N (3) 18.0 N (4) 20.0N

47. A force of 3 newtons and a force of 5 newtons act concurrently to produce a resultant of 8 newtons. The angle between the forces may be (1) 0° (2) 60° (3) 90° (4) 180°

48. A table exerts a 2.0-newton force on a book lying on the table. The force exerted by the book on the table is (1) 20. N (2) 2.0 N (3) 0.20 N (4) 0 N

49. The diagram at the right represents two concurrent forces acting on a point. Which vector best represents their resultant?

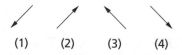

50. The resultant of two forces acting on the same point at the same time will be greatest when the angle between the forces is (1) 0° (2) 45° (3) 90° (4) 180°

51. What is the magnitude of the vector sum of the two concurrent forces represented in the diagram? (1) 2.5 N (2) 3.5 N (3) 3.0 N (4) 4.0 N

2.0 N

1.5 N

52. The resultant of two concurrent forces is minimum when the angle between them is (1) 0° (2) 45° (3) 90° (4) 180°

53. As the angle between two concurrent forces of 5.0 newtons and 7.0 newtons increases from 0° to 180°, the magnitude of their resultant changes from (1) 0 N to 35 N (2) 2.0 N to 12 N (3) 12 N to 2.0 N (4) 12 N to 0 N

54. Two concurrent forces act at right angles to each other. If one of the forces is 40 newtons and the resultant of the two forces is 50 newtons, the magnitude of the other force must be (1) 10 N (2) 20 N (3) 30 N (4) 40 N

55. If two 10.-newton concurrent forces have a resultant of zero, the angle between the forces must be (1) 0° (2) 45° (3) 90° (4) 180°

Thinking and Analyzing

56. Define force in your own words and provide an example.

57. What is true of two concurrent forces?

58. You and a friend are pulling on a desk. How can you adjust the angle between you, the desk, and your friend to make your efforts most efficient?

59. What is a net force and how is it determined?

60. Describe the condition of equilibrium.

61. Differentiate between static equilibrium and dynamic equilibrium.

62. What is the purpose of an equilibrant?

63. A 60.-N box is at rest on an inclined plane at a 30° angle from the horizontal. What is the magnitude of the force that acts to press the box against the surface of the plane?

64. Construct vector A representing a 100. N force directed due east and vector B representing a 200. N force directed at 30 degrees from vector A. State the scale the vectors are based on and construct them to scale. Then find the resultant vector by using the head-to-tail method. Obtain the magnitude and direction of the resultant vector by measurement. State your data and convert to force via the chosen scale.

65. Construct a vector representing a velocity of 80. m/s directed at 60 degrees N of E. State the scale upon which the vector is based and construct the vector to scale. Then resolve the vector by construction and measurement into an easterly and northerly component. State the magnitude and direction of each of these component velocities.

DYNAMICS

The laws of nature regarding motion have evolved over time. For a long time the dominant view was the one attributed to Aristotle. It claimed that in the absence of a force (a push, pull or any influence) acting on a body, the body remains at rest. Rest was thus presumed to be the "natural state" of a body. If an unbalanced force does act to influence a body, the body responds by moving. The stronger the force, the faster the motion of the body it acts on.

While this view sounds quite appealing and seems logical, it was eventually recognized that it conflicted with various observations. Objects continue to move, slide and roll even after the push that got them going no longer exists. This happened even in a vacuum, so air pressure (air rushing in to fill the vacuum left behind by the moving object) could not be the cause. Also, objects subjected to a constant unbalanced force, such as a freely falling body, continue to accelerate as long as the force was active. So greater speed could not be associated with the influence of a stronger force.

The First Law of Motion

The Aristotelian view was therefore replaced by the Newtonian system. In this view of things, the absence of a force leads to no change in motion. If the object is at rest, it remains at rest; if it is in motion, it maintains its speed and direction, forever, so long as no net force appears to influence its motion. It is difficult to demonstrate this principle on Earth because there are always forces present (such as friction, air resistance, and gravity) that act to slow down, and ultimately stop, a moving object. However, space vehicles continue to move for many years, even after their engines have been shut off.

The first law of motion is also known as the **law of inertia. Inertia** is the property of matter that resists change in motion. The inertia of an object is proportional to its mass. A large mass tends to resist changes in its motion to a greater extent than a smaller mass.

The Second Law of Motion

Newton's second law states: An unbalanced force acting on an object causes the object to accelerate in the direction of the force. In other words, if the resultant of all the forces acting on an object is not zero, the object's velocity will change in magnitude or direction or both. The acceleration of the object is directly proportional to the net force acting on it and inversely proportional to its mass.

One newton (N) is defined as the amount of force that imparts an acceleration of one meter per second squared to a mass of one kilogram. Newton's second law can be stated mathematically as

$$F = ma$$

where m is mass, in kg; a is acceleration, in m/s²; and F is the force, in N. The newton, therefore, is a derived unit: $1 \text{ N} = 1 \text{ kg} \cdot \text{m/s}^2$.

The graph in Figure 1-28 illustrates the direct proportionality between force and acceleration. Each line is the force vs. acceleration graph for an object with a particular mass. The slope of each line is equal to the object's mass (since $F/a = m$). Object B has twice as much mass as object A, so twice as much force is required to accelerate ob-

ject B at the rate of 1 m/s² than to accelerate object A at the same rate. Object C has three times as much mass as object B and so it takes three times the amount of force to accelerate C at the rate of 1 m/s² than it does to accelerate object B at the same rate.

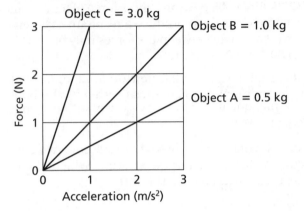

Figure 1-28.

11. A 120-N net force acts upon a 68-kg cart at rest. What acceleration results?
    Solution:

$$F = ma$$
$$a = \frac{F}{m} = \frac{120 \text{ N}}{68 \text{ kg}} = \frac{120 \text{ kg} \cdot \text{m/s}^2}{68 \text{ kg}}$$
$$= 1.8 \text{ m/s}^2$$

12. A force of F newtons causes a mass of m kilograms to accelerate at 24 m/s². What acceleration will occur under the following conditions?

    (*a*) The force is doubled to $2F$ newtons, and the mass remains the same.
    Solution: Since acceleration is directly proportional to force, if the force is doubled the acceleration will double. Hence,

$$a = 2(24 \text{ m/s}^2) = 48 \text{ m/s}^2$$

    (*b*) The force is F newtons and the mass is tripled.
    Solution: Since acceleration is inversely proportional to mass, if the mass is tripled the acceleration is divided by 3. Hence,

$$a = \frac{24 \text{ m/s}^2}{3} = 8 \text{ m/s}^2$$

The Third Law of Motion

When a cannon is fired, it recoils as the cannonball flies out. Air rushing out of a balloon in one direction forces the balloon to move in the opposite direction. Such effects are explained by **Newton's third law of motion,** which states: For every action there is an equal and opposite reaction. The words "action" and "reaction" refer to forces. The law means that when one object exerts a force on another, the second object exerts an equally strong but oppositely directed force on the first. Forces always occur in pairs that are equal in magnitude and opposite in direction. The members of the pair do not act on the same object, are not concurrent, and cannot be added together.

The Law of Universal Gravitation

The ancient natural philosophers believed that objects fall because Earth pulls on them. Newton insightfully proposed that Earth cannot be unique in having the ability to attract objects. All matter must attract other matter. This attraction is universal and is referred to as the **gravitational force.**

The gravitational forces between ordinary objects is extremely weak and therefore often undetectable. But if one or both of the objects contain an enormous amount of mass, the gravitational force between them is significant. For example, Earth, sun, and moon pull on each other with tremendous gravitational force, creating Earth's orbit and tides. The attraction between Earth and an object on its surface is also strong enough to be noticed. It is referred to as the object's **weight.**

Newton found that the gravitational force between any two objects is directly proportional to the product of their masses and inversely proportional to the square of the distance between them. This relationship is stated mathematically as

$$F \propto \frac{m_1 m_2}{r^2}$$

where m_1 and m_2 are the objects' masses and r is the distance between them. This proportionality can be changed to an equality by inserting a constant of proportionality into the equation

$$F = \frac{Gm_1 m_2}{r^2}$$

The constant G is called the **universal gravitational constant.** Careful experiments have determined that if the masses are expressed in kilograms, the distance in meters, and the force in newtons, the value of G is 6.67×10^{-11} N · m²/kg².

This gravitational law only applies to (1) masses whose sizes are small compared to the distance between them (point masses); and (2) spherical masses of uniform density—if the distance between them is measured from the center of one to the center of the other.

The relationship between gravitational force and distance is an example of an **inverse square relationship.** As the distance between the masses increases, the gravitational force between them decreases rapidly. For example, if the distance between two masses is doubled, the gravitational force between them is decreased to one-fourth its original value. If the distance between the masses is halved, the gravitational force between them is quadrupled. This inverse square relationship is illustrated by the graph in Figure 1-29.

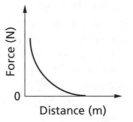

Figure 1-29. Inverse square relationship.

Sample Problems

13. Find the gravitational pull exerted by the moon on Earth (which is identical to the pull of Earth on the moon).
Solution:

$$\text{mass of Earth} = 6.0 \times 10^{24} \text{ kg}$$
$$\text{mass of the moon} = 6.0 \times 10^{22} \text{ kg}$$
$$\text{Earth-moon distance} = 3.7 \times 10^7 \text{ m}$$
$$F = \frac{Gm_1 m_2}{r^2}$$
$$= \frac{(6.67 \times 10^{-11} \text{ N} \cdot \text{m}^2/\text{kg}^2)(6.0 \times 10^{24} \text{ kg})(6.0 \times 10^{22} \text{ kg})}{(3.7 \times 10^7 \text{ m})^2}$$
$$= 2.0 \times 10^{22} \text{ N}$$

14. Find the gravitational force exerted by Earth on a 1-kg mass on its surface.
Solution: Since Earth is large and spherical the appropriate distance to use is the distance between Earth's center and the center of 1-kg mass. This distance is approximately equal to the radius of Earth.

$$\text{mass of object} = 1.0 \text{ kg}$$
$$\text{mass of Earth} = 6.0 \times 10^{24} \text{ kg}$$
$$\text{radius of Earth} = 6.4 \times 10^6 \text{ m}$$
$$F = \frac{Gm_1 m_2}{r^2}$$
$$= \frac{(6.67 \times 10^{-11} \text{ N} \cdot \text{m}^2/\text{kg}^2)(1.0 \text{ kg})(6.0 \times 10^{24} \text{ kg})}{(6.4 \times 10^6 \text{ m})^2}$$
$$= 9.8 \text{ N}$$

This is the force exerted by Earth on the 1-kg object which causes the object to fall. According to Newton's third law, the 1-kg object also pulls Earth toward it with the same force, but due to Earth's enormous mass, no noticeable acceleration of Earth results.

Gravitational Field

The fact that a mass exerts a force on another mass some distance away means that the space between the masses is unlike that where no masses are present. We say that every mass sets up a **gravitational field** in the space around itself. This field then acts on other masses so that an attraction results. The gravitational field strength g at any point in the field is defined as the force experienced by a 1-kg mass at that point in the field. This is expressed mathematically as

$$g = \frac{F}{m}$$

where F is the gravitational force in newtons experienced by a mass m. If the force exerted on a 5-kg object by a gravitational field at some point is 20 N, the intensity of the field at that point is 20 N/5 kg = 4 N/kg.

A gravitational field is a vector quantity. The direction of the gravitational field at any given point is the direction of the gravitational force exerted by the field on a mass placed in the field at that point.

Freely Falling Objects

Like all forces, gravitational force will cause an object to accelerate. An object is said to be **freely falling** if only Earth's gravitational pull acts on it and no other forces (such as friction or air resistance) are present. The acceleration of any freely falling object near Earth's surface is 9.81 m/s², regardless of the object's mass, size, or shape. The symbol g is used to represent this important constant.

$$g = 9.81 \text{ m/s}^2$$

The motion of freely falling objects can be described by using the equations for uniform acceleration where $a = g$.

The value $g = 9.81$ m/s² applies only to objects near sea level. At higher or lower elevations, the gravitational force will vary according to the inverse square relation and, therefore, the acceleration due to gravity will also vary.

15. Using the equations for uniform acceleration, determine the velocity and distance traveled by a freely falling object after 4.0 seconds.

Solution:

$$v_f = a\Delta t = g\Delta t$$
$$= (9.81 \text{ m/s}^2)(4.0 \text{ s}) = 39 \text{ m/s}$$
$$d = \tfrac{1}{2}a(\Delta t)^2 = \tfrac{1}{2}g(\Delta t)^2$$
$$= \tfrac{1}{2}(9.81 \text{ m/s}^2)(4.0 \text{ s})^2 = 78 \text{ m}$$

16. An object hits the ground after dropping 5000. m in free fall. What is its velocity as it hits the ground, and how long did it fall?

Solution:

final velocity:

$$v_f^2 = 2a\Delta d = 2g\Delta d$$
$$= 2(9.81 \text{ m/s}^2)(5000. \text{ m})$$
$$v_f = \sqrt{98{,}000 \text{ m}^2/\text{s}^2} = 313 \text{ m/s}$$

time of drop:

$$\Delta d = \tfrac{1}{2}g(\Delta t)^2$$
$$(\Delta t)^2 = \frac{2\Delta d}{g}$$
$$= \frac{2(5000. \text{ m})}{(9.81 \text{ m/s}^2)} = 1020 \text{ s}^2$$
$$\Delta t = \sqrt{1020 \text{ s}^2} = 32 \text{ s}$$

Weight

The **weight w** of an object is defined as the gravitational force it experiences. Since all freely falling objects at sea level experience the same acceleration g, we can use Newton's second law to obtain the formula

$$w = mg$$

Like all forces, weight is a vector quantity whose magnitude is expressed in newtons. The direction of the weight vector is always vertically downward toward the center of Earth. Note that since the magnitude of the gravitational force experienced by an object varies with distance from Earth, the weight of the object and its acceleration vary in the same way. A graph of weight vs. mass (Figure 1-30) for objects at sea level is a straight line whose slope is g.

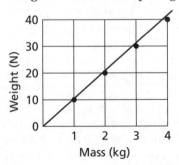

Figure 1-30. $g = 9.81$ N/kg $= 9.81$ *m/s²*.

17. What is the weight of a 100.-kg mass?
Solution:

$$w = mg = (100. \text{ kg})(9.81 \text{ m/s}^2)$$
$$= 981. \text{ kg} \cdot \text{m/s}^2 = 981. \text{ N}$$

18. What is the mass of a 100.-N weight?
Solution:

$$m = \frac{w}{g} = \frac{100. \text{ N}}{9.81 \text{ m/s}^2}$$
$$= \frac{100. \text{ kg} \cdot \text{m/s}^2}{9.81 \text{ m/s}^2} = 10.2 \text{ kg}$$

QUESTIONS

66. Which graph best represents the motion of a moving object with no unbalanced force acting on it?

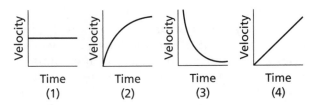

67. An 800-newton person is standing in an elevator. If the upward force of the elevator on the person is 600 newtons, the person is   (1) at rest   (2) accelerating upward   (3) accelerating downward   (4) moving downward at constant speed

68. An object with a mass of 2 kilograms is accelerated at 5 m/s². The net force acting on the mass is   (1) 5 N   (2) 2 N   (3) 10 N   (4) 20 N

69. The fundamental units for a force of one newton are   (1) meters/second²   (2) kilograms   (3) meters/second²/kilogram   (4) kilogram-meters/second²

70. The diagram below represents a constant force F acting on a box located on a frictionless horizontal surface. As the angle θ between the force and the horizontal increases, the acceleration of the box will   (1) decrease   (2) increase   (3) remain the same

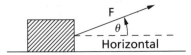

71. An object accelerates at 2.5 meters per second² when an unbalanced force of 10. newtons acts on it. What is the mass of the object?   (1) 1.0 kg   (2) 2.0 kg   (3) 3.0 kg   (4) 4.0 kg

Base your answers to questions 72 through 76 on this information: A 10.-kilogram object, starting from rest, slides down a frictionless incline with a constant acceleration of 2.0 m/s² for 4.0 seconds.

72. What is the velocity of the object at the end of the 4.0 seconds?   (1) 16 m/s   (2) 8.0 m/s   (3) 4.0 m/s   (4) 2.0 m/s

73. During the 4.0 seconds, the object moves a total distance of   (1) 32 m   (2) 16 m   (3) 8.0 m   (4) 4.0 m

74. To produce this acceleration, what is the force on the object?   (1) 10. N   (2) 2.0 × 10¹ N   (3) 5.0 N   (4) 2.0 × 10² N

75. What is the approximate weight of the object?   (1) 1 N   (2) 10 N   (3) 100 N   (4) 1,000 N

76. Which graph best represents the relationship between acceleration (a) and time (t) for the object?

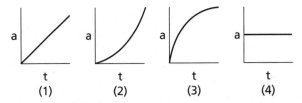

77. Which graph could represent the motion of an object with no unbalanced forced acting on it?

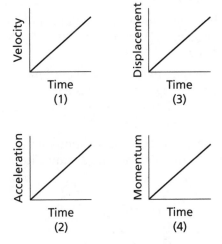

78. Two frictionless blocks having masses of 8.0 kilograms and 2.0 kilograms, rest on a horizontal surface. If a force applied to the 8.0-kilogram block gives it an acceleration of 5.0 m/s², then the same force will give the 2.0-kilogram block an acceleration of   (1) 1.2 m/s²   (2) 2.5 m/s²   (3) 10. m/s²   (4) 20. m/s²

79. An unbalanced force of 10.0 newtons causes an object to accelerate at 2.0 m/s². What is the mass of the object?   (1) 0.2 kg   (2) 5.0 kg   (3) 8.0 kg   (4) 20 kg

80. An unbalanced force of 10 newtons acts on a 20-kilogram mass for 5 seconds. The acceleration of the mass is   (1) 0.5 m/s^2 (2) 2 m/s^2 (3) 40 m/s^2 (4) 200 m/s^2

81. The graph below shows the relationship between the acceleration of an object and the unbalanced force producing the acceleration. The ratio ($\Delta F/\Delta a$) of the graph represents the object's   (1) mass   (2) momentum   (3) kinetic energy   (4) displacement

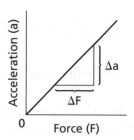

82. Two objects of equal mass are a fixed distance apart. If the mass of each object could be tripled, the gravitational force between the objects would   (1) decrease by one-third   (2) decrease by one-ninth   (3) triple   (4) increase 9 times

83. Which two quantities are measured in the same units?   (1) velocity and acceleration   (2) weight and force   (3) mass and weight   (4) force and momentum

84. What is the weight of a 5.0-kilogram object at Earth's surface?   (1) 5.0 kg   (2) 25 N   (3) 49 N   (4) 49 kg

85. What is the gravitational acceleration on a planet where a 2-kilogram mass has a weight of 16 newtons on the planet's surface?   (1) $\frac{1}{8}$ m/s^2 (2) 8 m/s^2 (3) 10 m/s^2 (4) 32 m/s^2

86. Which graph represents the relationship between the mass of an object and its distance from Earth's surface?

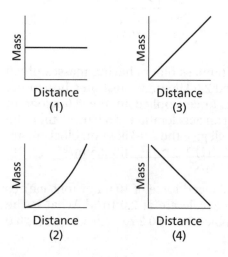

87. Which is constant for a freely falling object?   (1) displacement   (2) speed   (3) velocity   (4) acceleration

88. An object starting from rest falls freely near Earth's surface. Which graph best represents the motion of the object?

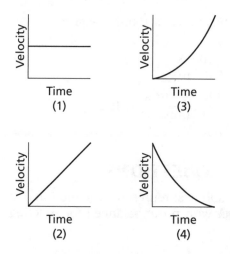

89. Starting from rest, an object rolls freely down an incline that is 10 meters long in 2 seconds. The acceleration of the object is approximately   (1) 5 m/sec   (2) 5 m/sec^2 (3) 10 m/sec   (4) 10 m/sec^2

90. An object, initially at rest, falls freely near Earth's surface. How long does it take the object to attain a speed of 98 meters per second?   (1) 0.1 s   (2) 10 s   (3) 98 s   (4) 960 s

91. Starting from rest, object *A* falls freely for 2.0 seconds, and object *B* falls freely for 4.0 seconds. Compared with object *A*, object *B* falls   (1) one-half as far   (2) twice as far   (3) three times as far   (4) four times as far

92. An object is thrown vertically upward from Earth's surface. Which graph best shows the relationship between velocity and time as the object rises?

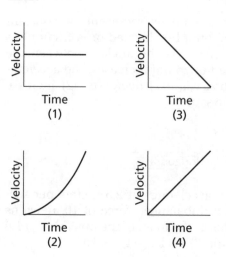

93. An astronaut drops a stone near the surface of the Moon. Which graph best represents the motion of the stone as it falls toward the Moon's surface?

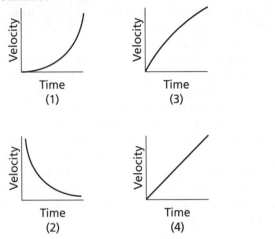

(1)

(3)

(2)

(4)

Thinking and Analyzing

94. Describe Newton's first law of motion. Use the words unbalanced force and inertia in your description.

95. According to Newton's first law of motion, an object in motion should continue in motion indefinitely. Why does a ball rolled across a field come to a stop?

96. When a train executes a sharp turn, passengers and objects inside the train tend to move toward the side of the train that is at the outer edge of the turn. Explain this phenomenon based on the laws of motion.

97. Describe Newton's second law of motion. Use the words unbalanced force and acceleration in your description.

98. How is acceleration related to the net force on an object and the mass of the object?

99. Draw a graph showing the relationship of force to acceleration for two objects, one of which has twice as much mass as the other.

100. A motorcyclist starts from rest and accelerates uniformly at the rate of 5.0 m/s² for 12 seconds. She then maintains her velocity for 30. seconds before decelerating to a stop at the uniform rate of 3.0 m/s². Construct a velocity-time graph representing the entire trip.

101. For each of the designations on the *v-t* graph below labeled A through E, describe the activity of the object whose motion is represented by the graph with regard to the following: (a) the direction of the object toward or away from the reference point, (b) changes taking place in that direction, if any, (c) whether the object's motion is uniform, accelerating or decelerating, (d) the velocity of the object when it is uniform and the acceleration rate of the object when its velocity is changing.

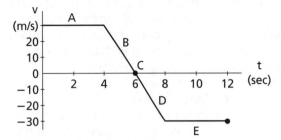

102. Describe the effect on the braking distance of a train if any one of the following quantities is doubled: (a) the initial velocity before braking begins, (b) the deceleration rate during braking. Support your conclusions by applying the motion equations with numerical examples to this situation.

103. What does Newton's third law of motion say about pairs of forces?

104. An astronaut opens the hatch of her spacecraft and wants to move away from the craft, into empty space. She cannot walk or swim away from the craft because there is no floor to walk on and no medium to swim through. What can she do to accomplish her goal of moving away from the craft? Explain your answer in terms of the laws of motion.

105. What does Newton's law of universal gravitation say?

106. How is the gravitational force related to mass and distance?

107. How is the gravitational field strength defined at a given point?

108. When is an object considered to be in free fall?

109. A 10. kg and a 20. kg object are released simultaneously from rest at the same height. Discuss the following quantities with regard to whether they are identical or different for the two objects as they fall freely toward the ground. Provide a basis for your answer for each quantity: (a) the time to reach the ground; (b) their speed as they arrive at the ground; (c) their acceleration rates; (d) the distance they travel in the first second of free fall.

110. What determines the weight of an object? How is weight different from mass?

FRICTION

Friction is the force that opposes the motion of one surface over another. This resistance to motion is the result of the contact between surfaces. Frictional force is always directed opposite to the motion and acts to slow down and ultimately stop the motion. The magnitude of the frictional force depends on the nature of the surfaces in contact (their roughness and composition) and on the amount of force pressing the two surfaces together. The nature of the surfaces is represented by their **coefficient of friction.** The force which presses the two surfaces together is called the **normal force,** because it always acts in a direction perpendicular to the surfaces. When an object moves over a horizontal surface, the magnitude of the normal force is equal to the weight of the object. When an object slides on an inclined plane, the magnitude of the normal force is equal to the component of the object's weight perpendicular to the surface.

The coefficient of friction μ is defined as the friction force F_f divided by the normal force F_N. This relationship can be expressed mathematically as

$$\mu = \frac{F_f}{F_N}$$

Sample Problem

19. A 60-N wooden box is pushed along a horizontal concrete sidewalk (Figure 1-31). The coefficient of friction between wood and concrete is 0.15. What frictional force must be overcome for the box to move at constant velocity?

Solution:

$F_f = \mu F_N$
$\quad = (0.15)(60 \text{ N}) = 9 \text{ N}$

$F_f = \mu F_N$
$\quad = (0.15)(60 \text{ N}) = 9 \text{ N}$

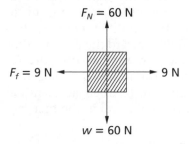

Figure 1-31.

Static Friction

The coefficient of friction between two surfaces is greatest when there is no relative motion between them and we wish to start one surface moving

over the other. The frictional force that must be overcome to start one surface moving over another is called **static friction.** Static friction is equal and opposite to the applied force parallel to the surfaces that is required to get this motion started. Thus static friction is sometimes called **starting friction.**

Kinetic friction is the force opposing the motion of an object sliding over a surface. Kinetic friction (or sliding friction) is always weaker than static friction. For nondeformable objects, kinetic friction is practically independent of the contact surface area and the relative velocity between the objects. When two rough surfaces slide across each other, they experience a strong force of sliding friction. Lubrication of the surfaces or making them smoother significantly reduces the amount of kinetic friction.

Rolling Friction

When one object rolls over another, it experiences a force of **rolling friction.** Rolling friction is generally weaker than sliding friction. This is why ball bearings are often placed between two surfaces that must move past each other.

Fluid Friction

Fluid friction is the force that resists the motion of an object through a fluid, such as water or air. Swimmers, boats, planes, and parachutes all experience fluid friction as they move. Fluid friction can be large enough to equal the weight of a falling object. This is how a parachute works. At first, a parachutist accelerates downward due to his or her weight. At a certain velocity, the fluid friction of the air exerted on the parachute becomes equal and opposite to the weight and the net force is zero. When this occurs, the parachutist ceases to accelerate and falls at a constant velocity.

QUESTIONS

111. The strongest frictional force between two surfaces is (1) static friction (2) kinetic friction (3) sliding friction (4) rolling friction

112. A 40.-N object requires 5.0 N to start moving over a horizontal surface. The coefficient of static friction is (1) 0.13 (2) 4.0 (3) 5.0 (4) 35

113. A 12-N cart is moving on a horizontal surface with a coefficient of kinetic friction of 0.10. What force of friction must be overcome to keep the object moving at constant speed? (1) 0.10 N (2) 1.2 N (3) 12 N (4) 120 N

114. The coefficient of friction between two dry sliding surfaces is 0.05. What value is possible if these surfaces are lubricated? (1) 5.00 (2) 0.02 (3) 0.05 (4) 0.08

115. If the normal force between two surfaces is doubled, the static friction force will (1) be halved (2) remain the same (3) be doubled (4) be quadrupled

116. If the normal force between two surfaces is doubled, the coefficient of static friction will (1) be halved (2) remain the same (3) be doubled (4) be quadrupled

117. In which situation is fluid friction not involved? (1) A boat moving in water (2) A parachute dropping (3) A plane flying (4) Climbing up a pole

Questions 118–124 relate to this situation: A 6.0-N block is moving to the right on a horizontal surface. The friction force during the motion is found to be 1.0 N.

118. In which direction does the friction force act on the block? (1) to the right (2) to the left (3) upward (4) downward

119. What is the magnitude of the normal force on the block? (1) less than 6.0 N (2) 6.0 N (3) more than 6.0 N

120. What is the coefficient of friction in this example? (1) 1.0 (2) 0.17 (3) 5.0 (4) 6.0

121. If the block is at rest, how much force will be needed to get it moving? (1) 1.0 N (2) less than 1.0 N (3) more than 1.0 N

122. If a weight is placed on top of the block, the force of friction will (1) remain the same (2) increase (3) decrease

123. If the same block slides on the surface at greater speed, the force of friction will be (1) the same (2) weaker (3) stronger

124. If the block is turned so that it slides on a side whose surface is smaller, the force of friction will (1) increase (2) remain the same (3) decrease

125. A constant unbalanced force of friction acts on a 15.0-kilogram mass moving along a horizontal surface at 10.0 meters per second. If the mass is brought to rest in 1.50 seconds, what is the magnitude of the force of friction? (1) 10.0 N (2) 100. N (3) 147. N (4) 150. N

Thinking and Analyzing

126. What is the friction force?

127. Upon what does the friction force depend?

128. A 40-N box is pushed along a horizontal surface. The coefficient of friction between the box and the surface is 1.0. What frictional force must be overcome for the box to move at constant velocity?

129. By how much does the frictional force determined in question 128 change if the weight of the box increases to 60 N?

130. Describe static friction. How is kinetic friction different from static friction?

131. You kick a box on the floor and it continues to move for some time after taking off in response to your push. Gradually, it slows to a stop after traveling some distance. Explain this sequence of events based on the laws of motion.

132. What is rolling friction? What is fluid friction? Provide an example of each.

133. How is it possible that a skydiver can fall at constant velocity?

134. A 10. kg crate rests on an inclined plane oriented 30° from the horizontal as illustrated in the diagram. Trace the figure onto another sheet of paper. Then sketch and label a vector to represent each of the forces acting on the crate. The tail of each of these vectors should be on the crate and the vectors should be correctly directed. Near each vector state its magnitude. Show all calculations.

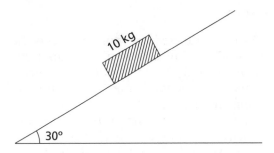

135. Repeat question 134 for the case in which the crate is sliding down the incline at the uniform rate of 4.0 m/s.

MOMENTUM

An object's **momentum** is defined as the product of its mass and its velocity. A fast-moving car has more momentum than a slow-moving car of the same mass, and a heavy bus has more momentum than a small car moving with the same velocity. The symbol for momentum is p.

$$p = mv$$

where m is the mass, in kilograms; and v is the velocity, in meters per second. The unit of momentum is the kg · m/s.

Momentum is a vector quantity whose direction is the same as the object's velocity. It is customary to assign a positive value to the velocity and momentum of an object that moves to the right and a negative value to the velocity and momentum of an object moving to the left.

Sample Problems

20. What is the momentum of a 15-kg bicycle moving at 12 m/s?
Solution:

$$p = mv$$
$$= (15 \text{ kg})(12 \text{ m/s}) = 180 \text{ kg} \cdot \text{m/s}$$

21. A bullet with a mass of 0.0025 kg has a momentum of 1.8 kg · m/s. What is the magnitude of its velocity?
Solution:

$$p = mv$$
$$v = \frac{p}{m} = \frac{1.8 \text{ kg} \cdot \text{m/s}}{0.0025 \text{ kg}} = 720 \text{ m/s}$$

Impulse

Impulse is defined as the product of the net force acting on an object and the time during which the force acts. The symbol for impulse is J.

$$J = F(\Delta t)$$

where F is the net force in newtons and Δt is the time interval in seconds. The unit for impulse is the newton second (N · s). Impulse is a vector quantity whose direction is the same as the net force acting on the object.

When a net force acts on an object, the object's velocity and momentum change. We can use Newton's second law to show that the change in momentum (Δp) is equal to the impulse imparted to the object.

Newton's second law:

$$F = ma \qquad (1)$$

definition of acceleration:

$$a = \frac{\Delta v}{\Delta t} \qquad (2)$$

Substituting (2) into (1):

$$F = m\frac{\Delta v}{\Delta t}$$
$$F(\Delta t) = m(\Delta v) = \Delta(mv)$$
$$J = \Delta p$$

Note that the unit for impulse and the unit for momentum are equivalent:

$$\text{N} \cdot \text{s} = (\text{kg} \cdot \text{m/s}^2) \cdot \text{s} = \text{kg} \cdot \text{m/s}$$

Sample Problems

22. A gust of wind exerts a 300.-N net force on a 1000.-kg sailboat for 15 s. What is the change in momentum and velocity of the boat?
Solution:

$$J = F\Delta t$$
$$= (300. \text{ N})(15 \text{ s}) = 4500 \text{ N} \cdot \text{s}$$
$$J = \Delta p = 4500 \text{ kg} \cdot \text{m/s}$$
$$p = m\Delta v$$
$$4500 \text{ kg. m/s} = (1000. \text{ kg})\Delta v$$
$$\Delta v = 4.5 \text{ m/s}$$

23. For what duration should a 10.-N force be applied to a 5.0-kg object to cause its velocity to slow down from 7.0 m/s to 4.0 m/s?
Solution:

$$\Delta v = v_f - v_i$$
$$= 4.0 \text{ m/s} - 7.0 \text{ m/s} = -3.0 \text{ m/s}$$
$$\Delta p = m\Delta v$$
$$= (5.0 \text{ kg})(-3.0 \text{ m/s}) = -15 \text{ kg} \cdot \text{m/s}$$
$$F(\Delta t) = \Delta p$$

(Note, F is negative since it opposes the motion.)

$$(-10. \text{ N})(\Delta t) = -15 \text{ kg} \cdot \text{m/s}$$
$$\Delta t = 1.5 \text{ s}$$

Conservation of Momentum

The **law of conservation of momentum** states that if no external force is acting on a system, the total momentum of the system remains unchanged. This means that when a set of objects interact, the total momentum before the event equals the total momentum after the event. For example, consider the total momentum of a set of billiard balls before and after a collision. Before the event, only the cue ball is moving toward the other assembled balls. After colliding with the cue ball, the balls scatter across the pool table. The resultant of the momentum vectors of all the moving balls after the collision is identical to the momentum vector of the cue ball before the collision.

In the simple case of a head-on interaction (collision or explosion) between two objects with masses m_1 and m_2, the law of conservation of momentum can be expressed mathematically as

total momentum before = total momentum after

$$m_1v_1 + m_2v_2 = m_1v_1' + m_2v_2'$$

where v_1 and v_2 are the velocities of the objects before the event, and v_1' and v_2' are their velocities after the event.

24. A 2-kg cart moving to the right at 5 m/s collides with an 8-kg cart at rest (Figure 1-32). As a result of the collision, the carts lock together.

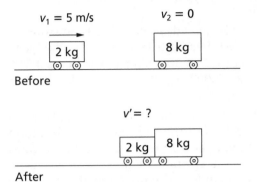

Figure 1-32.

What is the velocity of the carts after the event?

Solution:

$$m_1v_1 + m_2v_2 = m_1v_1' + m_2v_2'$$

Since $v_1' = v_2'$ we can call them both v' and factor v' from the equation to obtain:

$$m_1v_1 + m_2v_2 = (m_1 + m_2)v'$$

$$(2\text{kg})(5 \text{ m/s})$$
$$+ (8 \text{ kg})(0 \text{ m/s}) = (2 \text{ kg} + 8 \text{ kg})v'$$
$$10 \text{ kg} \cdot \text{m/s} = (10 \text{ kg})v'$$
$$v' = \frac{10 \text{ kg} \cdot \text{m/s}}{10 \text{ kg}}$$
$$= 1 \text{ m/s (to the right)}$$

25. A standard physics problem is the "explosion" of two carts initially at rest, which sends them moving in opposite directions. For example, Figure 1-33 shows a 6-kg cart and a 4-kg cart at rest.

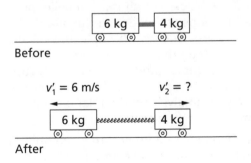

Figure 1-33.

Between them is a compressed spring. When the spring expands, it sends both carts in opposite directions. If the 6-kg cart moves to the left with a velocity of 6 m/s, what is the velocity of the other cart?

Solution:

$$m_1v_1 + m_2v_2 = m_1v_1' + m_2v_2'$$

$$(6\text{kg})(0 \text{ m/s})$$
$$+ (4 \text{ kg})(0 \text{ m/s}) = (6 \text{ k})(- 6 \text{ m/s}) + (4 \text{ kg})v_2'$$
$$(4 \text{ kg})v_2' = 36 \text{ kg} \cdot \text{m/s}$$
$$v_2' = 9 \text{ m/s}$$

Even though both cars are moving after the event, the resultant of their momentum vectors is zero, just as it was before the event. The 4-kg cart has a momentum of $(4 \text{ kg})(9 \text{ m/s})$, or $36 \text{ kg} \cdot \text{m/s}$, to the right, while the 6-kg cart has a momentum of $(6 \text{ kg})(-6 \text{ m/s})$, or $-36 \text{ kg} \cdot \text{m/s}$, to the left.

Momentum and Newton's Third Law of Motion

Recall that the third law states that every action produces an equal and opposite reaction. Thus, when two objects explode or collide, the forces they experience must be equal in magnitude and opposite in direction. Since the time during which these forces act (Δt) must be the same for both, the impulses $[F(\Delta t)]$ imparted to each object are equal in magnitude and opposite in direction. Because impulse equals change in momentum, we conclude that *the changes in momentum experienced by the objects as a result of the event are equal in magnitude and opposite in direction.*

QUESTIONS

136. A 1.0-kilogram mass changes speed from 2.0 meters per second to 5.0 meters per second. The change in the object's momentum is   (1) 3.0 kg-m/s   (2) 9.0 kg-m/s   (3) 21 kg-m/s   (4) 29 kg-m/s

137. A 20-kilogram mass moving at a speed of 3.0 meters per second is stopped by a constant force of 15 newtons. How many seconds must the force act on the mass to stop it?   (1) 0.20 s   (2) 1.3 s   (3) 4.0 s   (4) 5.0 s

138. An object traveling at 4.0 meters per second has a momentum of 16 kilogram-meters per second. What is the mass of the object?   (1) 64 kg   (2) 20 kg   (3) 12 kg   (4) 4.0 kg

139. Two carts resting on a frictionless surface are forced apart by a spring. One cart has a mass of 2 kilograms and moves to the left at a speed of 3 meters per second. If the second cart has a mass of 3 kilograms, it will move to the right at a speed of   (1) 1 m/s   (2) 2 m/s   (3) 3 m/s   (4) 6 m/s

140. A 15-newton force acts on an object in a direction due east for 3.0 seconds. What will be the change in momentum of the object? (1) 45 kg-m/s due east (2) 45 kg-m/s due west (3) 5.0 kg-m/s due east (4) 0.20 kg-m/s due west

141. A 5.0-kilogram cart moving with a velocity of 4.0 meters per second is brought to a stop in 2.0 seconds. The magnitude of the average force used to stop the cart is (1) 2.0 N (2) 4.0 N (3) 10. N (4) 20. N

142. A 5.0-newton force imparts an impulse of 15 newton-seconds to an object. The force acted on the object for a period of (1) 75 s (2) 20. s (3) 3.0 s (4) 0.33 s

143. A net force of 12 newtons acting north on an object for 4.0 seconds will produce an impulse of (1) 48 kg-m/s north (2) 48 kg-m/s south (3) 3.0 kg-m/s north (4) 3.0 kg-m/s south

144. Two disk magnets are arranged at rest on a frictionless horizontal surface as shown in the diagram. When the string holding them together is cut, they move apart under a magnetic force of repulsion. When the 1.0-kilogram disk reaches a speed of 3.0 meters per second, what is the speed of the 0.5-kilogram disk? (1) 0.50 m/s (2) 1.0 m/s (3) 3.0 m/s (4) 6.0 m/s

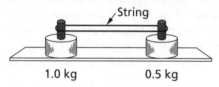

1.0 kg   0.5 kg

145. The diagram represents two identical carts, attached by a cord moving to the right at speed *V*. If the cord is cut, what would be the speed of cart *A*? (1) 0 (2) *V*/2 (3) *V* (4) 2*V*

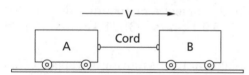

146. If a 3.0-kilogram object moves 10. meters in 2.0 seconds, its average momentum is (1) 60. kg-m/s (2) 30. kg-m/s (3) 15 kg-m/s (4) 10. kg-m/s

147. An impulse of 30.0 newton-seconds is applied to a 5.00-kilogram mass. If the mass had a speed of 100. meters per second before the impulse, its speed after the impulse could be (1) 250. m/s (2) 106 m/s (3) 6.00 m/s (4) 0 m/s

148. Two carts of masses of 5.0 kilograms and 1.0 kilogram are pushed apart by a compressed spring. If the 5.0-kilogram cart moves westward at 2.0 meters per second, the magnitude of the

velocity of the 1.0-kilogram cart will be (1) 2.0 kg-m/s (2) 2.0 m/s (3) 10. kg-m/s (4) 10. m/s

149. The direction of an object's momentum is always the same as the direction of the object's (1) inertia (2) potential energy (3) velocity (4) weight

150. An unbalanced force of 20 newtons is applied to an object for 10 seconds. The change in the momentum of the object will be (1) 200 kg-m/s (2) 2,000 kg-m/s (3) 10,000 kg-m/s (4) 20,000 kg-m/s

151. A 4.0-kilogram mass is moving at 3.0 meters per second toward the right and a 6.0-kilogram mass is moving at 2.0 meters per second toward the left on a horizontal frictionless table. If the two masses collide and remain together after the collision, their final momentum is (1) 24 kg-m/s (2) 12 kg-m/s (3) 1.0 kg-m/s (4) 0 kg-m/s

Thinking and Analyzing

152. What is momentum and how is it determined?

153. Show what the unit of momentum is and how it is derived.

154. How is the direction of momentum related to the direction of the object's velocity? What does it mean for an object to have a negative momentum?

155. A small car and a large truck filled with cargo each moves at 80 km/h. Which has the greater momentum? Explain.

156. What is impulse and how is it determined? How is impulse related to momentum?

157. A rubber, lead, and aluminum pellet are each fired at a block of wood. The rubber pellet bounces off the block. The aluminum pellet penetrates and remains embedded in the block. The lead pellet goes straight through the block, emerging from the other side at a somewhat reduced speed. Compare and contrast the magnitude of the force exerted by each pellet on the block. Base your analysis on the relationship between impulse and momentum.

158. What happens to momentum when objects interact in the absence of an external force?

159. Suppose two objects collide. After the collision, the momentum of Object A decreases. What must be true about the momentum of Object B. Why?

160. Relate changes in momentum to Newton's third law of motion.

TWO-DIMENSIONAL MOTION AND TRAJECTORIES

Up to now we have discussed the motion of objects traveling along a straight line, or in one dimension. Many objects, however, move within a plane, or in two dimensions. Any object that is launched by some force and continues to move by its own inertia is called a **projectile.** The path of a projectile is referred to as its trajectory.

The motion of a projectile is best described by separating the motion into horizontal (x) and vertical (y) components of the vector quantities displacement, velocity, and acceleration.

Projectiles Launched Horizontally

An object launched horizontally with a velocity v_x starts its motion with an initial vertical velocity of zero ($v_{iy} = 0$). Since no forces act in the horizontal direction (ignoring air resistance), the horizontal component of the object's velocity remains constant. The vertical component, however, is affected by Earth's gravitational pull and accelerates at the rate of 9.8 m/s^2. The resulting path of the object is a parabola.

The time it takes the object to reach the ground depends only on the height above the ground from which it is launched and the acceleration due to gravity. The horizontal component of its motion has no effect on this time. Balls A, B, and C in Figure 1-34 start with different horizontal velocities, but all three balls reach the ground at the same time. On the other hand, the horizontal distance traveled, or **range,** is dependent on the horizontal velocity and the time of flight.

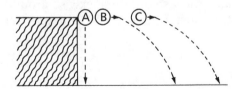

Figure 1-34. Ball A is released and falls straight down. Ball B is launched horizontally at 5 m/s. Ball C is launched horizontally at 10 m/s.

Projectiles Launched at an Angle

Golf balls, baseballs, and missiles are examples of projectiles launched at an angle to the surface of the earth. The maximum height achieved by such projectiles and their total horizontal displacement, or range, depend on the magnitude and direction of the velocity vector at the time of launch and on the acceleration due to gravity. Once the initial vertical and horizontal components of velocity have been determined, the motion of the projectile can be treated as two independent linear motion problems.

The horizontal and vertical components of the initial velocity vector can be determined by vector resolution. Figure 1-35 is a vector diagram of the initial velocity vector $\mathbf{v_i}$ of a projectile launched at some angle θ.

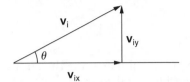

Figure 1-35.

The **maximum range** of a projectile launched at a given speed is achieved when the angle with the horizontal is 45°.

QUESTIONS

161. At what angle from the horizontal must a projectile be launched in order to achieve the greatest range?   (1) 20°   (2) 30°   (3) 45°   (4) 57.3°

162. At the same moment that a baseball is thrown horizontally by a pitcher, a ring drops vertically off his hand. Which statement about the baseball and the ring is correct, neglecting air resistance?   (1) The baseball hits the ground first. (2) The ring hits the ground first.   (3) They both hit the ground at the same time.

Thinking and Analyzing

163. When is an object considered to be a projectile?

164. What determines the time it takes for a horizontal projectile to reach the ground? Explain.

165. What is the range of a horizontal projectile and upon what does it depend?

166. How can you achieve the maximum range of a projectile launched at an angle?

UNIFORM CIRCULAR MOTION

An object undergoes **uniform circular motion** if it moves along a circular path at a constant speed. Although the magnitude of the object's velocity is constant, the velocity *direction* is constantly changing. A change in the velocity vector of an object means that the object is accelerating. The acceleration experienced by an object in uniform circular motion is called **centripetal acceleration**. Centripetal acceleration $\mathbf{a_c}$ is a vector quantity, directed toward the center of the circle. The magnitude of this acceleration vector is directly proportional to the square of the object's speed and inversely proportional to the radius of its path. Thus,

$$a_c = \frac{v^2}{r}$$

where v is the speed of the object along the circular path and r is the radius of the circle.

Since a circling object is accelerating, there must be a net force acting on it—it is not in equilibrium. The force that causes the centripetal acceleration is called the **centripetal force $\mathbf{F_c}$**. This force acts in the same direction as the centripetal acceleration—toward the center of the circle (Figure 1-36). The magnitude of the centripetal force is obtained from Newton's second law.

$$F_c = ma_c = m\,\frac{v^2}{r}$$

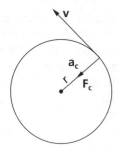

Figure 1-36.

The centripetal force is the net force on the circling object that acts to change the object's direction. The object's speed is constant because there are no tangential forces acting on the object.

Sample Problem

26. A 1.0-kg ball attached to the end of a rope 0.50 m long is swung in a circle. Its speed along the circular path is 6.0 m/s. Find the centripetal acceleration and force.

Solution:

$$a_c = \frac{v^2}{r} = \frac{(6.0 \text{ m/s})^2}{(0.50 \text{ m})} = 72 \text{ m/s}^2$$

$$F_c = ma_c = (1.0 \text{ kg})(72 \text{ m/s}^2) = 72 \text{ N}$$

QUESTIONS

Base your answers to questions 167 through 170 on the diagram below, which represents a 2.0-kilogram mass moving in a circular path on the end of a string 0.50 meter long. The mass moves in a horizontal plane at a constant speed of 4.0 meters per second.

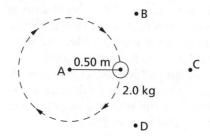

167. The force exerted on the mass by the string is (1) 8 N (2) 16 N (3) 32 N (4) 64 N

168. In the position shown in the diagram, the momentum of the mass is directed toward point (1) A (2) B (3) C (4) D

169. The centripetal force acting on the mass is directed toward point (1) A (2) B (3) C (4) D

170. The speed of the mass is changed to 2.0 meters per second. Compared to the centripetal acceleration of the mass when moving at 4.0 meters per second, its centripetal acceleration when moving at 2.0 meters per second would be (1) half as great (2) twice as great (3) one-fourth as great (4) four times as great

Base your answers to questions 171 through 175 on the diagram below, which represents a flat racetrack as viewed from above, with the radii of its two curves indicated. A car with a mass of 1000 kilograms moves counterclockwise around the track at a constant speed of 20 meters per second.

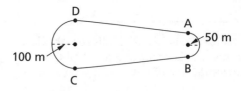

171. The net force acting on the car while it is moving from A to D is (1) 0 N (2) 400 N (3) 8,000 N (4) 20,000 N

172. The net force acting on the car while it is moving from D to C is (1) 0 N (2) 200 N (3) 4,000 N (4) 20,000 N

173. If the car moved from C to B in 20 seconds, the distance CB is (1) 100 m (2) 200 m (3) 300 m (4) 400 m

174. Compared with the centripetal acceleration of the car while moving from B to A, the centripetal acceleration of the car while moving from D to C is (1) the same (2) twice as great (3) one-half as great (4) 4 times greater

Note that question 175 has only three choices

175. Compared with the kinetic energy of the car while moving from A to D, the kinetic energy of the car while moving from D to C is (1) less (2) greater (3) the same

Base your answers to questions 176 through 180 on the diagram below, which represents a 5.0-kilogram object revolving around a circular track in a horizontal plane at a constant speed. The radius of the track is 20. meters and the centripetal force on the object is 4.0×10^2 newtons.

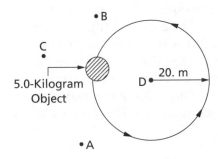

176. In the position shown, the object's centripetal acceleration is directed toward point (1) A (2) B (3) C (4) D

177. In the position shown, the object's velocity is directed toward point (1) A (2) B (3) C (4) D

178. The object's centripetal acceleration is (1) 0.012 m/s^2 (2) 20. m/s^2 (3) 80. m/s^2 (4) 1.0×10^2 m/s^2

179. The object's speed is (1) 20. m/s (2) 40. m/s (3) 60. m/s (4) 90. m/s

180. If the radius of the track is increased, the centripetal force necessary to keep the object revolving at the same speed would (1) decrease (2) increase (3) remain the same

Base your answers to questions 181 through 185 on the following diagram, which represents a car of mass 1,000 kilograms traveling around a horizontal circular track of radius 200 meters at a constant speed of 20 meters per second.

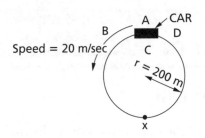

181. When the car is in the position shown, the direction of its centripetal acceleration is toward (1) A (2) B (3) C (4) D

182. The magnitude of the centripetal force acting on the car is closest to (1) 100 N (2) 1,000 N (3) 2,000 N (4) 4,000 N

183. If the speed of the car were doubled, the centripetal acceleration of the car would be (1) the same (2) doubled (3) $\frac{1}{2}$ as great (4) 4 times as great

Note that questions 184 and 185 have only three choices.

184. If additional passengers were riding in the car, at the original speed, the car's centripetal acceleration would be (1) less (2) greater (3) the same

185. As the car moves from its present position to position X, its kinetic energy (1) decreases (2) increases (3) remains the same

Thinking and Analyzing

186. Define uniform circular motion.

187. Why is an object in uniform circular motion accelerating?

188. Describe the magnitude and direction of centripetal acceleration.

189. Is an object undergoing uniform circular motion influenced by any force? If so, desribe the force.

190. How is the magnitude of the centripetal force determined?

191. Why does an object move in uniform circular motion even when a centripetal force is acting on it?

Free Fall

"What goes up, must come down," goes the old saying. This is true because of gravity. Gravity is the force that acts to pull objects toward the center of Earth. When the only force acting on a falling object is gravity, the object is said to be in free fall. An object in free fall accelerates as it falls because gravity acts as an unbalanced force in the downward direction. The acceleration due to gravity is 9.8 m/s^2.

Does this mean that a skydiver accelerates at a rate of 9.8 m/s^2 after jumping from an aircraft? The answer is no. In many cases, such as this, there is another force acting on falling objects—air resistance. Air resistance is a friction force that acts in the direction opposite to the direction of motion of the skydiver. In these cases, the objects are not falling freely.

Air resistance is not a constant value. Instead, it depends on the surface area and velocity of the falling object. Generally, the greater the surface area of the object perpendicular to the direction of motion, the greater is the air resistance on the object. And, generally, the greater the velocity of the object, the greater is the air resistance on the object. So as a falling object speeds up due to the force of gravity, the air resistance on the object increases. At some point, air resistance becomes equal to the force of gravity. When this happens, the downward force on the object is balanced by the upward force on the object. When forces are balanced, there is no acceleration. Does the object stop falling? Of course, not. The object continues to fall. However, its velocity no longer increases. The velocity at which this occurs is called terminal velocity.

QUESTIONS

1. Under what conditions is an object in free fall?
2. Describe the force(s) acting on an object in free fall. Include a diagram in your description.
3. What is air resistance?
4. Describe the force(s) acting on a skydiver before and after terminal velocity is reached. Include diagrams in your description.
5. How is a skydiver's parachute related to the motion of the skydiver? How does a parachute affect the motion of a skydiver?

Enrichment Mechanics

PROJECTILE MOTION

Using the equations of motion you learned earlier, you can calculate how far a projectile will travel in the horizontal direction and how long it will take to hit the ground. The motion equations are applied independently to the horizontal motion and the vertical motion. Those equations are listed in Table 1-3.

Table 1-3

Horizontal Components

$a_x = 0$	Ignoring air resistance, there is no force in the horizontal direction to produce an acceleration.
v_x = constant	The horizontal component of velocity remains constant.
$\Delta d_x = v_x \Delta t$	The horizontal displacement, or range.

Vertical Components

$a_y = g = 9.81$ m/s^2	Acceleration due to gravity near Earth is constant.
$v_{fy} = v_{iy} + a_y \Delta t$	When $v_{iy} = 0$, this equation reduces to $v_{fy} = ay \Delta t$.
$\Delta d_y = v_{iy} \Delta t + \frac{1}{2} a_y (\Delta t)^2$	When $v_{iy} = 0$, this equation reduces to $d_y = \frac{1}{2} a_y (\Delta t)^2$.

Sample Problems

27. A ball is tossed horizontally with a velocity of 15 m/s from a height of 100. m above the ground (Figure 1-37). How long will it take the ball to hit the ground?

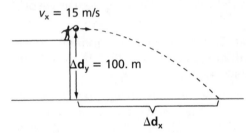

Figure 1-37

Solution:

$$\Delta d_y = v_{iy} \Delta t + \frac{1}{2} a_y (\Delta t)^2$$

$$100.\, \text{m} = (0\, \text{m/s})(\Delta t) + \frac{1}{2}(9.81\, \text{m/s}^2)(\Delta t)^2$$

$$\Delta t = \sqrt{\frac{100.\, \text{m}}{4.9\, \text{m/s}^2}} = 4.5\, \text{s}$$

What are the horizontal and vertical components of the ball's velocity as it strikes the ground?
Solution:

$$v_x = 15\, \text{m/s}$$

$$v_{fy} = v_{iy} + a_y \Delta t$$

$$= 0\, \text{m/s} + (9.81\, \text{m/s}^2)(4.5\, \text{s}) = 44\, \text{m/s}$$

How far did the ball travel horizontally in its flight?
Solution:

$$\Delta d_x = v_x \Delta t$$

$$= (15\, \text{m/s})(4.5\, \text{s}) = 68\, \text{m}$$

What is the magnitude of the resultant velocity vector as the ball strikes the ground?
Solution: The resultant velocity vector is the vector sum of the ball's vertical and horizontal components. Thus, using the Pythagorean theorem, we find

$$v_f^2 = v_{fx}^2 + v_{fy}^2$$

$$= (15\, \text{m/s})^2 + (44\, \text{m/s})^2$$

$$v_f = \sqrt{2161\, \text{m}^2/\text{s}^2} = 46\, \text{m/s}$$

28. In Figure 1-38, an airplane flying horizontally at 150 m/s drops a bomb from a height of 2500 m. How far in front of the target must the bomb be released?

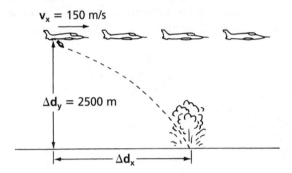

Figure 1-38.

Solution: First, find the time it takes for the bomb to hit the ground.

$$\Delta d_y = v_{iy}(\Delta t) + \frac{1}{2} a_y (\Delta t)^2$$

$$2500\, \text{m} = (0\, \text{m/s})(\Delta t) + \frac{1}{2}(9.81\, \text{m/s}^2)(\Delta t)^2$$

$$\Delta t = \sqrt{\frac{2500\, \text{m}}{4.9\, \text{m/s}^2}} = 23\text{s}$$

Now find the range.

$$\Delta d_x = v_x(\Delta t)$$

$$= (150\, \text{m/s})(23\, \text{s}) = 3.5 \times 10^3\, \text{m}$$

Thus the bomb must be released 3.5×10^3 m in front of the target.

Finding the Horizontal and Vertical Components of Velocity

Following the rules for vector resolution (Figure 1-39) you can determine the magnitude of the vertical and horizontal components of the initial velocity. The magnitude of the vertical component of the initial velocity vector $\mathbf{v_{iy}}$ is determined by the formula

$$v_{iy} = v_i \sin \theta$$

The magnitude of the horizontal component of the initial velocity vector $\mathbf{v_{ix}}$ is determined by the formula

$$v_{ix} = v_i \cos \theta$$

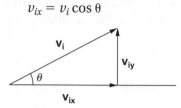

Figure 1-39.

29. A cannonball is fired from ground level at an angle of 60° with the ground at a speed of 72 m/s (Figure 1-40). What are the horizontal and vertical components of the velocity at the time of launch?

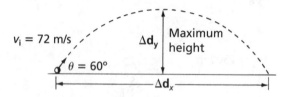

Figure 1-40.

Solution:

$$v_{ix} = v_i \cos \theta = (72 \text{ m/s})(\cos 60°)$$

$$= (72 \text{ m/s})(0.500) = 36 \text{ m/s}$$

$$v_{iy} = v_i \sin \theta = (72 \text{ m/s})(\sin 60°)$$

$$= (72 \text{ m/s})(0.866) = 62 \text{ m/s}$$

How long does it take the cannonball to reach its maximum height?

Solution: When the ball is at its highest point the vertical component of the velocity is zero. At that point the cannonball has stopped moving upward and is just about to begin moving downward. Thus,

$$v_{fy} = v_{iy} + a_y \Delta t$$

$$0 \text{ m/s} = 62 \text{ m/s} + (-9.81 \text{ m/s}^2)(\Delta t)$$

$$\Delta t = \frac{62 \text{ m/s}}{9.81 \text{ m/s}^2} = 6.3 \text{ s}$$

How high does the cannonball rise?
Solution:

$$\Delta d_y = v_{iy}\Delta t + \tfrac{1}{2}a_y(\Delta t)^2$$

$$= (62 \text{ m/s})(6.3 \text{ s}) + \tfrac{1}{2}(-9.81 \text{ m/s}^2)(6.3 \text{ s})^2$$

$$= 196 \text{ m}$$

What is the cannonball's total time of flight?
Solution: We have already found that the time going up is 6.3 s. To find the time going down:

$$\Delta d_y = v_{iy}\Delta t + \tfrac{1}{2}a_y(\Delta t)^2$$

$$196 \text{ m} = (0 \text{ m/s})(\Delta t)$$

$$+ \tfrac{1}{2}(9.81 \text{ m/s}^2)(\Delta t)^2$$

$$\Delta t = \sqrt{\frac{196 \text{ m}}{4.9 \text{ m/s}^2}} = 6.3 \text{ s}$$

$$\text{total time of flight} = 6.3 \text{ s} + 6.3 \text{ s}$$

$$= 12.6 \text{ s}$$

This answer can also be obtained by multiplying the time required to reach the maximum height by two.
What is the cannonball's range?
Solution:

$$\Delta d_x = v_x \Delta t$$

$$= (36 \text{ m/s})(12.6 \text{ s}) = 453 \text{ m}$$

QUESTIONS

Base your answers to questions 192 through 195 on the following information: An arrow is shot with an initial velocity of 50. m/s at an angle of 60° from the horizontal.

192. What is the vertical component of the arrow's initial velocity?   (1) 25 m/s   (2) 43 m/s   (3) 50. m/s   (4) 58 m/s

193. Neglecting air resistance, after how many seconds does the arrow reach its maximum height?   (1) 4.4 s   (2) 5.1 s   (3) 43 s   (4) 420 s

194. How high does the arrow rise?   (1) 95 m   (2) 190 m   (3) 220 m   (4) 284 m

195. How far has the arrow traveled horizontally by the time it returns to the ground?   (1) 110 m   (2) 220 m   (3) 380 m   (4) 450 m

KEPLER'S LAWS

Johannes Kepler deduced three laws describing planetary motion. These laws inspired Newton and led to his equations of motion and gravitation.

Kepler's First Law
Kepler's first law states that the path of each planet is an ellipse with the sun at one focus.

An **ellipse** is defined as a closed curve such that the sum of the distances from any point p on the curve to two fixed points called the foci is constant (Figure 1-41). A circle is an ellipse in which the two foci coincide at the center.

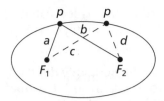

Figure 1-41. F_1 and F_2 are the foci and $a + b = c + d$.

The orbits of some planets are nearly circular while others are distinctly elliptical. For example, Pluto's elliptical orbit causes it to be closer to the sun than Neptune for about 20 during its 248-year path. This last occurred from 1979 to 1999. Earth's elliptical orbit brings it closest to the sun in January and farthest away in July. Many comets have elongated elliptical paths with the sun at one focus and the other far beyond the solar system (Figure 1-42).

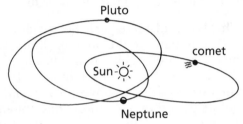

Figure 1-42.

Kepler's Second Law

Kepler's second law states that each planet moves in such a way that an imaginary line drawn from the sun to the planet sweeps out equal areas in equal periods of time. For example, the wedge-shaped sectors A_1, A_2, and A_3 in the ellipse illustrated in Figure 1-43 are all equal in area. If an imaginary line connecting the planet to the sun passes through area A_1 in one week, it passes through areas A_2 and A_3 in one week each as well. This means that the planet moves faster when it is closer to the sun. As a planet gets closer to the sun, its gravitational potential energy decreases and its kinetic energy increases.

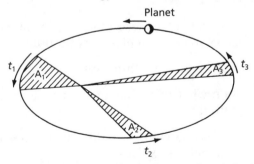

Figure 1-43. The planet moves faster when it is closer to the sun; $t_1 = t_2 = t_3$ and $A_1 = A_2 = A_3$.

Kepler's Third Law

Kepler's third law states that the ratio of the mean radius of orbit cubed (R^3) to the orbital period squared (T^2) is a constant for all the planets. This relationship is expressed mathematically as

$$\frac{R^3}{T^2} = k$$

where k is a constant. Kepler's third law is applicable to any group of satellites that orbit around a given body. The value of k depends on the mass of the particular body being orbited. In the case of the planets orbiting the sun, k is equal to 3.35×10^{18} m³/s². As the mass of the object being orbited decreases, k decreases. For example, the value of k for objects orbiting Earth is 1.02×10^{13} m³/s².

SATELLITE MOTION

A **satellite** is defined as any body revolving around a larger body. The nine planets are satellites of the sun, and the sixteen moons of Jupiter are satellites of Jupiter. Earth's satellites include the moon and the artificial objects placed in orbit about Earth.

Newton was the first to compare the motion of a satellite around Earth to the motion of a projectile. He concluded that a satellite is simply a projectile that "falls freely" toward Earth. We know that the greater the horizontal component of a projectile's velocity, the greater the horizontal distance it will travel before hitting the ground. It follows that if a projectile has a great enough horizontal velocity, the curved path of its motion will match Earth's curvature and it will rotate around, instead of fall into, Earth. If a satellite is too close to Earth, the drag of the atmosphere will slow it down and it will spiral inward toward Earth. If, on the other hand, its speed is too great, the satellite will spiral outward and escape from Earth's gravitational pull. The minimum speed an object must have to escape the influence of a body's gravitational pull is called the **escape velocity.**

Apparent Weightlessness

Astronauts in orbiting spaceships experience a state of "weightlessness" even though Earth's gravity still pulls them toward Earth. Indeed, it is this pull that provides the centripetal force that maintains the orbit. Why then does an astronaut's weight not register on a scale, and why do all the objects in the spaceship float freely? These effects occur because the spaceship is falling toward Earth together with the astronaut, the scale, and all the objects aboard. If the astronaut released a glove, for example, it would not fall to the floor because the floor, the glove, and the astronaut are all falling at the same rate.

Geosynchronous Orbit

Communication and weather satellites are usually placed in **geosynchronous orbits.** A geosynchronous orbit is one in which the satellite's orbital period is equal to the period of Earth's rotation about its own axis (24 hours). A satellite in geosynchronous orbit remains over the same spot on Earth's equator.

Kepler's third law can be used to determine the radius of orbit needed for an artificial satellite to have a desired orbital period. Since the value of R^3/T^2 is the same for all Earth satellites (both natural and artificial), we can simply equate R^3/T^2 for the moon and R^3/T^2 for the satellite. For example,

$$\frac{R_{\text{shuttle}}^3}{T_{\text{shuttle}}^2} = \frac{R_{\text{moon}}^3}{T_{\text{moon}}^2} = k_{\text{Earth}} = 1.02 \times 10^{13}\ \text{m}^3/\text{s}^2$$

We conclude that in order to be in geosynchronous orbit, a spaceship must orbit at a distance from the earth's center equal to approximately 6.6 times Earth's radius.

QUESTIONS

196. The path of a planet around the sun is best described as (1) a circle (2) an ellipse (3) a parabola (4) an epicycle

197. With respect to a planet's orbit, the sun is situated at (1) the center (2) one of the foci (3) a nodal point (4) a geocentric point

198. Until 1999 Neptune was farther from the sun than Pluto because Pluto (1) has switched orbits with Neptune temporarily (2) orbits Neptune (3) is denser than Neptune (4) has a very elongated orbit

Questions 199–205 are based on the following diagram of a planet orbiting the sun. It takes the planet one month to travel from point A to point B, and one month to travel from point C to point D.

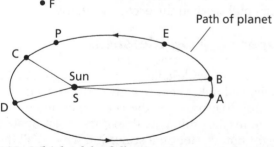

199. Which of the following statements is correct? (1) arc AB = arc CD (2) length SC = length SA (3) area SCD = area SAB (4) potential energy at C = potential energy at A

200. At which point does the planet have the greatest kinetic energy and speed? (1) A (2) C (3) E (4) the speed is the same at all of the above

201. If this planet is Earth, when is it located at point C? (1) January (2) June (3) July (4) September

202. If the planet's mass were suddenly doubled, the period of its revolution in orbit would (1) decrease (2) increase (3) remain the same.

203. When the planet is at point P, the direction of the planet's velocity is toward point (1) S (2) F (3) C (4) B

204. The direction of the planet's acceleration at point P is toward point (1) S (2) E (3) F (4) B

205. If the mass of the sun were suddenly to increase, then the value of R^3/T^2 would (1) decrease (2) increase (3) remain the same

206. What is true of a satellite in geosynchronous orbit? (1) It remains in the same position over a point on the equator. (2) It remains in a fixed position between Earth and the moon. (3) It remains in a fixed position between Earth and the sun. (4) Its period of revolution does not equal Earth's period of rotation.

207. The radius of orbit for an artificial satellite around Earth may be determined by equating R^3/T^2 for the satellite with R^3/T^2 for the (1) Earth (2) moon (3) sun (4) other planets

208. What occurs if an orbiting satellite's speed exceeds escape velocity? (1) It spirals back toward earth. (2) It achieves a geosynchronous orbit. (3) It spirals outward away from Earth. (4) Any of the above are possible.

Thinking and Analyzing

209. What is an ellipse and how do ellipses relate to Kepler's first law?

210. What is Kepler's second law and what is its significance in terms of planetary motion?

211. Describe Kepler's third law.

212. Upon what does the constant k depend in Kepler's third law?

213. What is a satellite? Can there be natural and artificial satellites? Explain.

214. Why must an object reach a certain speed if it is to become a satellite of Earth?

215. What is a geosynchronous orbit and how is Kepler's third law important in launching a satellite into such an orbit?

CHAPTER 2

Energy

Energy is needed to do work. The relationship between work and energy and the study of the various forms of energy are the subjects of this unit.

WORK

In physics, **work** is done whenever a force acts on an object in the direction of the object's motion. For example, a weight lifter does work as she lifts a weight from the ground to a position over her head because she pushes up as the weight goes up (Figure 2-1). If she then holds the weight at rest above her head, however, she is not doing any work since the weight is not in motion even though she may be straining to keep it there.

Figure 2-1.

The amount of work W is the product of the magnitude of the applied force F and the object's displacement Δd in the direction of the force. A short person, therefore, does less work in lifting a weight from the floor to a position over his head than a tall person. In situations where the force acts in the same direction as the object's motion we can write

$$W = F\Delta d$$

If only a component of the force acts in the direction of the object's motion, the amount of work done is equal to the product of the magnitude of that component and the displacement of the object. Work is a scalar quantity; it has magnitude but no direction.

The **joule** is the unit of work. One joule of work is done on an object when the force is one newton and the displacement is one meter. The joule (J) is a derived unit that can be expressed in terms of fundamental units.

$$1 \text{ joule} = 1 \text{ newton} \cdot \text{meter} = 1 \text{ N} \cdot \text{m}$$

$$1 \text{ J} = \frac{1 \text{ kg} \cdot \text{m}}{\text{s}^2} \cdot (\text{m}) = \frac{1 \text{ kg} \cdot \text{m}^2}{\text{s}^2}$$

Sample Problems

1. A crate is pushed along the floor with a force of 9.0 N for a distance of 5.0 m. How much work is done?

Solution:

$W = F\Delta d$

$\quad = (9.0 \text{ N})(5.0 \text{ m}) = 45 \text{ N} \cdot \text{m} = 45 \text{ J}$

2. A 5.0-kg weight is lifted a vertical distance of 2.0 m. How much work is done?

Solution: The force needed to lift an object at constant speed is equal to its weight, which in turn is equal to the product of its mass m and the acceleration due to gravity g. Thus,

$F = mg$

$\quad = (5.0 \text{ kg})(9.8 \text{ m/s}^2) = 49 \text{ kg} \cdot \text{m/s}^2 = 49 \text{ N}$

$W = F\Delta d = (49 \text{ N})(2.0 \text{ m}) = 98 \text{ J}$

Power

Power is the amount of work done per unit time. Like work, it is a scalar quantity. The symbol for power is P.

$$P = \frac{W}{t}$$

where W is work done in time t. Since $W = F\Delta d$ and $v = \Delta d/\Delta t$, we may write

$$P = F\frac{\Delta d}{\Delta t} = Fv$$

Thus, power can also be expressed as the product of the applied force and the velocity of the object.

The unit of power is the **watt** (W). One watt of power equals one joule of work done in one second. The watt is a derived unit and can be expressed in terms of fundamental units.

$$1 \text{ W} = 1\frac{\text{J}}{\text{s}} = \frac{1 \text{ N} \cdot \text{m}}{\text{s}} = 1\frac{\text{kg} \cdot \text{m}^2}{\text{s}^3}$$

Sample Problems

3. A hoist lifts an object weighing 1200 N a vertical distance of 15 m in 15 s. What work is done if the object rises at constant speed?
Solution:

$$W = F\Delta d = (1200 \text{ N})(15 \text{ m})$$
$$= 18,000 \text{ J}$$

What power is developed?
Solution:

$$P = \frac{W}{t} = \frac{18,000 \text{ J}}{15 \text{ s}} = 1200 \text{ W}$$

4. How long will it take an 800. W motor to push a boat through the water a distance of 1000. m with a force of 7.5 N?
Solution:

$$P = \frac{W}{t} = \frac{F\Delta d}{t}$$

$$800. \text{ W} = \frac{(7.5 \text{ N})(1000. \text{ m})}{t}$$

$$t = \frac{(7.5 \text{ N})(1000. \text{ m})}{800. \text{ W}}$$

$$= \frac{7500 \text{ N} \cdot \text{m}}{800. \text{ N} \cdot \text{m/s}} = 9.4 \text{ s}$$

5. A 60-N force exerted on an object causes it to move with a constant velocity of 5 m/s. What power is used?
Solution:

$$P = Fv$$

$$= (60 \text{ N})(5 \text{ m/s}) = 300 \text{ J/s} = 300 \text{ W}$$

QUESTIONS

1. A force of 80. newtons pushes a 50.-kilogram object across a level floor for 8.0 meters. The work done is   (1) 10 J   (2) 400 J   (3) 640 J   (4) 3,920 J

2. Energy is measured in the same units as (1) force   (2) momentum   (3) work   (4) power

3. If 700 watts of power is needed to keep a boat moving through the water at a constant speed of 10 meters per second, what is the magnitude of the force exerted by the water on the boat? (1) 0.01 N   (2) 70 N   (3) 700 N   (4) 7,000 N

4. A crane raises a 200-newton weight to a height of 50 meters in 5 seconds. The crane does work at the rate of   (1) 8×10^{-1} W   (2) 2×10^1 W   (3) 2×10^3 W   (4) 5×10^4 W

5. A constant force of 20. newtons applied to a box causes it to move at a constant speed of 4.0 meters per second. How much work is done on the box in 6.0 seconds?   (1) 480 J   (2) 240 J   (3) 120 J   (4) 80. J

6. An object has a mass of 8.0 kilograms. A 2.0-newton force displaces the object a distance of 3.0 meters to the east, and then 4.0 meters to the north. What is the total work done on the object? (1) 10. J   (2) 14 J   (3) 28 J   (4) 56 J

7. What is the minimum power required for a conveyor to raise an 8.0-newton box 4.0 meters vertically in 8.0 seconds?   (1) 260 W   (2) 64 W   (3) 32 W   (4) 4.0 W

8. As the power of a machine is increased, the time required to move an object a fixed distance (1) decreases   (2) increases   (3) remains the same

9. One elevator lifts a mass a given height in 10 seconds and a second elevator does the same work in 5 seconds. Compared with the power developed by the first elevator, the power developed by the second elevator is   (1) one-half as great (2) twice as great   (3) the same   (4) four times as great

Thinking and Analyzing

10. What requirements are necessary for work to be done?

11. What quantities do you need in order to calculate work? Explain.

12. How is power related to work?

13. How can power be defined in terms of force and velocity?

14. Identify the units of work and power, and provide the fundamental units for each.

15. Describe two different methods of increasing power for any given situation.

ENERGY

Energy is the ability to do work. The amount of energy a system possesses is equal to the amount of work the system can do. Work can be done only by the transfer of energy from one object or system to another. For example, a hammer swinging downward has energy—it has the ability to do work on a nail. It can drive a nail a certain distance with force. As this work is done, the hammer's energy is transferred to the nail. Like work, energy is a scalar quantity and is measured in joules.

Energy is found in many forms: electromagnetic, chemical, mechanical, heat, nuclear, and sound. One form of energy can be converted into any other. For example, the energy in steam can be used to drive a turbine. In this process, heat energy is converted to mechanical energy. The energy from the turbine can be used to generate electricity, thus converting mechanical energy into electrical energy. Finally, the electrical energy can be used to run an assortment of appliances.

Potential Energy

The energy that an object has owing to its position or condition is called **potential energy** (*PE*). For example, the position of an object above Earth's surface gives it gravitational potential energy because Earth's gravitational field can do work on it. The condition of a coiled spring, whether stretched or compressed, gives it elastic potential energy. Finally, energy stored in combustible fuel, such as gasoline, is an example of chemical potential energy.

The change in an object's potential energy is equal to the work required to bring the object to its new position or condition from its original position or condition (assuming no loss of energy due to friction or air resistance). For example, the elastic potential energy of a stretched spring is equal to the work done to stretch it.

$$\Delta PE = W$$

Gravitational Potential Energy

As an object is lifted from one position on Earth to another, work is done *against* Earth's gravitational attraction. After being lifted, there is an increase in the **gravitational potential energy** of the object. As an object is lowered from one position to another on Earth, work is done *by* Earth's gravitational field. This results in a decrease in the gravitational potential energy of the object. The change in gravitational potential energy is equal to the work done.

From the definition of work, we know that the amount of work done is equal to the product of the applied force and the displacement of the object in the direction of the force. Thus, we can write

$$\Delta PE = W = F\Delta d$$

When an object is lowered or raised, the force exerted by or against Earth's gravitational field is equal to the object's weight *mg*. The displacement of the object is the vertical distance Δh. Therefore, the change in the object's gravitational potential energy can be expressed as

$$\Delta PE = mg\Delta h$$

This equation only applies to displacements that are small compared with Earth's radius, when *g* is constant. Over larger distances, *g* varies and the equation is not applicable.

Frequently, we are interested only in the change in potential energy between two points and not in the true value of the potential energy at any point. It is convenient in such cases to choose a "base level"—a point that is arbitrarily assigned a potential energy value of zero. Base levels are usually the lowest point in an experiment, such as the ground, the floor in a room, a table top, or the lowest point in the swing of a pendulum. The change in the potential energy of an object between any point and the base level then becomes the potential energy value at that point, expressed by the formula

$$PE = mgh$$

where *PE* is equal to the potential energy of an object at any point *h* meters above the base level. At the base level, $h = 0$ and $PE = 0$.

Sample Problems

6. A 2.0-kg object is raised a vertical distance of 3.0 m. What is the resulting change in gravitational potential energy?
Solution:

$$\Delta PE = mg\Delta h$$
$$= (2.0\,\text{kg})(9.8\,\text{m/s}^2)(3.0\,\text{m})$$
$$= 59\,\text{kg} \cdot \text{m}^2/\text{s}^2 = 59\,\text{J}$$

7. A 5.0-kg object sits at the top of a flight of stairs at a height of 6.0 m above the ground, as shown in Figure 2-2. What is the gravitational potential energy of the object with the ground as the base level?

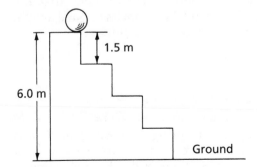

Figure 2-2.

Solution:

$$PE = mgh$$

$$= (5.0 \text{ kg})(9.8 \text{ m/s}^2)(6.0 \text{ m}) = 290 \text{ J}$$

How much potential energy will it lose if it falls down one step to a point 4.5 m above the ground?

Solution:

$$\Delta PE = mg\Delta h$$

$$= (5.0 \text{ kg})(9.8 \text{ m/s}^2)(6.0 \text{ m} - 4.5 \text{ m})$$

$$= 74 \text{ J}$$

Elastic Potential Energy

Elastic potential energy is the energy stored in a spring when it is compressed or stretched. The amount of potential energy stored in a spring is equal to the work done in stretching or compressing it from its original length. Springs are used in toys, scales, mattresses, and shock absorbers. For example, dart guns are equipped with springs. When a dart is loaded, it is pushed against the spring, compressing it. The work done to compress the spring is stored in the spring as elastic potential energy. As the spring is released and returns to its original length, it does work on the dart, sending it flying outward.

The force required to compress or stretch a spring is not constant. It is directly proportional to the distance that the spring has been compressed or stretched from its original length. The more a spring has been stretched or compressed, the harder it is to stretch or compress it further. The force F, in newtons, needed to keep a spring compressed or stretched at a distance x, in meters, is given by **Hooke's law**

$$F = kx$$

where k is a property of the spring known as the **spring constant.** The unit for the spring constant is the newton/meter (N/m).

The elastic potential energy stored in a spring is equal to one-half the product of the spring constant and the square of the distance that the spring has been stretched from its original length. This is expressed mathematically as

$$PE_s = \tfrac{1}{2}kx^2$$

8. A spring with a spring constant of 40 N/m is stretched a distance of 0.5 m from its original length. What force is required to keep it stretched this distance?

Solution:

$$F = kx$$

$$= (40 \text{ N/m})(0.5 \text{ m}) = 20 \text{ N}$$

What is the elastic potential energy in the stretched spring?

Solution:

$$PE_s = \tfrac{1}{2}kx^2$$

$$= \tfrac{1}{2}(40 \text{ N/m})(0.5 \text{ m})^2 = 5 \text{ N} \cdot \text{m} = 5 \text{ J}$$

What work was done to stretch the spring?

Solution:

$$W = \Delta PE_s = 5 \text{ J}$$

9. The data in Table 2-1 was collected during a demonstration in which a spring was stretched by attaching various weights to it as in Figure 2-3. Using Hooke's law, determine the spring constant of the spring, using any of the given data pairs.

Table 2-1

Force Applied (N)	Length Stretched (m)
0	0
40.	0.5
80.	1.0
120	1.5
160	2.0

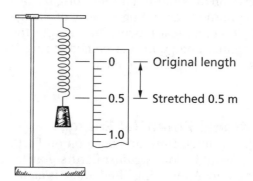

Figure 2-3.

Solution:

$$F = kx$$

$$k = \frac{F}{x} = \frac{40. \text{ N}}{0.5 \text{ m}} \text{ or } \frac{80. \text{ N}}{1.0 \text{ m}} \text{ or } \frac{120 \text{ N}}{1.5 \text{ m}}$$

$$\text{or } \frac{160 \text{ N}}{2.0 \text{ m}} = 80. \text{ N/m}$$

Refer to the force versus displacement graph of this data (Figure 2-4) and determine the slope of the line obtained.

$$\text{slope} = \frac{\Delta y}{\Delta x}$$

$$= \frac{160 \text{ N}}{2.0 \text{ m}} = 80. \text{ N/m}$$

Note that the slope of the force versus displacement is the spring constant k. The work done in stretching the spring is equal to the area under the graph.

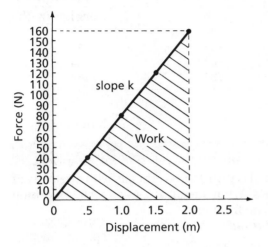

Figure 2-4. Graph of the data in Table 2-1.

Determine the elastic potential energy in the spring for each length measured in the demonstration.

Solution:

$$PE_s = \tfrac{1}{2}kx^2$$

$x = 0.5\text{ m}\ \ PE_s = \tfrac{1}{2}(80.\text{ N/m})(0.5\text{ m})^2 = 10.\text{ J}$

$x = 1.0\text{ m}\ \ PE_s = \tfrac{1}{2}(80.\text{ N/m})(1.0\text{ m})^2 = 40.\text{ J}$

$x = 1.5\text{ m}\ \ PE_s = \tfrac{1}{2}(80.\text{ N/m})(1.5\text{ m})^2 = 90.\text{ J}$

$x = 2.0\text{ m}\ \ PE_s = \tfrac{1}{2}(80.\text{ N/m})(2.0\text{ m})^2 = 160\text{ J}$

Kinetic Energy

Kinetic energy is the energy an object has because of its motion. Like all forms of energy, it is a scalar quantity. The symbol for kinetic energy is *KE* and its unit is the joule. The amount of kinetic energy an object of mass *m* has if it is moving with speed *v* is given by the formula

$$KE = \tfrac{1}{2}mv^2$$

The change in an object's kinetic energy is equal to the difference between its final kinetic energy and its initial kinetic energy. This is expressed as

$$\Delta KE = \tfrac{1}{2}mv_f^2 - \tfrac{1}{2}mv_i^2$$

The work done by a force as it acts on an object is equal to the sum of the change in the object's *KE* and *PE* and the work done against friction.

$$W = \Delta KE + \Delta PE + W_f$$

10. Find the kinetic energy of a 4-kg object moving at 5 m/s and 10 m/s.
Solution:

$$KE = \tfrac{1}{2}mv^2 = \tfrac{1}{2}(4\text{ kg})(5\text{ m/s})^2 = 50\text{ J}$$

$$KE = \tfrac{1}{2}mv^2 = \tfrac{1}{2}(4\text{ kg})(10\text{ m/s})^2 = 200\text{ J}$$

Note that, since kinetic energy depends on the *square of the velocity*, it is *quadrupled* when the velocity is *doubled*.

11. How much work must be done to accelerate a 1200-kg car from rest to a speed of 2.0 m/s, assuming there is no friction?
Solution: ΔPE and W_f are each equal to zero

$$W = \Delta KE = \tfrac{1}{2}mv_f^2 = \tfrac{1}{2}mv_i^2$$

$$= \tfrac{1}{2}(1200\text{ kg})(2.0\text{ m/s})^2 - \tfrac{1}{2}(1200\text{ kg})(0\text{ m/s})^2$$

$$= 2400\text{ J}$$

12. A new force of 5.0 N is applied to a 4.0-kg object over a distance of 6.0 m. What is the change in the object's kinetic energy, assuming there is no friction?
Solution: ΔPE and W_f are each equal to zero

$$\Delta KE = W = F\Delta d$$

$$= (5.0\text{ N})(6.0\text{ m})$$

$$= 30.\text{ J}$$

If the object was moving at 2.0 m/s before the force was applied, what is its velocity after the force is applied?
Solution:

$$\Delta KE = \tfrac{1}{2}mv_f^2 - \tfrac{1}{2}mv_i^2$$

$$30.\text{ J} = \tfrac{1}{2}(4.0\text{ kg})v_f^2 - \tfrac{1}{2}(4.0\text{ kg})(2.0\text{ m/s})^2$$

$$v_f^2 = 19\text{ m}^2/\text{s}^2$$

$$v_f = 4.4\text{ m/s}$$

Conservation of Energy

The **law of conservation of energy** states that the total energy of a closed system remains constant. A closed system is one where no external forces act and no external work is done on or by the system. Energy may be transferred among the objects in the system or be converted within the system from one form to another, but the total amount of energy within the system cannot change.

An example of conservation of energy is the conversion of potential to kinetic energy for a falling object on Earth. Table 2-2 lists the values of

Table 2-2. Energy of a Falling Object

Height h, meters	Velocity $v = \sqrt{2g\Delta h}$, meters per second	Potential Energy $PE = mgh$, joules	Kinetic Energy $KE = \frac{1}{2}mv^2$, joules	Total mechanical energy $PE + KE$, joules
(Release point) 8	0	784	0	784
7	4.4	686	98	784
4	8.9	392	392	784
2	10.8	196	588	784
(Ground) 0	12.5	0	784	784

potential and kinetic energy at various heights as a 10-kg object falls to the ground from a height of 8 m (assuming no friction or air resistance). The sum of the kinetic energy and potential energy at any point is called the total mechanical energy. It is fixed throughout the downward trip (at 784 J).

At the point of release, the object has potential energy but no kinetic energy. As the object falls, its potential energy is converted to kinetic energy, but the total mechanical energy remains constant. Midway through the fall, half of its energy is potential and half is kinetic. Just before the object hits the ground, all of its potential energy has been converted to kinetic energy.

We can summarize by stating that *if there is no loss of energy due to friction or air resistance, the gain in kinetic energy equals the loss in potential energy, and the loss in kinetic energy equals the gain in potential energy.* In other words, for a freely falling object initially at rest, PE (top) = KE (bottom) or $mg\Delta h = \frac{1}{2}mv^2$.

Since g is a constant, we can use this formula to calculate the velocity of an object after any change in its height (Δh). Furthermore, if we know the velocity of an object as it hits the ground, we can determine the height, h, from which it fell.

Sample Problem

13. A ball is thrown up vertically with a velocity of 17.5 m/s. What height does it reach, assuming there is no friction?

Solution:

$$mg\,\Delta h = \tfrac{1}{2}mv^2$$

$$\Delta h = \frac{v^2}{2g}$$

$$= \frac{(17.5 \text{ m/s})^2}{2(9.8 \text{ m/s}^2)}$$

$$= \frac{306 \text{ m}^2/\text{s}^2}{19.6 \text{ m/s}^2} = 15.6 \text{ m}$$

Conservation of energy can also be illustrated by the swing of a pendulum (Figure 2-5). If no energy is lost due to friction or air resistance, the motion and conversion of energy from potential to kinetic back to potential continues forever. At all points in the swing, the total energy of the pendulum remains constant. At the top of the swing the bob has only potential energy, and its velocity is zero. As the bob moves toward the

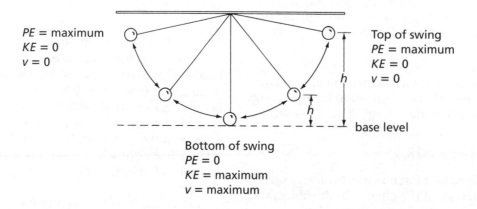

PE = maximum
KE = 0
v = 0

Top of swing
PE = maximum
KE = 0
v = 0

h

h

base level

Bottom of swing
PE = 0
KE = maximum
v = maximum

Figure 2-5. The swing of a pendulum.

bottom of the swing, it loses potential energy and gains kinetic energy as its velocity increases. The bottom of the swing is the base level; the potential energy there is zero and the kinetic energy is greatest. The kinetic energy at the bottom is equal to the potential energy at the top. The potential energy at any point in the swing is equal to *mgh* where *h* is the vertical distance to the base level.

Sample Problem

14. A 1.0-kg pendulum bob is released from a height of 0.50 m above the base level. Assuming there is no friction or air resistance, find the potential energy of the bob at the point of release.

Solution:

$$PE = mg\Delta h$$

$$= (1.0 \text{ kg})(9.8 \text{ m/s}^2)(0.50 \text{ m}) = 4.9 \text{ J}$$

Find the velocity of the bob at the bottom of its swing.

Solution:

$$KE \text{ (on the bottom)} = PE \text{ (on the top)}$$

$$KE = \tfrac{1}{2}mv^2$$

$$4.9 \text{ J} = \tfrac{1}{2}(1.0 \text{ kg})(v^2)$$

$$v^2 = \frac{9.8 \text{ J}}{1.0 \text{ kg}} = \frac{9.8 \text{ N} \cdot \text{m}}{1.0 \text{ kg}}$$

$$= \frac{9.8(\text{kg} \cdot \text{m/s}^2)\text{m}}{1.0 \text{ kg}} = 9.8 \text{ m}^2/\text{s}^2$$

$$v = 3.1 \text{ m/s}$$

The Work-Energy Relationship

In our discussion of the conservation of energy in the previous section, we were careful to limit ourselves to cases in which the forces of friction and air resistance were absent. Of course, in most situations, the forces of friction and air resistance are present, opposing the motion of moving objects. In the case of a falling object, if air resistance is present, some of the potential energy the object loses on the way down is converted into heat or internal energy. Some of the work done by gravity on the falling object will be spent fighting air resistance instead of accelerating the object and increasing its kinetic energy. Work done against air resistance or friction is always converted into heat or internal energy, which you will

learn about in the next section. The law of conservation of energy then means that the sum of kinetic energy, potential energy, and internal energy is constant.

$$\text{Total Energy} = PE + KE + \text{Internal Energy}$$

Sample Problem

15. In Figure 2-6 a 50.-kg jogger starts from rest at the bottom of a hill 6.0-m high (point *A*). When she reaches the top (point *B*) her velocity is 10. m/s. The work she does against air resistance and road friction between points *A* and *B* is 1500 J. Determine the total work required to jog straight up from point *A* to point *B*.

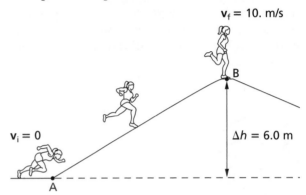

Figure 2-6.

Solution:

$$W = \Delta PE + \Delta KE + W_f$$

$$\Delta PE = mg\Delta h = (50. \text{ kg})(9.8 \text{ m/s}^2)$$

$$\times (6.0 \text{ m}) = 2900 \text{ J}$$

$$\Delta KE = \tfrac{1}{2}mv_f - \tfrac{1}{2}mv_i$$

$$= \tfrac{1}{2}(50. \text{ kg})(10. \text{ m/s})^2$$

$$- \tfrac{1}{2}(50. \text{ kg})(0 \text{ m/s})^2 = 2500 \text{ J}$$

$$W_f = 1500 \text{ J (given)}$$

$$\text{Total Work} = 2900 \text{ J} + 2500 \text{ J} + 1500 \text{ J}$$

$$= 6900 \text{ J}$$

Conservative Forces Forces, such as gravity, for which mechanical energy remains constant, are known as **conservative forces.** Forces, such as friction, that convert mechanical energy into internal energy and heat, are called **nonconservative forces.** In the example of the pendulum, we assumed that the kinetic energy at the bottom of the swing is equal to the potential energy at the top, even though the pendulum bob did not fall straight down but followed a curved path. This is true because the work done by or against gravity between two points is independent of the path taken between the points. Whether gravity pulls a bead down wire *A, B,* or *C* in Figure 2-7, it does the same amount of work—so long as the bead starts at point 1 and ends at point 2. The work done by or against a *conservative force* is always independent of the path taken. On the other hand, the work done on an object by or against a *nonconservative force* depends on the path taken. For example, the work done in overcoming the force of friction as a block is dragged over a rough surface is greater when the path taken by the block is longer. Potential energy can only be defined for a conservative force. It is impossible to describe how much work a force can do if the amount of work will be different for different paths.

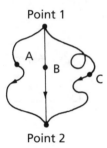

Figure 2-7.

QUESTIONS

16. A unit for kinetic energy is the (1) watt (2) joule (3) newton (4) kilogram-meter/second

17. A 2.0-newton book falls from a table 1.0 meter high. After falling 0.5 meter, the book's kinetic energy is (1) 1.0 J (2) 2.0 J (3) 10 J (4) 20 J

18. An object is lifted at constant speed a distance *h* above Earth's surface in a time *t*. The total potential energy gained by the object is equal to the (1) average force applied to the object (2) total weight of the object (3) total work done on the object (4) total momentum gained by the object

19. If a 5-kilogram mass is raised vertically 2 meters from the surface of Earth, its gain in potential energy is approximately (1) 0 J (2) 10 J (3) 20 J (4) 100 J

20. If the kinetic energy of a given mass is to be doubled, its speed must be multiplied by (1) 8 (2) 2 (3) $\sqrt{2}$ (4) 4

21. A 2.0-kilogram mass falls freely for 10. meters near Earth's surface. The total kinetic energy gained by the object during its free fall is approximately (1) 400 J (2) 200 J (3) 100 J (4) 50 J

22. If the velocity of a moving object is doubled, the object's kinetic energy is (1) unchanged (2) halved (3) doubled (4) quadrupled

23. Which mass has the greatest potential energy with respect to the floor? (1) 50-kg mass resting on the floor (2) 2-kg mass 10 meters above the floor (3) 10-kg mass 2 meters above the floor (4) 6-kg mass 5 meters above the floor

24. A ball is thrown upward from Earth's surface. While the ball is rising, its gravitational potential energy will (1) decrease (2) increase (3) remain the same

25. Ten joules of work are done in accelerating a 2.0-kilogram mass from rest across a horizontal frictionless table. The total kinetic energy gained by the mass is (1) 3.2 J (2) 5.0 J (3) 10. J (4) 20. J

26. Which graph best represents the relationship between potential energy (*PE*) and height above ground (*h*) for a freely falling object released from rest?

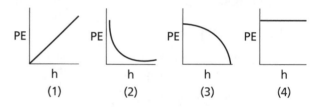

27. A 10.-kilogram object and a 5.0-kilogram object are released simultaneously from a height of 50. meters above the ground. After falling freely for 2.0 seconds, the objects will have different (1) accelerations (2) speeds (3) kinetic energies (4) displacements

28. At what point in its fall does the kinetic energy of a freely falling object equal its potential energy? (1) at the start of the fall (2) halfway between the start and the end (3) at the end of the fall (4) at all points during the fall

29. A 20.-newton block falls freely from rest from a point 3.0 meters above the surface of Earth. With respect to Earth's surface, what is the gravitational potential energy of the block-Earth system after the block has fallen 1.5 meters? (1) 20. J (2) 30. J (3) 60. J (4) 120 J

Base your answers to questions 30 through 34 on the diagram on page 45, which represents a 2.0-kilogram mass placed on a frictionless track at point A and released from rest. Assume the gravitational potential energy of the system to be zero at point E.

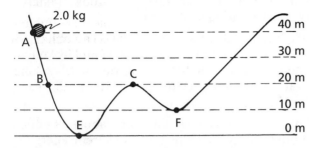

30. The gravitational potential energy of the system at point A is approximately (1) 80. J (2) 20. J (3) 8.0×10^2 J (4) 7.0×10^2 J

31. Compared with the kinetic energy of the mass at point B, the kinetic energy of the mass at point E is (1) $\frac{1}{2}$ as great (2) twice as great (3) the same (4) 4 times greater

32. As the mass travels along the track, the maximum height it will reach above point E will be closest to (1) 10. m (2) 20. m (3) 30. m (4) 40. m

33. If the mass were released from rest at point B, its speed at point C would be (1) 0 m/s (2) 0.50 m/s (3) 10. m/s (4) 14 m/s

Note that question 34 has only three choices.

34. Compared with the total mechanical energy of the system at point A, the total mechanical energy of the system at point F is (1) less (2) more (3) the same

Base your answers to questions 35 through 38 on the diagram below, which shows a 20-newton force pulling an object up a hill at a constant rate of 2 meters per second.

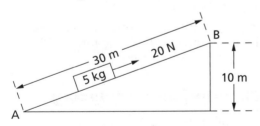

35. The work done by the force in pulling the object from A to B is (1) 50 J (2) 100 J (3) 500 J (4) 600 J

36. The kinetic energy of the moving object is (1) 5 J (2) 10 J (3) 15 J (4) 50 J

37. The work done against gravity in moving the object from point A to point B is approximately (1) 100 J (2) 200 J (3) 500 J (4) 600 J

38. Which graph best represents the relationship between velocity and time for the object?

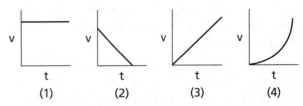

Base your answers to questions 39 through 42 on the diagram below, which represents a 10-kilogram object at rest at point A. The object accelerates uniformly from point A to point B in 4 seconds, attaining a maximum speed of 10 meters per second at point B. The object then moves up the incline. [Neglect friction.]

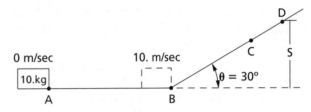

39. The kinetic energy of the object at point B is (1) 1000 J (2) 500 J (3) 100 J (4) 50 J

40. What distance did the object travel in moving from point A to point B? (1) 2.5 m (2) 10. m (3) 20. m (4) 100 m

41. As the mass moves up the incline, its potential energy (1) decreases (2) increases (3) remains the same

42. The object comes to rest at a vertical height of S (point D) when $\angle \theta = 30°$. If $\angle \theta$ were increased to 40°, the object would come to rest at a vertical height (1) less than S (2) greater than S (3) equal to S

Base your answers to questions 43 through 45 on the diagram below, which represents a simple pendulum with a 2.0-kilogram bob and a length of 10. meters. The pendulum is released from rest at position 1 and swings without friction through position 4. At position 3, its lowest point, the speed of the bob is 6.0 meters per second.

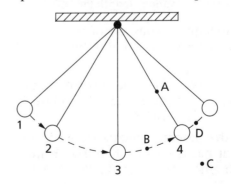

43. At which position does the bob have its maximum kinetic energy? (1) 1 (2) 2 (3) 3 (4) 4

44. What is the potential energy of the bob at position 1 in relation to position 3? (1) 18 J (2) 36 J (3) 72 J (4) 180 J

45. Compared with the sum of the kinetic and potential energies of the bob at position 1, the sum of the kinetic and potential energies of the bob at position 2 is (1) less (2) greater (3) the same

46. A 24-N force applied to a spring causes the spring to increase in length by 0.40 m. What is the spring constant? (1) 0.017 N/m (2) 9.6 N/m (3) 24.4 N/m (4) 60. N/m

47. A 2.0 N force is applied to a spring with a spring constant of 10. N/m. What is the resultant change in the length of the spring? (1) 0.20 m (2) 0.50 m (3) 5.0 m (4) 20. m

48. An unstretched spring has a length of 0.50 m and a spring constant of 100. N/m. What force is required to stretch this spring to a length of 0.60 m? (1) 10. N (2) 60. N (3) 100 N (4) 170 N

49. What is the potential energy stored in a spring with a spring constant of 100. N/m when it is stretched 0.10 m from the original length? (1) 0.50 J (2) 1.0 J (3) 5.0 J (4) 10. J

50. What work is required to make a spring's length increase by 3.0 m if its spring constant is 60. N/m? (1) 20. J (2) 180 J (3) 270 J (4) 540 J

Base your answers to questions 51 through 53 on the following graph taken from an experiment with a spring of original length 1.0 m.

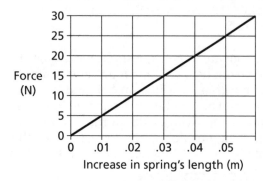

Increase in spring's length (m)

51. What is the spring constant of this spring? (1) 0.05 N/m (2) 5 N/m (3) 50 N/m (4) 500 N/m

52. How much force must be applied to this spring to change its length to 1.025 m? (1) 1.025 N (2) 6.0 N (3) 12.5 N (4) 513 N

53. What is the potential energy stored in the spring when it has been stretched 0.40 m from its original length? (1) 0.40 J (2) 40 J (3) 80 J (4) 100 J

54. Which of the following is not included in the work done by a force in moving an object? (1) change in momentum (2) change in potential energy (3) change in kinetic energy (4) work done against friction

55. When 800 J of work are done on an object, its potential energy increases by 300 J and its kinetic energy increases by 400 J. What was the work done against friction? (1) 100 J (2) 700 J (3) 800 J (4) 1500 J

56. In driving down a hill a car loses 500 J of potential energy but gains 1500 J of kinetic energy. If the work done to overcome friction was 200 J, determine the total work done by the engine to go down the hill. (1) 800 J (2) 1200 J (3) 1800 J (4) 2200 J

57. In the following diagram a cart starts from rest at ground level (point A). It is pulled up the inclined plane to the top at a constant speed where its potential energy is 20. J and its kinetic energy is 30. J (point B). The friction force was 3.0 N. The length of the inclined plane is 5.0 m. What is the total work done in moving the object from A to B? (1) 10. J (2) 15 J (3) 50. J (4) 65 J

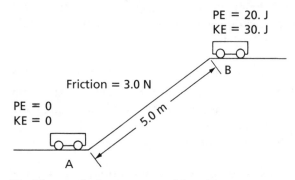

58. The work done on an object by a nonconservative force depends on: (1) the path taken (2) the object's mass (3) the object's velocity (4) the nature of the surfaces

59. An example of a nonconservative force is (1) gravitational force (2) elastic force (3) friction force (4) electrostatic force

Thinking and Analyzing

60. How is energy related to work?

61. Present two examples of different types of potential energy. In each example, identify the factors upon which the amount of potential energy is dependent and explain how it depends on those factors.

62. What is gravitational potential energy and how is it calculated?

63. A weight lifter raises a heavy barbell off the floor, raises it to a position over his head, holds it in place for some time, then lowers it slowly and steadily at constant speed back to the floor. For each of these three steps, state whether the work performed by the weightlifter is positive, negative, or zero. Explain your answers.

64. What is elastic potential energy and how is it calculated?

65. Define kinetic energy and define potential energy.

66. Which change will result in the greater increase in kinetic energy—doubling mass or doubling velocity?

67. Explain how the work done on an object is related to changes in the object's energy and the energy of the person doing the work?

68. In the absence of friction, what is true about the relationship between the potential energy of a ball just before being dropped from a cliff and the kinetic energy of the ball just before it reaches the ground? Explain.

69. What would happen to a swinging pendulum in the absence of friction?

70. Contrast a conservative force with a nonconservative force. Give an example of each.

71. A ball is released from a certain height, descends toward the ground, collides with the ground, and then rebounds upward to a position lower than its original position. Describe the changes, if any, in the various forms of energy involved in each of these steps.

72. An archer draws the arrow of a bow-and-arrow system through some distance while stretching the bow. The arrow is then released, rises upward to some height, then falls back down to the ground. Describe the changes, if any, in the various forms of energy involved in all steps of this process, beginning with the archer drawing the arrow and ending with the arrow colliding into the ground.

73. Explain why the work performed by a conservative force does not depend on the path taken between two points despite the fact that the distance traveled will be different.

74. Does the force of gravity acting on a spaceship in circular orbit around Earth do work? Explain your answer.

75. Does the normal force exerted by a table on a book that rests on the table do work? Explain your answer.

Reading Comprehension

Heat Exchange

Some devices we use every day operate on the principles of the laws of thermodynamics, which will be discussed in the next section. Examples of such devices include refrigerators, air conditioners, and heat pumps. Many of these devices transfer heat from a cooler environment to a warmer one. This is much like pumping water uphill. Heat is supposed to flow from hot to cold, just as water is supposed to flow downhill, not the other way around.

  Let us consider the operation of a typical electric refrigerator. A refrigerator consists of three basic parts: the evaporator, the compressor, and the condenser. The refrigerator also needs a refrigerant, a substance that absorbs heat quickly and in large amounts. During the refrigeration cycle the liquid refrigerant in the evaporator evaporates (boils), becoming a gas. The liquid absorbs the heat it needs to boil from inside the refrigerator, cooling it. The gas then moves on to the compressor, which compresses the gas and sends it on to the condenser. In the condenser, the compressed gas is returned to the liquid state, releasing the heat it absorbed from the refrigerator to the air in the room. To sum up the process, the refrigerant absorbs heat at a low temperature, and then through the action of mechanical work by the compressor, the gas is compressed and raised to a high enough temperature to allow it to give up the heat it absorbed.

  In reality, the mechanical energy used to cool a given area is always greater than the energy lost by the area. The additional energy is used to overcome friction. Thus, you cannot cool your kitchen by opening the refrigerator door—in fact, this will actually heat the kitchen.

An air conditioner operates in much the same way. The main difference is that the air conditioner cools the inside of a room or building, transferring the heat to the air outside the building. This is why, as you are walking outside, you feel a blast of hot air when you pass a working air conditioner. A heat pump, which operates in a similar manner, transfers heat from outside a building inside to heat the building.

QUESTIONS

1. How is the action of a refrigerator comparable to pumping water uphill?
2. What happens to the heat energy lost by the refrigerant as it condenses?
3. From where does the liquid refrigerant get the heat it needs to boil?
4. Which part of the refrigerator does work on the refrigerant?
5. In what way is a heat pump different from an air conditioner?

Enrichment Energy

INTERNAL ENERGY

Temperature

The temperature of an object indicates how hot or cold the object is with respect to a chosen standard. It is a property that originates from the motions and vibrations of the molecules in matter. When the average kinetic energy of the molecules increases, the temperature of the object increases. Conversely, the temperature of an object decreases when the average kinetic energy of its molecules decreases.

Temperature Scales

Celsius Scale   Temperature is a scalar quantity measured with respect to arbitrarily selected temperatures called **fixed points.** On the **Celsius scale** the freezing point of water at standard pressure has been assigned the value of 0 degrees, and the boiling point of water at standard pressure has been assigned the value of 100 degrees. One **Celsius degree** (C°) is defined as one-hundredth $\left(\frac{1}{100}\right)$ of the interval between these two points. Temperatures higher than 100°C or lower than 0°C are defined by extending the scale above and below the fixed points.

Absolute Temperature and the Kelvin Scale

The **Kelvin scale** measures the **absolute temperature** of matter. Absolute temperature is directly proportional to the average kinetic energy of the molecules. If the average kinetic energy of the molecules is doubled, the absolute temperature is also doubled. A typical graph of absolute temperature versus average kinetic energy appears in Figure 2-8.

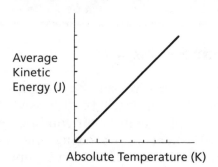

Figure 2-8.

The fixed point of the Kelvin scale is called **absolute zero.** It is the lowest possible temperature; no object can have a lower temperature. An object at a temperature of absolute zero cannot transfer any thermal energy to its surroundings. In the graph in Figure 2-8, absolute zero appears to represent a gas with zero kinetic energy. However, according to modern theory, at absolute zero the molecules retain a minimum possible amount of energy, referred to as the zero-point energy.

The Kelvin (K) is a fundamental unit. A change of 1 Kelvin is equivalent to a change of 1 Celsius degree, but the zero point on the Kelvin scale corresponds to −273 on the Celsius scale (Figure 2-9). Thus, we can convert from one scale to the other by using the formula

$$K = °C + 273$$

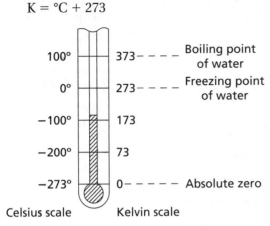

100°   373 – – – – Boiling point of water

0°   273 – – – – Freezing point of water

−100°   173

−200°   73

−273°   0 – – – – – Absolute zero

Celsius scale   Kelvin scale

Figure 2-9. The Kelvin and Celsius scales.

Sample Problems

16. Convert 56°C to K
    Solution:

    $$K = °C + 273$$
    $$= 56 + 273 = 329$$

Convert 56 K to °C
    Solution:

    $$°C = K − 273$$
    $$= 56 − 273 = −217$$

17. The temperature of a substance changes from −10°C to 25°C. What is the temperature change on the Kelvin scale?

    Solution: The size of a Celsius degree is equal to the size of a Kelvin. Therefore, a 35°C rise in temperature corresponds to a 35 K rise.

Internal Energy and Heat

The **internal energy** of an object is the total kinetic and potential energy associated with the motions and relative positions of the molecules of the object, apart from any kinetic and potential energy the object as a whole may possess. The amount of internal energy an object has depends on its temperature, mass, phase, and intermolecular bonds. The internal energy of an object can be changed either by changing the kinetic energy of its molecules, or by changing the potential energy of its molecules, or both.

    Heat energy refers to energy that is transferred from a warm object to a cooler one due to

the temperature difference between them. Whenever this occurs, the internal energies of both objects are changed. Heat is a scalar quantity and is measured in joules. It is important to understand the difference between internal energy, temperature, and heat. For example, even though the Arctic Ocean is at a much lower temperature than a cup of boiling water, it has far more internal energy and can release far more heat. This is because temperature is a measure of the *average kinetic energy* of the molecules, while internal energy is the *total kinetic and potential energy* of the molecules. The Arctic Ocean is colder because the average kinetic energy of its molecules is lower than the average kinetic energy of the molecules in the cup of boiling water. However, the Arctic Ocean has so many more molecules that the total kinetic and potential energy of its molecules is much greater than the total kinetic and potential energy of the molecules in the cup of boiling water.

    In our discussion of work and energy, we noted that mechanical energy is converted into internal energy when work is done against friction. The increase in internal energy in turn raises the average kinetic energy of the molecules. As a result, whenever we rub our hands together, or drive a nail into wood, or drag an object over a rough surface, we can detect an increase in the temperature of these objects.

QUESTIONS

76. As the temperature of a substance increases, the average kinetic energy of its molecules (1) decreases (2) increases (3) remains the same

77. The direction of exchange of internal energy between objects is determined by their relative (1) inertias (2) momentums (3) temperatures (4) masses

78. What temperature reading on the Kelvin scale is equivalent to a reading of zero degrees Celsius? (1) −273°K (2) −100°K (3) 100°K (4) 273°K

79. The internal energy of water depends on its (1) temperature, only (2) phase, only (3) temperature and mass, only (4) temperature, mass, and phase

80. When an object moves at a constant speed against friction on a horizontal tabletop, there is an increase in the object's (1) temperature (2) momentum (3) potential energy (4) acceleration

81. A change in temperature of 100 Celsius degrees is equal to a change in Kelvin temperature of (1) 373 K (2) 200 K (3) 100 K (4) 50 K

82. Doubling the absolute temperature of an ideal gas will affect the molecules of the gas by doubling their average (1) kinetic energy (2) potential energy (3) momentum (4) velocity

83. The sum of the kinetic energy and potential energy of the molecules of a solid is called (1) temperature (2) specific heat (3) heat energy (4) internal energy

84. Which graph best represents the relationship between the average kinetic energy of the molecules of an ideal gas and the absolute temperature of the gas?

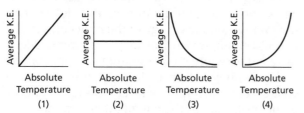

85. The internal energy of a substance is at a minimum when its temperature is (1) 0° Celsius (2) 0 Kelvin (3) 273° Celsius (4) 273 Kelvin

Specific Heat

Every material has its own characteristic response to heat. In order to achieve the same temperature change in equal masses of different substances, different amounts of heat energy are required. The **specific heat** c of a substance is defined as the amount of heat energy 1 kg of the substance must absorb or liberate in order for its temperature to increase or decrease by 1°C. Table 2-3 lists the specific heats of a few substances in kJ/kg · °C.

Table 2-3. Specific Heats

Material	Specific Heat (kJ/kg · °C)
Water:	
Ice	2.05 (sol.)
Water	4.19 (liq.)
Steam	2.01 (gas)
Alcohol (ethyl)	2.43 (liq.)
Aluminum	.90 (sol.)
Iron	.45 (sol.)
Lead	.13 (sol.)

The amount of heat energy that must be absorbed or liberated when the temperature of the substance changes by any given amount is the product of the mass of the substance, its specific heat, and the change in temperature. This is expressed mathematically as

$$Q = mc\Delta T_c$$

where Q is the heat energy in joules, m is the mass of the substance in kilograms, c is the specific

heat of the substance in kJ/kg · °C, and ΔT_c is the temperature change in °C. This formula can only be used when there is no change in phase as the material is heated or cooled. As shown in Table 2-3, different phases of the same element or compound usually have different specific heats.

Sample Problems

18. Given that 4.86 kJ of heat energy added to 1.00 kg of a liquid raises its temperature by 2.00°C, what is the liquid?

Solution:

$$Q = mc\Delta T_c$$

$$4.86 \text{ kJ} = (1.00 \text{ kg})(c)(2.00°C)$$

$$c = 2.43 \text{ kJ/kg} \cdot °C$$

The liquid is ethyl alcohol.

19. How much heat energy is required to raise the temperature of 8.0 kg of aluminum from 20.°C to 25°C?

Solution:

$$Q = mc\Delta T_c$$

$$= (8.0 \text{ kg})(0.90 \text{ kJ/kg} \cdot °C)(5.0°C)$$

$$= 36 \text{ kJ}$$

20. By how many degrees will the temperature of 6.0 kg of lead increase if 11.7 kJ of heat are added to the metal?

Solution:

$$Q = mc\Delta T_c$$

$$11.7 \text{ kJ} = (6.0 \text{ kg})(0.13 \text{ kJ/kg} \cdot °C)(\Delta T_c)$$

$$\Delta T_c = \frac{11.7 \text{ kJ}}{(6.0 \text{ kg})(0.13 \text{ kJ/kg} \cdot °C)} = 15°C$$

Conservation of Internal Energy

Whenever there is a transfer of internal energy without conversion to or from other forms of energy, the total internal energy of a closed system remains constant. For example, if two liquids at different temperatures are mixed, the sum of the internal energies of the liquids before they are mixed is equal to the total internal energy of the mixture. The **law of conservation of internal energy** states that when materials having different temperatures are put into contact, *the heat gained by the cooler material is equal to the heat lost by the warmer material.* Heat energy flows from the warmer material to the cooler material until both materials are at the same temperature and a condition of **thermal equilibrium** is achieved.

21. If 1.0 kg of water at 20.°C is mixed with 2.0 kg of water at 35°C, the final temperature of the mixture is 30.°C. Show that internal energy is conserved.

Solution:

Heat gained by the water at 20°C

$$Q = mc\Delta T_c$$
$$= (1.0 \text{ kg})(4.19 \text{ kJ/kg} \cdot {}^\circ\text{C})(30.{}^\circ\text{C} - 20.{}^\circ\text{C})$$
$$= 42 \text{ kJ}$$

Heat lost by the water at 35°C

$$Q = mc\Delta T_c$$
$$= (2.0 \text{ kg})(4.19 \text{ kJ/kg} \cdot {}^\circ\text{C})(35{}^\circ\text{C} - 30.{}^\circ\text{C})$$
$$= 42 \text{ kJ}$$

The heat gained by the cooler water is equal to the heat lost by the warmer water, and the total internal energy is conserved. Note that ΔT_c is always kept positive by always subtracting the lower temperature from the higher temperature.

22. A 6.00-kg piece of iron at 100.°C is immersed in 3.00 kg of water at 20.0°C. Determine the final temperature T_f when thermal equilibrium is established.

Solution:

heat gained by water = heat lost by iron

$$m_w c_w \Delta T_w = m_i c_i \Delta T_i$$

$$(3.00 \text{ kg})(4.19 \text{ kJ/kg} \cdot {}^\circ\text{C})(T_f - 20.0{}^\circ\text{C})$$
$$= (6.00 \text{ kg}) \times (0.45 \text{ kJ/kg} \cdot {}^\circ\text{C})$$
$$\times (100.{}^\circ\text{C} - T_f)$$
$$12.6(T_f - 20.0{}^\circ\text{C}) = 2.70(100.{}^\circ\text{C} - T_f)$$
$$T_f - 20.0{}^\circ\text{C} = 0.214(100.{}^\circ\text{C} - T_f)$$
$$1.21\, T_f = 41.4$$
$$T_f = 34.2{}^\circ\text{C}$$

23. A 10.-kg block of metal at 0°C is placed into 15 kg of water at 74°C. The temperature at thermal equilibrium is 65°C. What is the specific heat of the metal?

Solution:

heat gained by metal = heat lost by water

$$m_m c_m \Delta T_m = m_w c_w \Delta T_w$$

$$(10. \text{ kg})(c_m)(65{}^\circ\text{C} - 0{}^\circ\text{C})$$
$$= (15 \text{ kg})(4.19 \text{ kJ/kg} \cdot {}^\circ\text{C})(74{}^\circ\text{C} - 65{}^\circ\text{C})$$
$$650 c_m = 566$$
$$c_m = 0.87 \text{ kJ/kg} \cdot {}^\circ\text{C}$$

Note that the temperature at equilibrium is much closer to the original temperature of the water than to that of the metal. Water must absorb a greater amount of heat energy in order to increase its temperature than most other materials, and must release more heat in order to cool. This property explains why large bodies of water moderate coastal climates.

Change of Phase

Under ordinary conditions, matter can exist in three states, or **phases:** liquid, solid, and gas. When a crystalline material changes phase, its internal energy changes but its temperature does not. For example, heat energy is absorbed when a solid melts and a liquid vaporizes, but their temperatures remain constant throughout the phase change. As a liquid freezes and a gas condenses, heat energy is released but there is no decrease in temperature during these processes. The heat energy absorbed or released during a phase change produces a change in the molecular potential energy associated with bonds between the molecules, but the average kinetic energy of the molecules remains the same.

Heat of Fusion

The **heat of fusion** of a material is defined as the amount of heat energy one kilogram of the material at its melting point must absorb to change from the solid to the liquid phase with no change in temperature. The same amount of heat energy is released when one kilogram of the material freezes at its freezing point. (For pure crystalline substances, the melting point and freezing point are the same.) The amount of heat energy Q_f absorbed or released by a material of mass m as it changes from the solid to the liquid or the liquid to the solid phase is expressed by the formula

$$Q_f = mH_f$$

where H_f is the heat of fusion of the material.

For example, the heat of fusion of ice is 335 kJ/kg. This means that one kilogram of ice at 0°C (the melting point) needs to absorb 335 kJ of heat energy in order to melt completely into water at 0°C.

Heat of Vaporization

The **heat of vaporization** of a material is the amount of heat energy that must be absorbed by one kilogram of the material at its boiling point in order to change from the liquid to the gaseous phase with no change in temperature. The same amount of heat energy is released when one kilogram of the material condenses from a gas into a liquid. The amount of heat energy Q_v absorbed or released by a material of mass m as it changes from the liquid to the gas or the gas to the liquid phase is expressed by the formula

$$Q_v = mH_v$$

where H_v is the heat of vaporization of the material. For example, the heat of vaporization of water is 2311 kJ/kg. This means that one kilogram of water at 100°C (the boiling point) must absorb 2311 kJ of heat energy in order to be completely vaporized to steam at 100°C.

Figure 2-10 is a typical graph of temperature versus heat for 1 kg of a material. As the first 10 kJ of heat energy is absorbed by the material in the solid phase, its temperature rises from 40°C to 60°C. The material's melting point is 60°C, so the next 20 kJ of heat absorbed does not increase the temperature. When the material has completely liquefied, its temperature begins to rise again as more heat energy is added. As 20 kJ of heat energy is absorbed by the material in the liquid phase, its temperature rises from 60°C to 80°C. The material's boiling point is 80°C, so the next 50 kJ of heat added does not change the temperature. Instead the liquid is completely converted into a gas that is still at 80°C. Finally, the temperature of the gas rises from 80°C to 90°C as another 20 kJ of heat energy is absorbed.

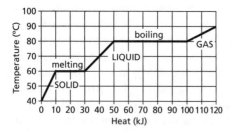

Figure 2-10. The graph represents the temperature of 1 kilogram of a material as heat is added.

Sample Problems

24. The following questions are based on the temperature vs. heat graph in Figure 2-10.

What is the heat of fusion of the material?
Solution:

$$Q_f = mH_f$$

$$20 \text{ kJ} = (1 \text{ kg})(H_f)$$

$$H_f = 20 \text{ kJ/kg}$$

What is the heat of vaporization of the material?
Solution:

$$Q_v = mH_v$$

$$50 \text{ kJ} = (1 \text{ kg})(H_v)$$

$$H_v = 50 \text{ kJ/kg}$$

What is the specific heat of the material in the liquid phase?
Solution:

$$Q = mc\Delta T$$

$$20 \text{ kJ} = (1 \text{ kg})(c)(80°C - 60°C)$$

$$c = 1 \text{ kJ/kg} \cdot °C$$

25. The heat of fusion of lead is 25 kJ/kg and its melting point is 328°C. How much heat is liberated as 3.0 kg of liquid lead solidifies at 328°C?
Solution:

$$Q_f = mH_f$$

$$= (3.0 \text{ kg})(25 \text{ kJ/kg}) = 75 \text{ kJ}$$

26. How much heat energy is required to convert 5.00 kg of ice at 0°C, into 5.00 kg of steam at 100.°C?
Solution:

Total heat

= heat to melt ice (at 0°C)

   + heat to raise temperature of water (from 0°C to 100°C)

   + heat to vaporize water (at 100°C)

$$= mH_f + mc\Delta T_c + mH_v$$

$$= (5.00 \text{ kg})(335 \text{ kJ/kg}) + (5.00 \text{ kg})$$
$$\times (4.19 \text{ kJ/kg} \cdot °C)(100°C - 0°C)$$
$$+ (5.00 \text{ kg})(2311 \text{ kJ/kg})$$

$$= 1.68 \times 10^3 \text{ kJ} + 2.10 \times 10^3 \text{ kJ}$$
$$+ 11.6 \times 10^3 \text{ kJ}$$

$$= 15.4 \times 10^3 \text{ kJ} = 1.54 \times 10^4 \text{ kJ}$$

Factors Affecting the Boiling and Freezing Points of Water

If salt is dissolved in water, it lowers the freezing point of the water and raises its boiling point. This effect is intensified as more salt is dissolved in the water. For example, a concentrated saltwater solution might not freeze until its temperature is lowered to −11°C and might not boil until its temperature is raised to 104°C. This is why salt is sprinkled on icy roads. Ions from the salt diffuse into the ice, forming a mixture with a freezing point below 0°C.

If salt is added to boiling water, the water stops boiling because the saltwater solution has a higher boiling point. The temperature of the solution must increase above 100°C, to the new boiling point, for the solution to resume boiling.

For similar reasons, antifreeze solutions are added to the water in car radiators. These substances lower the freezing point and raise the boiling point of the water, making it less likely to freeze or boil away during extreme weather conditions.

Pressure also affects the boiling and freezing points of water. Increased pressure lowers the freezing point of water and raises its boiling point. When an ice skater moves over the ice, the ice directly under the skate's blade is subjected to high pressure and its freezing point is lowered to a temperature less than 0°C. The ice under the blade melts, creating a thin layer of water over which the blade can slide with very little friction. As the skater moves on, the water freezes again.

A pressure cooker is designed to contain water, steam, and food at high pressures. This raises the boiling point of the water. As a result, the water in the cooker does not boil at 100°C. Instead its temperature rises above 100°C and the food is cooked faster. At low pressures, water boils at temperatures below 100°C. This explains why baking a cake requires more time at the top of a mountain, where the pressure is lower, than at sea level where the pressure is greater. At very low pressures, water can even boil at room temperature.

QUESTIONS

Base your answers to questions 86 through 90 on the following graph, which shows the relationship between the temperature of one kilogram of a pure substance and the heat energy emitted by the substance.

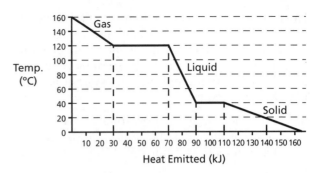

86. The melting point of the substance is (1) 20°C   (2) 40°C   (3) 120°C   (4) 160°C

87. The specific heat of the substance in the gaseous phase is   (1) 0.75 kJ/kg · °C   (2) 1.3 kJ/kg · °C   (3) 30 kJ/kg · °C   (4) 40 kJ/kg · °C

88. The heat of vaporization of the substance is (1) 120 kJ/kg   (2) 70 kJ/kg   (3) 3 kJ/kg   (4) 40 kJ/kg

89. What is the physical state of the substance at a temperature of 120°C?   (1) liquid, only   (2) solid, only   (3) gas and liquid   (4) liquid and solid

90. Compared with the specific heat of the substance in the liquid phase, the specific heat of the substance in the solid phase is (1) less (2) greater   (3) the same

91. As heat is added to a solid at a temperature below its melting point, its average molecular kinetic energy   (1) decreases   (2) increases   (3) remains the same

Base your answers to questions 92 through 96 on Table 2-4 on page 53 and this information:

Table 2-4. Heat Constants

	Specific Heat (average) (kJ/kg · C°)	Melting Point (°C)	Boiling Point (°C)	Heat of Fusion (kJ/kg)	Heat of Vaporization (kJ/kg)
Alcohol (ethyl)	2.43 (liq.)	−117	79	109	855
Aluminum	0.90 (sol.)	660	2467	396	10500
Ammonia	4.71 (liq.)	−78	−33	332	1370
Copper	0.39 (sol.)	1083	2567	205	4790
Iron	0.45 (sol.)	1535	2750	267	6290
Lead	0.13 (sol.)	328	1740	25	866
Mercury	0.14 (liq.)	−39	357	11	295
Platinum	0.13 (sol.)	1772	3827	101	229
Silver	0.24 (sol.)	962	2212	105	2370
Tungsten	0.13 (sol.)	3410	5660	192	4350
Water { ice	2.05 (sol.)	0	—	334	—
water	4.19 (liq.)	—	100	—	2260
steam	2.01 (gas)	—	—	—	—
Zinc	0.39 (sol.)	420	907	113	1770

Heat is added to 0.500 kilograms of alcohol at −120.°C at a rate of 1.00 kilojoule per minute, until all of the alcohol has vaporized. [Assume that the pressure on the alcohol remains constant at 1.00 atmosphere and that the system is completely insulated.]

92. At its melting point, how long does it take to change all of the alcohol from a solid to a liquid? (1) 54.5 min (2) 218 min (3) 250 min (4) 440 min

93. Through how many Celsius degrees will the alcohol remain in the liquid phase? (1) 196 (2) 178 (3) 78 (4) 37

94. How long does it take to change the alcohol from −22°C to 28°C? (1) 122 min (2) 100 min (3) 71 min (4) 61 min

95. At which temperature can the alcohol exist as both a liquid and a gas? (1) 100°C (2) 79°C (3) 0°C (4) −115°C

96. At its boiling point, how much heat does it take to evaporate all of the alcohol? (1) 1750 kJ (2) 79 kJ (3) 109 kJ (4) 428 kJ

Base your answers to questions 97 through 101 on Table 2-4 on page 53 and this information: A 10-kilogram mass of tungsten is heated from 50°C to 400°C.

97. The total amount of heat energy needed to heat the tungsten from 50°C to 400°C is (1) 192 kJ (2) 585 kJ (3) 1460 kJ (4) 455 kJ

98. Which of the following materials would require the same amount of heat as the tungsten to undergo the same temperature change? (1) 10 kg of copper (2) 10 kg of zinc (3) 10 kg of silver (4) 10 kg of platinum

99. In order to change the tungsten to a liquid, the tungsten at 400°C would have to rise in temperature a *minimum* of (1) 3,010 C° (2) 3,370 C° (3) 4,000 C° (4) 5,000 C°

100. How much heat energy would be required to change the 10 kilograms of tungsten to a liquid at its melting point? (1) 56,600 kJ (2) 1920 kJ (3) 192 kJ (4) 19.2 kJ

101. It is difficult to melt tungsten in metallic containers because tungsten has a (1) low specific heat (2) high specific heat (3) low melting point (4) high melting point

Base your answers to questions 102 through 106 on Table 2-4 on page 53 and this information: Heat is added to 20 kilograms of water that is at an initial temperature of 20°C. Assume that the atmospheric pressure remains constant throughout the process.

102. The heat required to bring the water to its boiling point is (1) 168 kJ (2) 1680 kJ (3) 3352 kJ (4) 6704 kJ

103. The water is at its boiling point. The heat energy required to vaporize all of the water is (1) 20 kJ (2) 2311 kJ (3) 6700 kJ (4) 46,220 kJ

104. While the water is boiling, what happens to the average kinetic energy of the water molecules? [Assume that the pressure remains constant.] (1) It decreases. (2) It increases. (3) It remains the same.

105. If a piece of red-hot iron is thrust into the boiling water, the temperature of the water will (1) decrease (2) increase (3) remain the same

106. Compared with the heat needed to raise the temperature of 20 kilograms of water 10C°, the heat needed to raise the temperature of 20 kilograms of steam 10C° is (1) less (2) more (3) the same

Base your answers to questions 107 through 111 on the graph below, which represents the temperature vs. heat of 2.0 kilograms of a substance originally in the solid state.

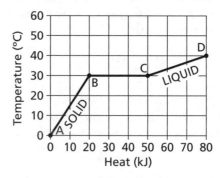

107. The melting point of the substance is (1) 10°C (2) 20°C (3) 30°C (4) 50°C

108. How much heat energy is necessary to raise the temperature of the substance in the liquid phase from 30°C to 40°C? (1) 15 kJ (2) 30 kJ (3) 50 kJ (4) 60 kJ

109. The total amount of heat energy necessary to raise the temperature of the substance from a solid at 30°C to a liquid at 40°C is (1) 20 kJ (2) 30 kJ (3) 60 kJ (4) 80 kJ

110. During which interval is the average kinetic energy of the molecules of the substance unchanged? (1) *AB* (2) *BC* (3) *CD* (4) *AC*

111. The specific heat of the substance in the solid phase is approximately (1) 1.0 kJ/kg · °C (2) 0.25 kJ/kg · °C (3) 0.33 kJ/kg · °C (4) 1.5 kJ/kg · °C

Base your answers to questions 112 through 116 on the following diagram, which represents a cooling curve for 10. kilograms of a substance as it cools from a vapor at 160°C to a solid at 20°C. Energy is removed from the sample at a rate of 2.0 kilojoules per minute.

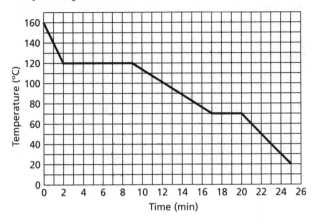

112. The boiling point of the substance is (1) 0°C   (2) 70°C   (3) 100°C   (4) 120°C

113. The heat of vaporization of the substance is (1) 0.30 kJ/kg   (2) 0.60 kJ/kg   (3) 0.70 kJ/kg   (4) 1.4 kJ/kg

114. During the liquid phase, the specific heat of the substance is   (1) 0.0080 kJ/kg · °C   (2) 0.016 kJ/kg · °C   (3) 0.032 kJ/kg · °C   (4) 0.064 kJ/kg · °C

115. While the substance is cooling during the liquid phase, the average kinetic energy of the molecules of the substance   (1) decreases   (2) increases   (3) remains the same

116. Compared with the specific heat of the vapor phase of the substance, the specific heat of the liquid phase is   (1) less   (2) greater   (3) the same

117. What is a possible freezing point for salt water at atmospheric pressure?   (1) −2.0°C   (2) 0°C   (3) 0.5°C   (4) 2.0°C

118. What is a possible boiling point for salt water at atmospheric pressure?   (1) 90°C   (2) 98°C   (3) 100°C   (4) 102°C

119. What is a possible boiling point for pure water at pressures higher than normal?   (1) 90°C   (2) 98°C   (3) 100°C   (4) 102°C

120. Salt is put on icy sidewalks because it   (1) releases heat to the ice   (2) removes heat from the ice   (3) lowers the freezing point of water   (4) prevents water from ever freezing

121. What will occur if a large amount of salt is added to a pot of boiling water on a hot stove? (1) The water boils more vigorously.   (2) The salt starts to boil instead of the water.   (3) The boiling stops temporarily.   (4) The boiling stops permanently.

122. Water can boil at room temperature if the pressure is   (1) much less than 1 atmosphere   (2) 1 atmosphere   (3) slightly more than 1 atmosphere   (4) much more than 1 atmosphere

123. The ice directly under the blade of an ice skate melts because increased pressure   (1) adds heat to the ice   (2) removes heat from the ice   (3) lowers the freezing point of water   (4) raises the freezing point of water

Thinking and Analyzing

124. Describe the characteristics of the Celsius scale.

125. What is absolute temperature and what scale is used to measure it?

126. Compare and contrast the Celsius and Kelvin scales.

127. What is the significance of absolute zero?

128. What happens to heat energy and temperature during a phase change?

129. Define heat of fusion and heat of vaporization.

130. Two factors affect water's freezing and boiling points, what are they and what is their effect?

Kinetic Theory of Gases

Gases are composed of molecules in constant random motion. In gases of low density, the average distance between molecules is very large compared with the diameter of each molecule. Hence, the volume occupied by the gas is much larger than the volume of its molecules. The forces between the molecules are negligible, except during collisions. Collisions between gas molecules usually result in a transfer of energy between the molecules, but the total internal energy of the system is constant. A gas that conforms to this model is called an **ideal gas.**

Pressure

The pressure exerted by a gas is due to collisions of gas molecules with the walls of the container. **Pressure** is defined as the force per unit surface area. A pressure of 1 newton per meter squared (N/m^2) is called 1 pascal (Pa). A pressure of $1.01 \times 10^5 \, N/m^2$ (101 kilopascals) is called 1 atmosphere. The amount of pressure exerted by the molecules of a gas against the walls of the container depends on how hard and frequently the molecules hit the walls. These factors in turn depend on the numbers of molecules in the container, and the average kinetic energy of the molecules (or the absolute temperature of the gas, which is proportional to the average kinetic energy of the molecules).

The Gas Laws

The product of the pressure and the volume of an ideal gas is directly proportional to the product of the number of molecules in the gas and its absolute temperature. This proportionality is expressed mathematically as

$$PV \propto nT$$

where P is the pressure of the gas, V is its volume, T is its absolute temperature, and n is the number of molecules in the gas.

Case One: Temperature Is Constant When the absolute temperature of a given mass of gas is kept constant, the product of the pressure and the volume remains fixed. This means that the pressure and the volume are inversely proportional to each other. If the volume of the container is decreased, more molecules will strike the walls per second and the pressure will increase. Conversely, if the volume is increased, fewer molecules will strike the container walls per second and the pressure will decrease. This relationship between the volume and the pressure of a fixed mass of gas at a constant temperature is known as **Boyle's law** and is expressed mathematically as

$$PV = k$$

where k is a constant. If the volume is halved, the pressure of the gas is doubled and if the volume is tripled, the pressure is divided by three. This relationship is illustrated graphically in Figure 2-11.

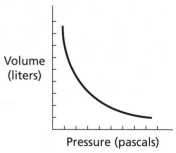

Figure 2-11. Boyle's law.

Case Two: Pressure Is Constant When the pressure of a fixed mass of gas is kept constant, the volume is directly proportional to the absolute temperature. If the absolute temperature of the gas is increased, the average kinetic energy of the molecules increases. In order for the pressure to remain the same, the volume must increase so that the faster moving molecules will

have to travel greater distances before colliding with the container walls. Conversely, if the absolute temperature is decreased, the volume must decrease in order for the pressure to remain the same. This relationship between the volume and the absolute temperature of a fixed mass of gas at a constant pressure is known as **Charles' law** and is expressed mathematically as

$$V \propto T$$

If the absolute temperature of a fixed mass of gas is doubled, its volume must also double if the pressure remains constant. If the volume is tripled, the absolute temperature is also tripled. The relationship is illustrated graphically in Figure 2-12.

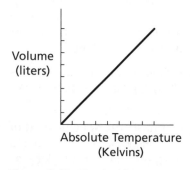

Figure 2-12. Charles' law.

Case Three: Volume Is Constant When the volume of a fixed mass of gas is kept constant, the pressure is directly proportional to the absolute temperature. As the absolute temperature increases, the average kinetic energy of the molecules increases. The molecules collide with the container walls with greater force and frequency, and the pressure increases correspondingly. This relationship is expressed as

$$P \propto T$$

If the absolute temperature is multiplied by five, the pressure is also multiplied by five. This relationship is illustrated graphically in Figure 2-13.

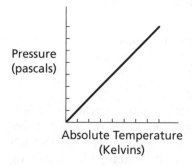

Figure 2-13. Absolute temperature versus pressure.

27. A fixed mass of gas at initial pressure P_1 and temperature T_1 occupies a volume V_1. If the pressure is tripled, but the temperature remains the same, what is the final volume?

Solution:

$$P_1 V_1 = P_2 V_2$$

$$P_1 V_1 = (3P_1)V_2$$

$$\frac{V_1}{3} = V_2$$

If the absolute temperature is doubled but the pressure remains the same, what is the new volume?

Solution: Since absolute temperature and volume are directly proportional

$$\frac{V_1}{T_1} = \frac{V_2}{T_2}$$

$$\frac{V_1}{T_1} = \frac{V_2}{2T_1}$$

$$V_2 = 2V_1$$

The absolute temperature is halved but the volume remains the same. What is the new pressure?

Solution: Since pressure is directly proportional to absolute temperature

$$\frac{P_1}{T_1} = \frac{P_2}{T_2}$$

$$\frac{P_1}{T_1} = \frac{P_2}{\frac{1}{2}T_1}$$

$$P_2 = \frac{1}{2}P_1$$

THE LAWS OF THERMODYNAMICS

Thermodynamics is the study of heat and its relationship to other forms of energy and to work. The principles of thermodynamics are based on the law of conservation of energy and can be summarized in three fundamental laws.

The First Law

The **first law of thermodynamics** states that the amount of heat energy added to a system is equal to the increase in the internal energy of the system plus the work done by the system. For example, consider the results of adding heat to a gas in a sealed container. If the container does not expand, no work is done by the gas and all of the added heat is used to increase the internal energy of the gas. On the other hand, if the lid of the container is replaced by a movable piston and the gas is allowed to expand as heat is added, the gas will do work as it exerts a force on the outwardly moving piston (Figure 2-14). In this case, the increasin the internal energy of the gas must equal the amount of heat energy added minus the amount of work done on the piston in order that energy be conserved.

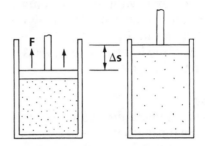

Figure 2-14. Heat added equals the increase in internal energy plus the work done.

The Second Law

The **second law of thermodynamics** states that unless external work is done to produce the effect, heat cannot flow from a cold to a hotter region. If objects at different temperatures are brought into contact, heat energy is transferred from the hotter to the colder object. The reverse will occur only if external work is done. For example, in order to remove heat from a cool refrigerator and transfer it to a warm kitchen, an electric motor must expend energy and do work to drive the process.

The fact that heat does not flow on its own from a colder to a hotter region can be explained in terms of **entropy.** *During all natural processes, the entropy, or amount of disorder, of a system tends to increase.* Disorder is simply the absence of organization. If heat were to flow from a cold to a hotter object, all the faster moving molecules would end up in one region and all the slower molecules in another. The molecules would then be organized according to their kinetic energies and disorder would *decrease.* According to the principle of increasing entropy, this can never occur. Instead, heat will always flow from the hotter to the colder object. As the temperature difference between the objects diminishes to zero the organization of molecules in terms of kinetic energy is eliminated and the system becomes less organized.

The second law has important consequences. It places limitations on the transfer and conversion of heat energy and, therefore, on the usefulness of all the heat energy around us. For example, a heat engine converts heat energy into useful mechanical energy as heat flows through it from a hot to a colder region. However, a heat engine can only convert a fraction of the heat energy into mechanical energy. Most of the heat is absorbed by the cold region and cannot be used to do work. If there is no cold region to transfer the heat to, no work can be obtained. This is why an ocean liner cannot be powered by the enormous reservoir of heat energy in the ocean. The extraction of heat from the water, without there being a colder region in contact with it, would necessitate the expenditure of energy (as in the case of the refrigerator). Thus, all of the internal energy stored in the ocean is practically useless.

The Third Law

The **third law of thermodynamics** states that it is impossible to reduce the temperature of a system to absolute zero. In order to lower the temperature of a system, heat must be removed from the system. One way to remove heat from a system is to place it in contact with another system at a lower temperature. In order to lower the temperature of a system to absolute zero, it would have to be placed in contact with a system whose temperature was lower than absolute zero. Since absolute zero is the lowest possible temperature, this is impossible.

Another way to remove heat from a system is to allow the system to do work. This method can be used to lower the temperature of gases. The lowest known condensation temperature of any gas is 3.2 K for the light isotope of helium. Below 3.2 K all substances are in the liquid or solid phase, so absolute zero cannot be achieved in this way either.

Scientists have been able to reach temperatures lower than 1 K by pumping away the vapor emitted by supercold liquids and by using a variety of magnetic effects. However, the closer to 0 K a system gets, the more difficult it is to further reduce its temperature. Absolute zero has never been achieved and is assumed to be unattainable.

QUESTIONS

131. The pressure exerted by a gas is due to (1) nuclear forces in the atoms of the gas (2) gravitational forces between gas atoms (3) collisions of molecules with each other (4) collisions of molecules with the container's walls.

132. Which of the following is not true of low density gases? (1) Gas molecules are in constant random motion. (2) Forces between molecules are large and significant. (3) Distances between molecules are large compared with their diame-

ters. (4) The total volume of the gas molecules is small compared with the volume of the gas.

133. If the pressure of a gas is doubled while temperature remains constant, the volume of the gas will (1) be halved (2) remain the same (3) be doubled (4) be quadrupled

134. If the temperature of a gas increases while the pressure remains constant, the volume of the gas (1) decreases (2) remains the same (3) increases

135. If the temperature of gas increases while its volume remains constant, the pressure will (1) decrease (2) remains the same (3) increase

136. Which graph illustrates the relationship between the absolute temperature and volume of a gas at constant pressure?

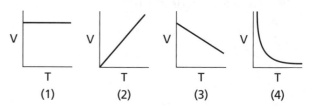

137. Which graph illustrates the relationship between the pressure and the volume of a gas at constant temperature?

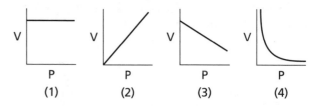

138. Which graph illustrates the relationship between the absolute temperature and the pressure of a gas at constant volume?

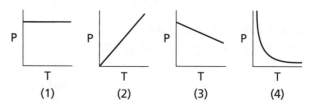

139. When the absolute temperature of a given mass of gas is constant, the relationship between its volume and pressure is best described as (1) unrelated (2) directly related (3) directly proportional (4) inversely proportional

140. On page 59, is a sketch of a cylinder in an automobile engine. After the fuel is ignited the internal energy of the cylinder (and its contents) increases by 300 J. As the piston is pushed forward, 500 J of work is done by the system. How much heat energy was added to the cylinder when the fuel ignited? (1) 200 J (2) 300 J (3) 500 J (4) 800 J

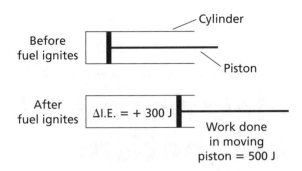

Before fuel ignites
Cylinder
Piston

After fuel ignites
$\Delta I.E. = + 300\ J$
Work done in moving piston = 500 J

141. In the system below, heat energy is flowing from region A at 0°C to region B at 50°C. Which statement is true about this situation? (1) It is impossible. (2) It occurs naturally. (3) It occurs only if external work is done on the system. (4) It occurs only if the mass of A is greater than the mass of B.

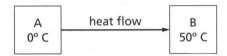

A 0° C → heat flow → B 50° C

142. An increase in the entropy of a system means the system is (1) hotter (2) less ordered (3) more ordered (4) cooler

143. There is a tendency in nature for systems to proceed toward (1) absolute zero (2) greater energy (3) less energy (4) less order

144. Which statement describes the thermodynamics involved when water evaporates to a gas? (1) the water absorbs energy, and entropy increases (2) the water absorbs energy, and entropy decreases (3) the water releases energy, and entropy increases (4) the water releases energy, and entropy decreases

145. The total energy of the universe is (1) decreasing (2) constant (3) increasing

146. The total entropy of the universe is (1) decreasing (2) constant (3) increasing

147. According to the third law of thermodynamics, a substance can be cooled to (1) 0 K (2) below 0 K (3) a little above 0 K (4) −273 K

Thinking and Analyzing

148. Describe and contrast the inter-related concepts of heat, internal energy, and temperature. How does altering the amount of any one of these quantities affect the amounts of the other two quantities?

149. A hot and a cold object come in contact with each other. Describe what changes, if any, occur to the internal energy, temperature, and specific heat of each of these two objects. Which of these changes are of necessity equally shared by the two objects and which need not be equally shared?

150. Describe two independent methods for removing some of an object's internal energy.

151. Define specific heat and explain the significance of a high specific heat.

152. Describe two reasons for the fact that the specific heat of one type of material may be different from that of another material.

153. Explain why the presence of a body of water has a moderating effect on the temperature of the surrounding materials.

154. What is meant by the term "entropy"?

155. Explain why and how the entropy of an object changes as some of its internal energy is converted to kinetic energy and as some of its kinetic energy is converted to internal energy.

156. One thousand red marbles and 1000 blue marbles are placed inside a sealed container. The container is then shaken vigorously. Explain how the second law of thermodynamics applied to this situation, affects your expectations for the arrangement of the marbles in the container after shaking it. If the marbles are initially organized in the container, with all the red marbles on top of the blue marbles, what will shaking the container do to the entropy of this system? Explain your answer.

157. Explain why it is quite easy to convert kinetic energy or potential energy into internal energy, but it is much more difficult to do the reverse—change internal energy into kinetic or potential energy.

158. Summarize the three laws of thermodynamics.

159. In what way does the second law of thermodynamics place limitations on the operation of a heat engine?

160. Describe the model of an ideal gas.

161. What is pressure and why do gases exert pressure?

162. What factors affect gas pressure?

163. How are the pressure and volume of a gas related to the number of molecules in the gas and the absolute temperature of the gas?

164. Describe Boyle's law and give an example.

165. Describe Charles' law and give an example.

CHAPTER 3

Electricity and Magnetism

STATIC ELECTRICITY

Static electricity involves the phenomena associated with charges at rest. The term "at rest" means that there is no net flow of charge in any direction. There are many familiar effects of static electricity. For example, a person shuffling across a carpeted floor and then touching a metal doorknob can expect to experience a shock.

The behavior of objects that have a static charge can be demonstrated with pith balls. If a rubber rod or a glass rod is rubbed against fur or silk fabric and then brought near a light, suspended pith ball, the ball approaches the rod, makes contact with it, and then moves away from it. After that, the ball remains as far from the rod as possible. A pith ball touched by a stroked rubber rod and a pith ball touched by a stroked glass rod experience a force of attraction and move toward each other. On the other hand, two pith balls touched by the same type of stroked rod experience a force of repulsion and move away from each other.

Structure of the Atom

The study of such phenomena indicates that all matter is electrical in nature. The basic unit of matter is the **atom** (Figure 3-1). Every atom consists of three types of particles: **protons, neutrons,** and **electrons.** Each electron carries a negative charge and each proton carries a positive

charge. Neutrons carry no charge. The amount of negative charge on an electron is the same as the amount of positive charge on a proton. Therefore, an atom with an equal number of protons and electrons has no net charge.

Protons and neutrons are located at the center of the atom, in the **nucleus,** which occupies a tiny fraction of the volume of the atom. Protons and neutrons are hundreds of times more massive than electrons and are held tightly together by strong nuclear forces. Electrons orbit the nucleus at various distances. The outermost electrons are often loosely bound to the nucleus by electrical forces and can be removed from the atom.

An object becomes charged if it either loses or gains electrons. An object that loses electrons and is left with fewer electrons than protons has a net positive charge. An object that gains electrons and has more electrons than protons has a net negative charge.

Electrons can only be transferred intact (fragments of electrons do not exist). As a result, any deficiency or excess of charge must consist of a whole-number multiple of the charge on one electron or proton. The charge on one electron is known as one **negative elementary charge.** The charge on one proton is referred to as one **positive elementary charge.**

The unit of charge is the **coulomb** (C). One coulomb is equal to the charge carried by 6.25×10^{18} electrons. Therefore the charge on one electron is equal to $1/6.25 \times 10^{18}$ C, or 1.6×10^{-19} C.

The Fundamentals of Electricity

From the observation of charged objects, the fundamental principles governing all electrical phenomena emerge:

1. There are two kinds of electric charge: positive charge and negative charge.

2. Just as gravitational force exists between masses, there is an electrical force between charges. Unlike gravitational force, which is one of attraction only, charges can be attracted to or

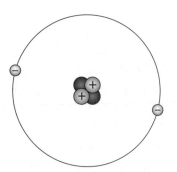

Figure 3-1. Model of an atom.

repelled by other charges. A positive charge will repel another positive charge, and a negative charge will repel another negative charge. A positive charge and a negative charge will attract each other. In other words, *like charges repel and unlike charges attract.*

3. All ordinary objects are electrically neutral, that is, they contain equal amounts of positive and negative charge.

Although both types of charge exist all around us, we are generally unaware of them because the electric forces they exert balance one another. For example, between two neutral objects there are forces of attraction between unlike charges balanced by equally strong forces of repulsion between like types of charge. Thus, the net force exerted on either object is equal to zero.

Conservation of Charge   In all cases of charge transfer, the **law of conservation of charge** applies. Charge is never created or destroyed. A gain of charge in one place must correspond with a loss of that type of charge in another place.

Coulomb's Law

Experiments performed by Charles Coulomb demonstrate that for two charged objects that are much smaller than the distance between them (**point charges**), the electric force between the charges is directly proportional to the product of the amounts of charge and inversely proportional to the square of the distance between them. This relationship is known as **Coulomb's law.** Doubling the distance between two charges results in a force that is one-fourth as strong. Tripling the distance between the charges results in a force that is one-ninth as strong.

As indicated by Newton's third law of motion, the force exerted by one charge on a second charge is equal in magnitude and opposite in direction to the force exerted by the second charge on the first.

Coulomb's law can be expressed as

$$F = \frac{kq_1q_2}{d^2}$$

where F is the force exerted by either charge on the other, in newtons; q_1 and q_2 are the amounts of charge, in coluombs; d is the distance between the charges, in meters; and k, the **electrostatic constant,** is equal to $9.0 \times 10^9 \, \text{N} \cdot \text{m}^2/\text{C}^2$.

Sample Problems

1. How strong is the repulsive force exerted on two point charges that each carry $1.0 \times 10^{-6} \, \text{C}$ of negative charge and are 0.3 m apart?

Solution:

$$F = \frac{kq_1q_2}{d^2}$$

$$= \frac{(9.0 \times 10^9 \, \text{N} \cdot \text{m}^2/\text{C}^2)(1.0 \times 10^{-6} \, \text{C})}{(1.0 \times 10^{-6} \, \text{C})}$$
$$ \frac{}{(0.3 \, \text{m})^2}$$

$$= \frac{9.0 \times 10^{-3} \, \text{N} \cdot \text{m}^2}{9.0 \times 10^{-2} \, \text{m}^2} = 0.1 \, \text{N}$$

2. Two identical point charges separated by 25 m exert a repulsive force on each other of 25 N. What is the magnitude of the charge on each object?
Solution:

$$F = \frac{kq_1q_2}{d^2} \quad \text{and} \quad q_1 = q_2$$

$$25 \, \text{N} = \frac{(9.0 \times 10^9 \, \text{N} \cdot \text{m}^2/\text{C}^2)(q^2)}{(25 \, \text{m})^2}$$

$$q^2 = \frac{(25 \, \text{N})(25 \, \text{m})^2}{(9.0 \times 10^9 \, \text{N} \cdot \text{m}^2/\text{C}^2)}$$

$$= 1.7 \times 10^{-6} \, \text{C}^2$$

$$q = 1.3 \times 10^{-3} \, \text{C}$$

QUESTIONS

Base your answers to questions 1 through 3 on the following diagram, which represents a system consisting of two charged metal spheres with equal radii.

A |← 12 m →| B
+2.0 × 10⁻⁴C   −8.0 × 10⁻⁴C

1. What is the magnitude of the electrostatic force exerted on sphere *A*?   (1) $1.1 \times 10^{-9} \, \text{N}$ (2) $1.3 \times 10^{-8} \, \text{N}$ (3) 120 N   (4) 10. N

2. Compared with the force exerted on sphere *B* at a separation of 12 meters, the force exerted on sphere *B* at a separation of 6.0 meters would be   (1) $\frac{1}{2}$ as great   (2) 2 times as great   (3) $\frac{1}{4}$ as great   (4) 4 times as great

3. If the two spheres were touched together and then separated, the charge on sphere *A* would be   (1) $-6.0 \times 10^{-4} \, \text{C}$ (2) $2.0 \times 10^{-4} \, \text{C}$ (3) $-3.0 \times 10^{-4} \, \text{C}$ (4) $-8.0 \times 10^{-4} \, \text{C}$

4. The following diagram represents two charges at a separation of *d*. Which would produce the greatest increase in the force between the two charges?

q₁   q₂
○——————— d ———————○

(1) doubling charge q_1, only   (2) doubling d, only (3) doubling charge q_1 and d, only   (4) doubling both charges and d

5. The electrostatic force of attraction between two small spheres that are 1.0 meter apart is F. If the distance between the spheres is decreased to 0.5 meter, the electrostatic force will then be (1) $F/2$ (2) $2F$ (3) $F/4$ (4) $4F$

6. If the charge on one of two small charged spheres is doubled while the distance between them remains the same, the electrostatic force between the spheres will be (1) halved (2) doubled   (3) tripled   (4) unchanged

7. Charge A is $+2.0 \times 10^{-6}$ coulomb and charge B is $+1.0 \times 10^{-6}$ coulomb. If the force that A exerts on B is 1.0×10^{-2} newton, the force that B exerts on A is   (1) 1.0×10^{-2} N   (2) 2.0×10^{-2} N (3) 3.0×10^{-2} (4) 5.0×10^{-1} N

Base your answers to questions 8 through 10 on the following diagram, which shows two *identical* metal spheres. Sphere A has a charge of $+12$ coulombs and sphere B is a neutral sphere.

+ 12 coulumbs

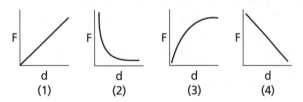

8. When sphere A and B are in contact, the total charge of the system is   (1) neutral   (2) $+6$ C (3) $+12$ C   (4) -24 C

9. When spheres A and B are separated, the charge on A will be   (1) $+12$ C   (2) $\frac{1}{4}$ the original amount   (3) $\frac{1}{2}$ the original amount   (4) 4 times the original amount

10. After spheres A and B are separated, which graph best represents the relationship of the force between the spheres and their separation?

Thinking and Analyzing

11. Describe the flow of charge around charges that are at rest.

12. In what way do two objects with like charges behave differently than two objects with opposite charges?

13. Describe the particles that make up the atom.

14. How does an object become charged?

15. What can you conclude about the numbers of protons and electrons in an object that is electrically neutral?

16. What does the law of conservation of charge demand?

17. Explain what is meant by the statement, "The electric force depends on the inverse of the square of the distance between charges." Provide three sample sets of data to illustrate your explanation.

ELECTRIC FIELDS

A charge in empty space experiences no electric forces, but a charge near another charge does. The reason for this difference is that a charge creates an **electric field** that permeates the surrounding space and affects other nearby charges.

As long as no other charge is present, an electric field does nothing. When another charge (referred to as a **test charge**) is introduced into the field, the field exerts a force on it. The presence of an electric field can be detected by its effect on a charged object introduced into the region.

Electric Field Intensity
Fields, like forces, are vector quantities: they have magnitude and direction. The magnitude of an electric field is referred to as its **intensity.** The intensity of an electric field at a particular point is defined as the magnitude of the force that the field exerts on a test charge of one coulomb at that point. The inverse square law applies to electric fields around point charges. The direction of the electric field at any given point is defined as the direction of the force that the field exerts on a positive test charge at that point. The intensity and direction of an electric field are different at different positions in the vicinity of a charge, and therefore, the magnitude and direction of the electric force also vary from point to point.

Electric Potential Energy
The electric force, like the gravitational force, can push or pull an object through a distance and thereby do work. Just as a mass has gravitational potential energy because of its position in a gravitational field, a charged object has **electric potential energy** due to its position in an electric field.

If an electric field does work on any charged object, such as when the field created by one positive charge repels another positive charge, electric potential energy decreases. Similarly, electric potential energy decreases when the field created by a positive charge attracts a negative charge, pulling the charges closer together. This is analogous to a falling object on Earth. When the gravitational field does work, gravitational potential energy decreases. In accordance with the law of conservation of energy, the lost potential energy is converted to an equal amount of energy of some other type, such as kinetic energy or heat.

If work is done against an electric field, such as when a positive charge is moved closer to another positive charge, electric potential energy increases. Similarly, electric potential energy increases when a negative charge is moved away from a positive charge. This is analogous to lifting an object on Earth. When work is done against the gravitational field, gravitational potential energy increases. Once again, the gain in potential energy must correspond to a loss of energy of some other type, in order that energy be conserved. The work done by (or against) an electric field in moving a charge from one point to another is independent of the path taken. In other words, the electric force is a conservative force, as is gravity.

Electric Potential

The **electric potential** at any given point in an electric field is defined as the total amount of work required to bring one coulomb of positive charge from infinity to that point. At a point in a field created by a positive charge, the force is repulsive. Thus, the work done against the field in moving the positive test charge from infinity to the point is positive. The closer the point is to the positive charge that set up the field, the greater the electric potential.

At a point in a field created by a negative charge, the force is attractive. Thus, the work done in moving the positive test charge from infinity to the point is negative (the field does work on the charge). The closer the point is to the negative charge that set up the field, the smaller the electric potential.

In summary, electric potential at any given point in an electric field is positive if work must be done *against* the field to move a positive test charge from infinity to that point, and negative if work is done *by* the field to move a positive test charge from infinity to that point.

Potential Difference

The work required to move a test charge of one coulomb from one point to another in an electric field is equal to the difference in the electric potential between the two points. We refer to this difference in electric potential as the **potential difference** between the two points.

From the amount of work W, in joules, required to move a charge q, in coulombs, between two points in an electric field, the potential difference V between those two points can be obtained by using the formula

$$V = \frac{W}{q}$$

Thus, potential difference is expressed in joules per coulomb. One joule per coulomb is more commonly referred to as one **volt.** Since the potential difference between two points is measured in volts, it is also known as the **voltage.**

If it takes 6 J of work to push a 3 C charge from one point to another in an electric field, the potential difference between the two points is 6 J/3 C, or 2 V. If a manufacturer labels a battery 9 V, it means that the electric field created by the two charged terminals will do 9 J of work on every coulomb that is pushed by the battery from one terminal to the other. Since the quantity of work done is independent of the path taken between the terminals, the characteristics of the materials and appliances connected to the battery play no role in determining the voltage.

If the voltage between two points is known, the work done in moving any given amount of charge between those points can be found by using the formula

$$W = qV$$

Sample Problems

3. What is the potential difference between the terminals of a battery if 60. J of work are done when 3.0 C are pushed through a wire from one terminal to the other?

Solution:

$$V = \frac{W}{q}$$

$$= \frac{60.\,J}{3.0\,C} = 20.\,J/C = 20.\,V$$

4. How much work does the same battery do on every electron pushed through the wire?

Solution:

$$W = qV$$

$$= (1.6 \times 10^{-19}\,C)(20.\,V)$$

$$= 3.2 \times 10^{-18}\,J$$

The Electron Volt

A convenient unit of work and energy when working with small charges, such as electrons and protons, is the **electron volt** (eV). One electron volt is defined as the work required to move one elementary charge between two points with a 1-V potential difference between them. Using the equation $W = qV$, this amount of work is

$$W = (1.6 \times 10^{-19}\,\text{C})(1\,\text{V})$$

$$= (1.6 \times 10^{-19}\,\text{C})(1\,\text{J/C})$$

$$= 1.6 \times 10^{-19}\,\text{J}$$

One electron volt, therefore, is equivalent to 1.6×10^{-19} J. When this amount of work is done on a charge, the charge gains 1 eV of energy.

Base your answers to questions 18 and 19 on the following diagram, which represents two small, charged conducting spheres, identical in size, located 2.0 meters apart.

A |← — 2.00 meters — →| B

+5.00 × 10⁻⁶coulomb   −4.00 × 10⁻⁶coulomb

18. What is the net combined charge on both spheres?   (1) $+1.0 \times 10^{-6}$ C   (2) -1.0×10^{-6} C   (3) $+9.0 \times 10^{-6}$ C   (4) -9.0×10^{-6} C

19. The force between these spheres is (1) 1.8×10^{-2} N (2) 3.6×10^{-2} N (3) 4.5×10^{-2} N (4) 9.0×10^{-2} N

20. What is the magnitude of the force acting on an electron when it is in the 10^6 N/C electric field? (1) 1.6×10^{-25} N (2) 1.6×10^{-13} N (3) 1.0×10^6 N (4) 1.6×10^{25} N

21. As an electron moves from a negatively charged plate to a positively charged plate, the force on the electron due to the electric field (1) decreases (2) increases (3) remains the same

22. The electron above is replaced by a proton. Compared with the magnitude of the force on the electron, the magnitude of the force on the proton will be (1) less (2) greater (3) the same

Base your answer to question 23 on the following diagram, which represents two charged metal spheres.

q = +.020 coulomb   q = −.020 coulomb

|← — 1 m — →|

23. What is the magnitude of the force between the two spheres?   (1) 3.6×10^6 N   (2) 1.8×10^8 N   (3) 3.6×10^9 N   (4) 9.0×10^9 N

Thinking and Analyzing

24. How does a charge experience an electric force when it is placed near a second charge?

25. What is meant by the intensity of an electric field?

26. How is the direction of an electric field determined?

27. What is the electric potential at a given point?

28. What does it mean to say that there is a potential difference between two points?

29. How is potential difference calculated?

ELECTRIC CURRENT

Conduction in Solids

Just as water can be made to flow through a network of pipes by the action of a pump, charged particles (usually electrons) can be made to flow through certain materials by the action of an electric field. For this flow of electric charge, or **electric current,** to occur, the following conditions must be satisfied:

1. The materials must be **conductors,** substances that allow electrons to flow through them. Some materials, called **insulators,** strongly resist such a flow.

2. The conductor must be connected to a **source,** a device that creates an electric field, such that a potential difference exists between the ends of the conductor. Two common sources are the battery and the generator.

3. The source and the conductor must form a closed loop, called a **circuit,** with no gaps across which electrons cannot travel. If such a gap exists, electrons will gather on one side of the gap, and the flow of charge will not occur.

Before scientists learned that electrons flow in an electric current, they assumed that current consisted of positive charges flowing from the positive to the negative terminal of a battery. This flow of positive charges is called **conventional current**.

Conductors and Insulators

Metals are good conductors because their atoms do not hold firmly onto their outermost electrons. These "free" electrons can easily be pushed through the metal, from atom to atom. The greater the number of free electrons per unit volume in a material, the better a conductor it makes.

Nonmetallic solids are good insulators because they hold on strongly to their electrons. It is difficult or impossible to get electrons to flow through such materials.

The Ampere

The amount of charge flowing past a given point in a conductor is expressed in coulombs per second. If one coulomb passes a point in a conductor each second, the current in the conductor is one **ampere.** The ampere (A) is a fundamental unit.

The current in a conductor can be found by using the formula

$$I = \frac{\Delta q}{\Delta t}$$

where Δq is the amount of charge, in coulombs, passing a given point in a conductor in an amount of time Δt, in seconds, and I is the current, in amperes. For example, if 8 C pass a point in a conductor in 4 s, the current is 8 C/4 s, or 2 A.

Ohm's Law

The amount of current passing through a conductor at a particular temperature is directly proportional to the potential difference across the ends of the conductor. For example, if the potential difference is doubled, the amount of current is doubled. This relationship is known as **Ohm's law.** Ohm's law is generally not applicable to conductors other than metallic solids.

Ohm's law can be stated mathematically as

$$V = IR$$

where V is the potential difference, in volts; I is the current, in amperes; and R is a constant. This constant is different for different materials and, for any particular material, is different at different temperatures.

The greater the R value of a material, the smaller the amount of current for a particular voltage. Thus, the greater the R value, the poorer the conductivity. The R value of a material, therefore, is a measure of the material's **resistance** to the flow of electrons through it.

The resistance of a metallic conductor at a given temperature is equal to the slope of a graph of current versus potential difference for that conductor (Figure 3-2).

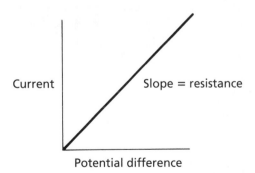

Figure 3-2. The slope of the current-potential difference graph is the resistance.

Resistance

A material that allows a current of one ampere to flow through it when the potential difference across it is one volt is said to have a resistance of one **ohm.** The symbol for the ohm is the Greek letter omega (Ω).

Sample Problems

5. What is the resistance of a metallic conductor that allows a current of 2 A to flow through it when connected to a source that provides a potential difference of 120 V?
  Solution:

$$V = IR$$
$$120\,V = (2\,A)(R)$$
$$R = 60\,\Omega$$

6. If a wire has a resistance of 60 Ω and the potential difference across the wire is 30 V, what is the current flowing through it?
  Solution:

$$V = IR$$
$$30\,V = (I)(60\,\Omega)$$
$$I = 0.5\,A$$

The resistance of a solid conductor, such as a metallic wire, depends upon the conductor's composition, length, cross-sectional area, and temperature:

1. Resistance is directly proportional to length. A wire that is twice as long as a similar wire has twice as much resistance.

2. Resistance is inversely proportional to cross-sectional area. A wire with twice the cross-sectional area of another wire (all other factors being equal) has one-half as much resistance.

3. The resistance of a metallic conductor increases as temperature rises, but the resistance of some nonmetallic, liquid, and gas conductors decreases as the temperature increases.

Some materials become such good conductors at very low temperatures, near absolute zero (0 K), that their resistance is effectively reduced to zero. Because electrons encounter virtually no resistance in passing through them, these materials are known as **superconductors.** A current of electrons incurs no loss of energy to heat while passing through a superconducting material.

Scientists recently discovered that certain materials act as superconductors at substantially higher temperatures. This discovery may eliminate the need for costly cooling to achieve super-conductivity.

4. The resistance of a conductor of given dimensions depends upon the material of which it is made. Copper, for example, is a better conductor and offers less resistance to the flow of charge than aluminum.

5. **Resistivity,** represented by the Greek letter ρ (rho), is the measure of the resistance of a wire 1 m long with a uniform cross-sectional area of 1 m^2. You know that the resistance of a conductor is directly proportional to its length and inversely proportional to its cross-sectional area. This is expressed mathematically as $R = \rho\frac{l}{A}$, where R is the resistance, ρ is the resistivity of the metal, l is the length of the conductor, and A is the cross-sectional area. If the resistivity of a metal is known, you can calculate the resistance any wire made of that material. Table 3-1 gives the resistivity of several metals.

Table 3-1. Resistivity of Selected Metals at 20°C

Metal	Resistivity ($\Omega \cdot m$)
Aluminum	2.82×10^{-8}
Copper	1.72×10^{-8}
Gold	2.44×10^{-8}
Nichrome	150×10^{-8}
Silver	1.59×10^{-8}
Tungsten	5.60×10^{-8}

Sample Problem

7. What is the resistance of 30.-cm length of copper wire that has a cross-sectional area of 0.50 cm^2?

Solution:

$$R = \rho\frac{l}{A}$$

$$= 1.72 \times 10^{-8}\Omega \cdot m \left(\frac{0.30\ m}{0.50 \times 10^{-4}\ m^2} \right)$$

$$R = 1.0 \times 10^{-4}\Omega$$

Electric Power and Energy

As electrons are pushed through a circuit, work is done on them. Electric potential energy is converted into other forms of energy, such as heat, light, mechanical energy, or a combination of these, depending on the particular circuit. The electrons do not gain kinetic energy as they move through a circuit, because they undergo collisions with the atoms of the conductor. Although the

electrons accelerate in between collisions due to the electric force acting on them, the kinetic energy they gain is transferred to the atoms during the collisions. As a result, the average kinetic energy of the atoms increases, and the temperature of the conductor increases.

Electric power is the rate at which electric potential energy is converted into another form of energy. The unit of power is the **watt** (W). One watt is equal to a rate of energy conversion of one joule/second.

The power (P), in watts, can be obtained by using the formula

$$P = VI$$

where V is the potential difference, in volts; and I is the current, in amperes.

For example, if the potential difference between the ends of a conductor is 8 V and the current is 5 A, then the power is 40 W. This means that 40 J of electric potential energy is expended every second and converted into another form of energy. The formula $P = VI$ can be combined with Ohm's law to obtain two other equations for calculating power

$$P = I^2R \qquad \text{and} \qquad P = \frac{V^2}{R}$$

The total amount of electric energy converted to another form when a current flows through a circuit during a period of time (t) may be obtained from the formula

$$W = Pt$$

where W is the total energy converted, in joules.

For example, if a 40-W circuit operates for 20 s, then 40 J of energy is converted during each of the 20 s of operation. The total amount of energy converted is then 800 J.

The formula $W = Pt$ can be combined with the formulas $P = VI$ and $P = I^2R$ to yield

$$W = VIt \qquad \text{and} \qquad W = I^2Rt$$

Sample Problem

8. A light bulb whose resistance is 240. Ω is connected to a 120.-V source. What is the current through the bulb?

Solution:

$$V = IR$$

$$120.\ V = (I)(240.\ \Omega)$$

$$I = 0.500\ A$$

What is the power of the bulb? (There are two formulas you can use.)

Solution:

$$P = VI$$
$$= (120.\text{ V})(0.500\text{ A}) = 60.0\text{ W}$$

or

$$P = I^2R$$
$$= (0.500\text{ A})^2(240.\ \Omega) = 60.0\text{ W}$$

After operating for 10 minutes (600. s), how many joules of heat and light energy are produced? (There are two formulas you can use.)

Solution:

$$W = VIt$$
$$= (120.\text{ V})(0.500\text{ A})(600.\text{ s}) = 3.60 \times 10^4\text{ J}$$

or

$$W = I^2Rt$$
$$= (0.500\text{ A})^2(240.\ \Omega)(600.\text{ s}) = 3.60 \times 10^4\text{ J}$$

Circuit Combinations

Frequently we connect many appliances to one source so that electrons flow through all of them simultaneously. The appliances may be connected in **series,** in **parallel,** or in combinations of these.

Two fundamental principles apply to the operation of all circuits, no matter how complicated the connections. First, in accordance with the law of conservation of charge, no charge is ever created or destroyed. Thus, for any circuit, the sum of the currents entering any junction is equal to the sum of the currents leaving it. This is known as **Kirchoff's first law.** Second, in accordance with the law of conservation of energy, the total energy output of the circuit is equal to the total electric energy made available to the circuit by the source. This is referred to as **Kirchoff's second law.**

Schematic diagrams facilitate the study of electric circuits. Some of the symbols used to represent various circuit elements are shown in Figure 3-3.

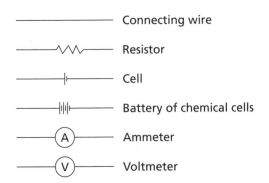

————————	Connecting wire
—————/\/\/\/——————	Resistor
—————|⊢—————	Cell
—————|⊩|⊩—————	Battery of chemical cells
—————(A)—————	Ammeter
—————(V)—————	Voltmeter

Figure 3-3. Electric circuit symbols.

A **resistor** is any conductor with a measurable resistance. The resistors in a circuit are usually various types of appliances. The connecting wires are assumed to have negligible resistance.

A **cell** is illustrated by a set of parallel lines. The long line represents the positive terminal and the short line represents the negative terminal. A **battery,** or combination of cells, is illustrated with a set of long and short parallel lines for every cell it contains.

An **ammeter** is a device used to measure current and is usually calibrated in amperes. It is so designed that its insertion into a circuit does not have a significant effect on the current.

A **voltmeter** is used to measure the potential difference between two points in a circuit. It is usually calibrated in volts. It is so designed that its insertion into the circuit has no significant effect on the potential difference.

Series Circuits

In a **series circuit** only one path exists through which current can flow. A series circuit with three resistors is shown in Figure 3-4. Since the circuit consists of a single conducting path, the currents in all the resistors must be the same, in accordance with Kirchoff's first law. This principle is represented by the relationship

$$I_t = I_1 = I_2 = I_3 = \cdots = I_n$$

where I_t is the total current, and I_1, I_2, and I_3 are the currents through resistors R_1, R_2, and R_3, respectively. (There is no limit to the number of resistors permitted.)

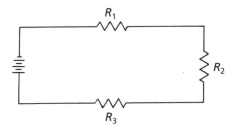

Figure 3-4. Series circuit.

The work done per coulomb of charge as it goes through a particular resistor is equal to the potential difference between the ends of that resistor. This potential difference is referred to as the **voltage drop** across the resistor. Thus, Kirchoff's second law can be stated as: The sum of the voltage drops across all the resistors in series must equal the potential difference produced by the source. This is represented by the formula

$$V_t = V_1 + V_2 + V_3 + \cdots + V_n$$

where V_t is the voltage created by the source and V_1, V_2, and V_3 are the voltage drops across resistors R_1, R_2, and R_3, respectively (up to the nth resistor).

The total resistance, R_t, is found by adding all the individual resistances in the series combination

$$R_t = R_1 + R_2 + R_3 = \cdots + R_n$$

By combining these principles with Ohm's law and the formulas introduced earlier, the voltage drop, current, and power of all resistors in series can be calculated.

Sample Problem

9. The circuit diagram in Figure 3-5 represents three appliances connected in series to a 90.-V source. If their resistances are 2.0 Ω, 3.0 Ω, and 5.0 Ω, respectively, find the voltage drop across each appliance, the amount of current passing through each appliance, and the power of each appliance.

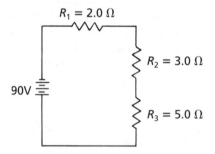

Figure 3-5.

Solution:
First, find the total resistance.

$$R_t = R_1 + R_2 + R_3$$
$$= 2.0\ \Omega + 3.0\ \Omega + 5.0\ \Omega = 10.0\ \Omega$$

Next, determine the current by applying Ohm's law to the total voltage and the total resistance.

$$V_t = I_t R_t$$
$$90.\ \text{V} = (I_t)(10.\ \Omega)$$
$$I_t = 9.0\ \text{A}$$

Since $I_t = I_1 = I_2 = I_3$, we know that $I_1 = 9.0$ A, $I_2 = 9.0$ A, and $I_3 = 9.0$ A.

Next, find the voltage drop across each appliance by applying Ohm's law to each resistance.

$$V_1 = I_1 R_1 = (9.0\ \text{A})(2.0\ \Omega) = 18\ \text{V}$$
$$V_2 = I_2 R_2 = (9.0\ \text{A})(3.0\ \Omega) = 27\ \text{V}$$
$$V_3 = I_3 R_3 = (9.0\ \text{A})(5.0\ \Omega) = 45\ \text{V}$$

At this point check to make sure that the sum of the individual voltage drops equals the voltage of the source.

$$V_t = V_1 + V_2 + V_3$$
$$= 18\ \text{V} + 27\ \text{V} + 45\ \text{V} = 90.\ \text{V}$$

Next, determine each appliance's power by applying $P = VI$ to each.

$$P_1 = V_1 I_1 = (18\ \text{V})(9.0\ \text{A}) = 160\ \text{W}$$
$$P_2 = V_2 I_2 = (27\ \text{V})(9.0\ \text{A}) = 240\ \text{W}$$
$$P_3 = V_3 I_3 = (45\ \text{V})(9.0\ \text{A}) = 410\ \text{W}$$

The voltage drop and power of an appliance in series is directly proportional to its resistance. The greater the appliance's resistance, the greater its voltage drop and power.

Parallel Circuits

In a **parallel circuit,** current flows through two or more alternate paths, called **branches.** Every appliance in our homes is a branch in such a network of branches. The part of the circuit through which the full amount of current flows is called the **main line.** Each branch of the circuit is independent of the others. A break in one branch only stops the current in that branch, and current continues to flow through the others (Figure 3-6).

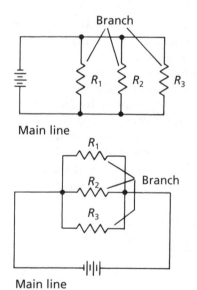

Figure 3-6. Parallel circuits.

Since electric force is a conservative force, the amount of work done per coulomb of charge is equal to the potential difference created by the source irrespective of the particular branch through which the charge passes. It follows that the voltage drop across each resistor connected in parallel is the same. This is expressed mathematically as

$$V_t = V_1 = V_2 = V_3 = \cdots = V_n$$

where V_t is the voltage of the source, and V_1, V_2, and V_3 are the voltage drops across resistors R_1, R_2, and R_3, respectively (up to the nth resistor).

In accordance with Kirchoff's first law, the sum of the branch currents must equal the current in the main line. Mathematically this is stated as

$$I_t = I_1 + I_2 + I_3 + \cdots + I_n$$

where I_t is the current in the main line and I_1, I_2, and I_3 are the currents in branches 1, 2, and 3, respectively (up to the nth branch).

The total current can be found by replacing all the parallel resistors with one whose resistance, R_{eq}, is provided by the formula

$$\frac{1}{R_{eq}} = \frac{1}{R_1} + \frac{1}{R_2} + \frac{1}{R_3} + \cdots + \frac{1}{R_n}$$

where R_1, R_2, and R_3 are the resistances of branches 1, 2, and 3, respectively (up to the nth branch). The total current I_t, can then be found by using Ohm's law

$$I_t = \frac{V_t}{R_{eq}}$$

R_{eq} is referred to as the **combined,** or **equivalent resistance** of the parallel circuit.

By combining these principles with the formulas introduced earlier, the current, voltage drop, and power of each branch in a parallel circuit can be calculated.

Sample Problems

10. What is the current, voltage drop, and power of each of three appliances connected in parallel to a 72-V source in Figure 3-7, if their resistances are 12 Ω, 24 Ω, and 8.0 Ω?

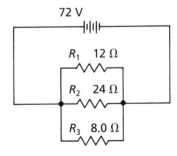

72 V

R_1 12 Ω
R_2 24 Ω
R_3 8.0 Ω

Figure 3-7.

Solution: First, the equivalent resistance of the circuit is determined by applying the formula

$$\frac{1}{R_{eq}} = \frac{1}{R_1} + \frac{1}{R_2} + \frac{1}{R_3}$$

$$= \frac{1}{12\ \Omega} + \frac{1}{24\ \Omega} + \frac{1}{8.0\ \Omega} = \frac{1}{4.0\ \Omega}$$

$$R_{eq} = 4.0\ \Omega$$

Note that the equivalent resistance of the circuit is less than the resistance of any one of the branches. The effect of adding more branches to a parallel circuit is to decrease the equivalent resistance of the circuit and to draw a greater amount of current from the source.

Next, Ohm's law is applied to determine the total current through the circuit.

$$V_t = I_t R_{eq}$$

$$72\ \text{V} = (I_t)(4.0\ \Omega)$$

$$I_t = 18\ \text{A}$$

Now the voltage drop across each of the three appliances in parallel is found

$$V_t = V_1 = V_2 = V_3 = 72\ \text{V}$$

Next, the current in each branch is determined by applying Ohm's law to each one

$$I_1 = \frac{V_1}{R_1} = \frac{72\ \text{V}}{12\ \Omega} = 6.0\ \text{A}$$

$$I_2 = \frac{V_2}{R_2} = \frac{72\ \text{V}}{24\ \Omega} = 3.0\ \text{A}$$

$$I_3 = \frac{V_3}{R_3} = \frac{72\ \text{V}}{8.0\ \Omega} = 9.0\ \text{A}$$

At this point we check to see if the branch currents add up to the total current.

$$I_t = I_1 + I_2 + I_3$$

$$= 6.0\ \text{A} + 3.0\ \text{A} + 9.0\ \text{A} = 18\ \text{A}$$

Note that the amount of current in each branch is inversely proportional to the resistance of the branch. The greater the resistance of the branch, the smaller the current.

The power of each branch can now be determined by applying $P = VI$ to each.

$$P_1 = V_1 I_1 = (72\ \text{V})(6.0\ \text{A}) = 430\ \text{W}\ (432\ \text{W})$$

$$P_2 = V_2 I_2 = (72\ \text{V})(3.0\ \text{A}) = 220\ \text{W}\ (216\ \text{W})$$

$$P_3 = V_3 I_3 = (72\ \text{V})(9.0\ \text{A}) = 650\ \text{W}\ (648\ \text{W})$$

The total power of the parallel circuit (430 W + 220 W + 650 W = 1300 W) would be the same if the branches were replaced by one path with a resistance equal to the equivalent resistance, R_t. The power would then be 72 volts × 18 amperes, or 1300 watts.

11. Figure 3-8 represents two appliances connected in series to a 100-V source. The resistances of R_1 and R_2 are 3 Ω and 7 Ω respectively.

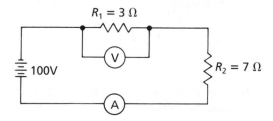

Figure 3-8.

What is the current recorded by the ammeter?
Solution:

$$V_t = I_t R_{eq}$$
$$100\text{ V} = (I_t)(10\text{ Ω})$$
$$I_t = 10\text{ A}$$

What is the voltage drop recorded by the voltmeter?
Solution:

$$V_1 = I_1 R_1$$
$$= (10\text{ A})(3\text{ Ω}) = 30\text{ V}$$

How much electric energy is expended in R_1 in 2 seconds?
Solution:

$$W_1 = V_1 I_1 t$$
$$= (30\text{ V})(10\text{ A})(2\text{ s}) = 600\text{ J}$$

QUESTIONS

30. The diagram represents a positive test charge located near a positively charged sphere. The greatest increase in the electric potential energy of the test charge relative to the sphere would be caused by moving the charge to point   (1) A (2) B (3) C (4) D

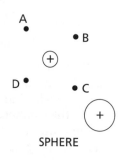

31. How much work is done in moving 6 electrons through a potential difference of 2.0 volts? (1) 6.0 eV   (2) 2.0 eV   (3) 3.0 eV   (4) 12 eV

32. If 6.0 joules of work is done to move 2.0 coulombs of charge from point A to point B, what is the electric potential difference between points A and B?   (1) 6.0 V   (2) .33 V   (3) 3.0 V   (4) 12 V

33. The work required to move a charge of 0.04 coulomb from one point to another point in an electric field is 200 joules. What is the potential difference between the two points?   (1) 0.0002 V (2) 8 V   (3) 200 V   (4) 5,000 V

34. A unit of electric potential difference is the (1) ampere   (2) joule   (3) volt   (4) coulomb

35. The electron volt is a unit of   (1) charge   (2) potential difference   (3) current   (4) energy

Base your answers to questions 36 through 38 on the following diagram, which represents a source connected to two large, parallel metal plates. The electric field intensity between the plates is 3.75×10^4 newtons per coulomb.

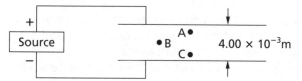

36. What is the potential difference of the source? (1) 9.38×10^5 V   (2) 4.00×10^3 V   (3) 3.75×10^2 V   (4) 1.50×10^2 V

37. What would be the magnitude of the electric force on a proton at point A?   (1) 1.60×10^{-19} N (2) 6.00×10^{-15} N   (3) 0 N   (4) 3.75×10^4 N

38. Compared with the work done in moving an electron from point B to point C, the work done in moving an electron directly from point A to point C is   (1) less   (2) greater (3) the same

39. Compared with the number of free electrons in a conductor, the number of free electrons in an insulator of the same volume is   (1) less   (2) greater   (3) the same

40. Most metals are good electrical conductors because   (1) their molecules are close together (2) they have high melting points   (3) they have many intermolecular spaces through which the current can flow   (4) they have a large number of free electrons

41. When 20. coulombs of charge pass a given point in a conductor in 4.0 seconds, the current in the conductor is   (1) 80. A   (2) 0.20 A   (3) 16 A (4) 5.0 A

42. Which graph best represents the relationship between the current in a metallic conductor and the applied potential difference?

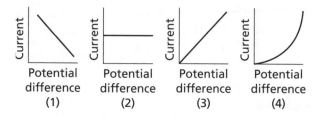

43. A potential difference of 12 volts is applied across a circuit which has a 4.0-ohm resistance. What is the magnitude of the current in the circuit? (1) 0.33 A (2) 48 A (3) 3.0 A (4) 4.0 A

44. The ratio of the potential difference across a metallic conductor to the current in the conductor is known as (1) potential drop (2) conductivity (3) resistance (4) electromagnetic force

45. If the current in a wire is 2.0 amperes and the potential difference across the wire is 10. volts, what is the resistance of the wire? (1) 5.0 Ω (2) 8.0 Ω (3) 12 Ω (4) 20. Ω

46. Which condition must exist between two points in a conductor in order to maintain a flow of charge? (1) a potential difference (2) a magnetic field (3) a low resistance (4) a high resistance

47. If 4 joules of work are required to move 2 coulombs of charge through a 6-ohm resistor, the potential difference across the resistor is (1) 1 V (2) 2 V (3) 6 V (4) 8 V

48. As the temperature of a metal conductor is reduced, the resistance of the conductor will (1) decrease (2) increase (3) remain the same

49. The resistance of a metallic wire conductor is inversely proportional to its (1) tensile strength (2) cross-sectional area (3) length (4) temperature

50. If the cross-sectional area of a fixed length of wire were decreased, the resistance of the wire would (1) decrease (2) increase (3) remain the same

51. A piece of wire has a resistance of 8 ohms. A second piece of wire of the same composition, diameter, and temperature, but one-half as long as the first wire, has a resistance of (1) 8 Ω (2) 2 Ω (3) 16 Ω (4) 4 Ω

52. The resistivity of nichrome is 115×10^{-6} $\Omega \cdot cm$. What is the resistance of a 755-cm length of nichrome wire that has a cross-sectional area of 0.312 cm²? (1) 4.75×10^{-8} Ω (2) 1.15×10^{-4} Ω (3) 3.62×10^{-1} Ω (4) 2.05×10^{6} Ω

53. A 1500-cm length of aluminum wire (cross-sectional area 0.330 cm²) has a resistance of 1.28×10^{-2} Ω, what is the resistivity of aluminum? (1) 2.8×10^{-6} Ω · cm (2) 3.8×10^{-6} Ω · cm (3) 5.6×10^{-6} Ω · cm (4) 6.8×10^{-6} Ω · cm

54. If energy is used in an electric circuit at the rate of 20. joules per second, then the power supplied to the circuit is (1) 5.0 W (2) 20. W (3) 25. W (4) 100. W

55. What is the current in a 1,200-watt heater operating on 120 volts? (1) 0.10 A (2) 5.0 A (3) 10. A (4) 20. A

56. The potential difference across a 100.-ohm resistor is 4.0 volts. What is the power dissipated in the resistor? (1) 0.16 W (2) 25 W (3) 4.0×10^{2} W (4) 4.0 W

57. Three resistors of 10 ohms, 20 ohms, and 30 ohms are connected in series to a 120-volt source. The power developed is (1) greatest in the 10-ohm resistor (2) greatest in the 20-ohm resistor (3) greatest in the 30-ohm resistor (4) the same in all three resistors

58. Compared with the potential drop across the 10-ohm resistor shown in the diagram, the potential drop across the 5-ohm resistor is (1) the same (2) twice as great (3) one-half as great (4) four times as great

59. The diagram represents a circuit with two resistors in series. If the total resistance of R_1 and R_2 is 24 ohms, the resistance of R_2 is (1) 1.0 Ω (2) 0.50 Ω (3) 100. Ω (4) 4.0 Ω

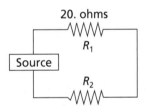

60. In the circuit shown in the diagram below, the rate at which electrical energy is being expended in resistor R_1 is (1) less than in R_2 (2) greater than in R_2 (3) less than in R_3 (4) greater than in R_3

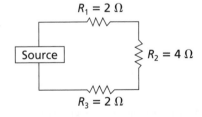

Base your answers to questions 61 and 62 on the diagram, which represents an electrical circuit.

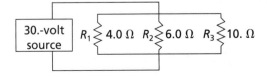

61. The equivalent resistance of R_1, R_2, and R_3 is approximately (1) 10 Ω (2) 2 Ω (3) 20 Ω (4) 7 Ω

62. The current in R_1 is (1) 3.8 A (2) 7.5 A (3) 15 A (4) 60. A

63. Compared with the current in the 10.-ohm resistor in the circuit shown below, the current in the 5.0-ohm resistor is (1) one-half as great (2) one-fourth as great (3) the same (4) twice as great

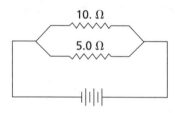

64. The following diagram represents a segment of a circuit. What is the current in ammeter A? (1) 1 A (2) 0 A (3) 3.5 A (4) 7 A

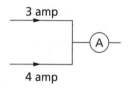

65. Two resistors of 10 ohms and 5 ohms are connected as shown in the diagram. If the current through the 10-ohm resistor is 1.0 ampere, then the current through the 5.0-ohm resistor is (1) 15 A (2) 2.0 A (3) 0.50 A (4) 0.30 A

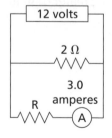

66. Two resistors are connected in parallel to a 12-volt battery as shown in the diagram. If the current in resistance R is 3.0 amperes, the rate at which R consumes electrical energy is (1) 1.1×10^2 W (2) 36 W (3) 24 W (4) 4.0 W

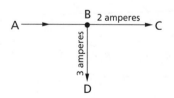

67. The diagram below represents a segment of an electrical circuit. What is the current in wire AB? (1) A (2) 2 A (3) 5 A (4) 6 A

Base your answers to questions 68 through 71 on the following diagram, which represents resistors R_1 and R_2 connected to a constant power source of 40 volts. A_1, A_2, and A_3 represent ammeters.

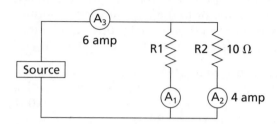

68. What is the reading of ammeter A_1? (1) 1 A (2) 2 A (3) 3 A (4) 4 A

69. The potential difference across R_1 is (1) 10 V (2) 12 V (3) 20 V (4) 40 V

70. Compared with the power supplied to R_1, the power supplied to R_2 is (1) less (2) greater (3) the same

71. If a third resistor is connected in parallel with R_1 and R_2, the effective resistance of the circuit will (1) decrease (2) increase (3) remain the same

Base your answers to questions 72 through 76 on the following diagram, which represents an electric circuit. The voltmeter, V, reads 12 volts.

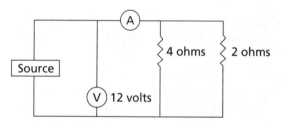

72. Ammeter A should read (1) 6 A (2) 2 A (3) 3 A (4) 9 A

73. The resistance of the circuit is (1) less than 2 Ω (2) 2 Ω (3) between 2 Ω and 6 Ω (4) 6 Ω

74. What is the current in the 4-ohm resistor? (1) 6 A (2) 2 A (3) 3 A (4) 4 A

75. At what rate is energy supplied to the 4-ohm resistor? (1) 0.33 W (2) 12 W (3) 36 W (4) 48 W

76. What is the total energy supplied to both resistors in 30 seconds? (1) 24 J (2) 108 J (3) 720 J (4) 3,240 J

Base your answers to questions 77 through 81 on the following diagram, which represents three resistors connected in parallel across the 24-volt source. The ammeter reads 3 amperes.

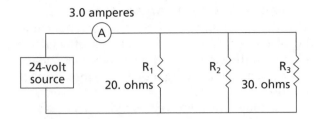

3.0 amperes

24-volt source | R_1 20. ohms | R_2 | R_3 30. ohms

77. The equivalent resistance in the circuit is (1) 0.13 Ω (2) 8.0 Ω (3) 58 Ω (4) 72 Ω

78. The current in R_1 is (1) 0.83 A (2) 1.5 A (3) 3.0 A (4) 1.2 A

79. The potential difference across R_3 is (1) 8.0 V (2) 24 V (3) 48 V (4) 72 V

80. If the ratio of the current R_3 to the current in R_2 is 4:5, the resistance of R_2 is (1) 5.0 Ω (2) 8.0 Ω (3) 24 Ω (4) 60. Ω

81. The power supplied to the circuit is (1) 220 W (2) 190 W (3) 72 W (4) 24 W

Thinking and Analyzing

82. What conditions are necessary for an electric current to flow through a material?

83. Compare insulators and electrical conductors.

84. Name and describe two common sources.

85. Describe the motion of individual electrons that join the current in a conducting wire as they make their way through the wire.

86. What unit describes the rate of flow of charge in a conductor? Define that unit.

87. What values are related by Ohm's law?

88. What is indicated by the R value in Ohm's law?

89. Define the ohm.

90. How is the resistance of a solid conductor related to its length and cross-sectional area?

91. Relate the temperature and state of a conductor to its resistance.

92. What is a superconductor and why are superconducting materials important?

93. Why does the temperature of a conductor increase as a current passes through it?

94. What is electric power and what unit is used to describe it?

95. Summarize Kirchoff's first and second laws.

96. Compare the structure of a series circuit with that of a parallel circuit.

97. Sketch an electric circuit in which a battery is connected to three resistors, A, B, and C, an ammeter, and a voltmeter. Resistors A and B are in parallel with each other and both are in series with resistor C. The ammeter is to measure the current through resistor B, and the voltmeter is to measure the potential drop across resistor C. Use the standard symbols for all these devices.

MAGNETISM

Natural Magnets

The ancients discovered that long slender pieces of certain ores, when free to rotate, always align themselves in the same direction: one end points north (toward Earth's magnetic north pole), the other south (toward the magnetic south pole). Objects that behave this way are called **magnets.** They point toward the earth's magnetic poles so dependably that sailors and navigators rely on them to determine direction. A magnet so used is called a **compass.**

The end that points north is referred to as the **north pole (N-pole)** of the magnet, and the end that points due south is the **south pole (S-pole).** When two or more magnets are brought together, they exert forces on each other; like poles repel, unlike poles attract. Earth itself is a giant magnet that affects the orientation of all magnetic compasses on Earth.

Some substances, such as iron, become **magnetized** when placed near a magnet. When this happens, the magnetic poles created in the non-magnet are so arranged that an attraction to the magnet results. Thus, a magnet is attracted to a nonmagnet when the nonmagnet has at least temporarily become magnetized by the close proximity of the magnet. Different substances offer varying degrees of susceptibility to this type of magnetization.

Breaking a magnet into pieces does not isolate the poles from each other. Instead, all the pieces become magnets, each with its own two poles. Objects that are magnets always have both poles; single poles do not exist. (See Figure 3-9.) Heating a magnet weakens its magnetism, but cooling does not ordinarily strengthen it.

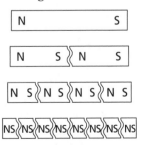

Figure 3-9. Breaking a magnet results in new, complete magnets.

Magnetic Fields

Just as charges create electric fields that act on other charges, magnets create **magnetic fields** that act on other magnets. Magnetic fields, like electric and gravitational fields, are **vector quantities,** with magnitude (intensity) and direction.

A magnetic field's direction at a given point is defined as the direction in which the N-pole of a test magnet is made to point by the action of the field at that point. The field's magnitude, or **intensity,** is determined by the force it exerts on a test magnet at a given point. A more precise definition of intensity will be presented in the enrichment section (pp. 90–91).

Magnetic fields, like electric fields, can be represented by field lines if certain rules are adopted. First, at any point in the field, the direction of the field is tangent to the field line at that point, with the arrow on the line indicating the direction in which the N-pole of the test magnet would point. Second, the concentration of field lines in a region indicates the intensity of the field in the region. Where the field is more intense, the field lines are more crowded together. Based on these rules, the field lines in the vicinity of a bar-shaped magnet are as shown in Figure 3-10.

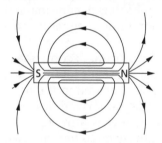

Figure 3-10. Magnetic field around a bar magnet.

A simple and useful field picture exists between two magnets with opposite poles facing each other, as shown in Figure 3-11. Note that the field between the poles is uniformly intense and the field lines are parallel to one another. Magnet field lines always form closed loops and never intersect one another.

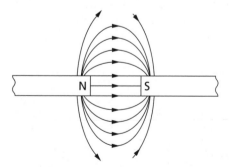

Figure 3-11. Magnetic field between opposite poles.

Currents Act on Magnets

With the development of electric currents came the discovery that a flow of charge affects any magnet in the vicinity of the current. This means that currents create magnetic fields, just as magnets do.

The magnetic field created by a current is best described by field lines. Magnetic field lines in the vicinity of a straight current-carrying wire can be represented as concentric circles around the wire, with each circle forming a plane perpendicular to the current.

A test magnet placed on the right side of the upward-moving current in Figure 3-12 experiences a force that makes its N-pole point out of the page, toward the reader. A test magnet placed on the left side, will have its N-pole point into the page, away from the reader. Behind the current, the N-pole points to the reader's right; in front, it points to the left. These directions are reversed for a downward-moving current.

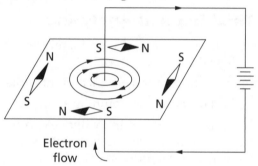

Figure 3-12. The magnetic field around a straight current-carrying conductor.

In the vicinity of a coil-shaped current-carrying wire (called a **solenoid**) or a single loop of current-carrying wire, the magnetic field lines appear as shown in Figure 3-13. Inside the solenoid or loop, the field lines are parallel to one another and perpendicular to the circles of current.

Field lines emerge from one end of the solenoid. At some distance from the solenoid they begin to curve back, until the arrows point in the opposite direction. The lines curve back again and complete the loop by reentering the other side of the solenoid.

A test magnet placed inside the coil in Figure 3-13 experiences a force that makes its N-pole point to the right. The N-pole of a magnet situated outside, but near either end of the solenoid A is also forced to point to the right. At other locations, a magnet's N-pole is forced to point in the direction indicated by the local field line.

Note: The field created by a solenoid looks very much like that of a bar magnet. We will return to this important fact in a later section (p. 75).

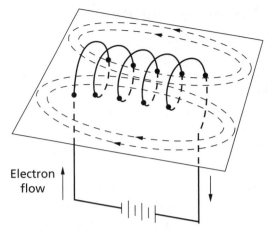

Figure 3-13. The magnetic field around a solenoid.

When certain materials, such as iron, are inserted inside a solenoid they become magnetized in such a way that the magnetic field of the solenoid becomes stronger. A solenoid whose magnetic field is in this way intensified is referred to as an **electromagnet.** Materials that behave this way are said to be **ferromagnetic.**

Magnets Act on Currents

Further experimentation with magnets and currents revealed that not only do currents affect magnets but magnets also exert forces on currents. A straight current-carrying wire situated in a magnetic field experiences a force if the charges move perpendicularly to the field, or at least a component of their motion is perpendicular to the field. No force appears if the direction of the current is parallel to the field. The force is greatest when the angle between the field lines and the current is exactly 90°.

The force exerted on the wire is perpendicular to both the direction of the current and the direction of the magnetic field.

Currents Act on Currents

Since currents create magnetic fields and magnetic fields exert forces on currents, it follows that one current exerts a force on another. (No electric force exists between current-carrying wires, since they are electrically neutral.)

Two straight, parallel wires carrying current in the same direction attract each other. If the currents move in opposite directions, the wires repel each other (see Figure 3-14). The force on either current is always equal in magnitude and opposite in direction to the force on the other current. If the currents are perpendicular to each other, no forces appear.

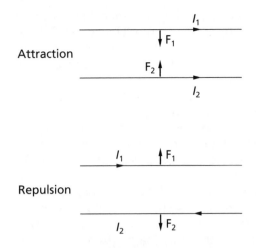

Figure 3-14. The direction of current in the wires determines the directions of the forces exerted by the wires.

The Magnetic Force

All the various forces described in this section—those exerted by magnets on magnets, magnets on currents, currents on magnets, and currents on currents—are different manifestations of one and the same principle of nature: **moving charges exert forces on other moving charges.** This force is independent of the electric force between charges; we call it the **magnetic force.** Each moving charge creates a magnetic field. The intensity of the field created by a moving charge is proportional to the amount of charge and to the velocity of the charge. Intensity weakens with distance from the moving charge.

Magnets behave as they do because the electrons in their atoms spin in the same direction, as illustrated in Figure 3-15. As we look at the N-pole of a magnet, the electron rotations are clockwise; as we look at the S-pole, they are counterclockwise. Magnets are, in effect, solenoids, with each

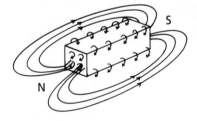

Figure 3-15.

atom supplying one of the "coils" of current. This is why a bar magnet's field lines look like those of a solenoid.

In nonmagnets the atomic currents (as the electron rotations are called) are not all oriented in one direction. The magnetic field created by one atom is cancelled by the oppositely directed field created by another atom. The net result is no magnetic field. The object neither exerts a magnetic force nor responds to the presence of a magnetic field.

Bringing two magnets together is the same as bringing two solenoids together. The magnetic field of each exerts a twisting force (torque) on the other. Each attempts to realign the other's atomic currents. As a result, like poles repel and unlike poles attract.

A magnet seeks to align the atomic currents within a nonmagnet so that they all rotate in the same direction. When this realignment occurs, the nonmagnet becomes magnetized. Many substances, however, resist the twisting of their atoms, and it is difficult to magnetize them.

Heating a magnet weakens its magnetism because the increased kinetic energy of the atoms and the more violent collision between them disrupt the uniform orientation of the atomic currents in one direction. Breaking a magnet produces many new magnets, each with two poles, because each piece is still a solenoid, albeit a smaller one.

QUESTIONS

98. In the following diagram, what is the direction of the magnetic field at point *A*?   (1) to the left   (2) to the right   (3) toward the top of the page   (4) toward the bottom of the page

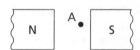

99. Which diagram correctly shows a magnetic field configuration?

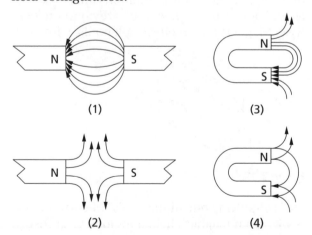

100. As two parallel conductors with currents in the same direction are moved apart, their force of (1) attraction increases   (2) attraction decreases (3) repulsion increases   (4) repulsion decreases

Thinking and Analyzing

101. What is a magnet?

102. What enables a paper clip to be held by a magnet even though the paper clip is not ordinarily magnetic?

103. What happens to a magnet if it is cut in half? What happens if it is cut into four pieces?

104. Describe the direction and intensity of a magnetic field.

105. What two rules must you obey when you represent magnetic fields by field lines?

106. Compare and contrast electric and magnetic fields with regard to the following: (a) the effect each type of field has on a charged particle at rest in the field, (b) the effect each type of field has on a charged particle that moves parallel to the field lines, (c) the orientation of the force each type of field exerts with respect to the direction of the field in the vicinity of the charge.

107. In what way are electric currents related to magnetic fields?

108. A bar magnet is dropped and allowed to fall perpendicularly to the plane of a closed loop of conducting wire, through the center of the loop. It is observed that the fall magnet's acceleration rate is less than the 9.8 m/s^2 of free fall. Explain why this is so.

109. What is an electromagnet?

ELECTROMAGNETISM

Electromagnetic Induction

If a straight piece of metal wire (or some other conductor) is moved through a magnetic field perpendicularly to the field lines, the field exerts a force on the electrons in the wire. The electrons in the wire move with the wire, and magnetic fields act on moving charges. The direction of the force on the moving electrons is perpendicular to both the magnetic field lines and the wire's direction of motion (see Figure 3-16), and may product a current in the wire.

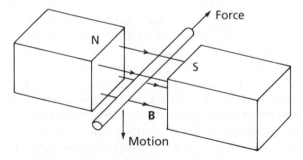

Figure 3-16. Force on electrons in a wire moving across a magnetic field.

A current—one that can make a bulb glow, for example—is created if the wire moving in the magnetic field is connected to a complete circuit. This current continues as long as the wire moves across the field lines.

Electromagnetic induction also occurs when the intensity (or strength) of a magnetic field varies over time. As the field becomes stronger or weaker, the number of magnetic field lines in the region enclosed by a loop of wire varies. This gives rise to current in the loop, even if the wire is stationary.

The current created by a changing magnetic field or by moving a wire across a magnetic field is referred to as **induced current,** and the potential difference (voltage) so created is referred to as **induced EMF** (electromotive force). The magnitude of the induced voltage is proportional to the rate of change in the number of flux lines enclosed by the loop per unit time. The faster the number of flux lines changes, the greater the induced voltage (and current) in the loop.

Since the changing magnetic field leads to a force on electrons even when the wire is at rest, we say **changing magnetic fields create electric fields.** Electric fields exert forces on charges whether or not the charges are in motion; magnetic fields act only on moving charges.

The physicist James Clerk Maxwell proposed that the converse statement should also be true, that *changing electric fields create magnetic fields.* This has indeed been found to be the case.

QUESTIONS

110. The following diagram shows a copper wire located between the poles of a magnet. Maximum electric potential will be induced in the wire when it is moved at a constant speed toward which point? (1) *A* (2) *B* (3) *C* (4) *D*

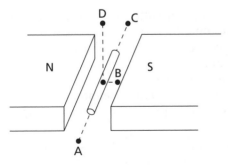

111. A conductor is moving perpendicularly to a uniform magnetic field. Increasing the speed of the conductor will cause the potential difference induced across the ends of the conductor to (1) decrease (2) increase (3) remain the same

112. The following diagram shows the cross section of a wire which is perpendicular to the page and a uniform magnetic field directed to the right. Toward which point should the wire be moved to induce the maximum electric potential? (Assume the same speed would be used in each direction.) (1) 1 (2) 2 (3) 3 (4) 4

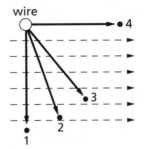

Thinking and Analyzing

113. Under what two conditions might a current be induced?

114. Upon what does the magnitude of an induced voltage depend?

115. A stationary charge is exposed to a magnetic field and an electric field. Which field will have an effect on the charge?

ELECTROMAGNETIC APPLICATIONS

Current-Carrying Loops in Magnetic Fields

If a solenoid or a single loop of current-carrying wire is placed in a magnetic field, the wire experiences a torque (twisting force) that rotates the plane of the loop (and every individual loop in the case of a solenoid) until the plane of the loop is perpendicular to the magnetic field lines (see Figure 3-17). When this occurs, the magnetic field created by the loop of current inside the loop becomes *parallel* to and points in the same direction as the external magnetic field. The strength of the torque is proportional to the amount of current in the loop and to the intensity of the external field.

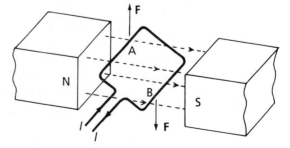

Figure 3-17. Forces on a current-carrying loop of wire in a magnetic field.

This twisting action exerted on coils of current in magnetic fields is the basis of the operation of many useful devices, including the ammeter, the voltmeter, and the electric motor.

Ammeter (-(A)-) Current is measured with an ammeter. The ammeter is placed in series with the circuit (or part of the circuit) whose current is to be measured.

Voltmeter (-(V)-) Potential difference, or voltage, is measured with a voltmeter. The voltmeter is connected in parallel with the part of the circuit whose voltage is to be measured.

Motors An electric motor is a device that converts electrical energy into rotational kinetic energy. Its operation is based on the torque exerted by a magnetic field on a loop of current in the field. A wire loop situated between opposite magnetic poles is connected to a battery, one end to the positive terminal and the other end to the negative terminal (see Figure 3-18).

The Generator The process of inducing current and EMF by moving a conducting wire across magnetic field lines is used today to provide millions of homes with electric power. The most common device for

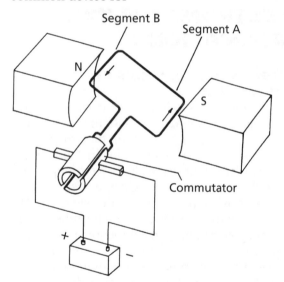

Figure 3-18. A motor.

this purpose is the **generator.** A simple generator consists of a loop of wire that is made to rotate between two opposite magnetic poles. As the loop rotates, the current and potential difference generated vary in magnitude and alternate in direction. This is called **alternating current** (ac).

Transformers (▮▮▮) A **transformer** is a device inserted into a circuit carrying alternating current

(ac) in order to change the voltage to some higher or lower value. It is used with fluorescent and neon lights, thermostats, bells, and many other appliances that require voltages greater or smaller than the 120 volts supplied by all electric utility companies in the U.S.

QUESTIONS

116. Which statement best describes the torque experienced by a current-carrying loop of wire in an external magnetic field?
(1) It is due to the current in the loop of wire, only.
(2) It is due to the interaction of the external magnetic field and the magnetic field produced by current in the loop.
(3) It is inversely proportional to the length of the conducting loop in the magnetic field.
(4) It is inversely proportional to strength of the permanent magnetic field.

117. The torque on the armature of an operating electric motor may be increased by
(1) decreasing the current in the armature
(2) decreasing the magnetic field strength of the field poles
(3) increasing the potential difference applied to the armature
(4) increasing the distance between the armature and the field poles

118. A motor is to rotational mechanical energy as a generator is to
(1) chemical potential energy
(2) induced electrical energy
(3) thermal internal energy
(4) elastic potential energy

119. A student uses a voltmeter to measure the potential difference across a circuit resistor. To obtain a correct reading, the student must connect the voltmeter
(1) in parallel with the circuit resistor
(2) in series with the circuit resistor
(3) before connecting the other circuit components
(4) after connecting the other circuit components

120. In a transformer, two coils of wire are wound around a common iron core. To operate properly, the transformer requires
(1) an alternating-current source connected to the primary coil

(2) a direct-current source connected to the secondary coil

(3) more turns in the primary coil than in the secondary coil

(4) more turns in the secondary coil than in the primary coil

121. Describe how you would connect an ammeter in a circuit.

122. Describe how you would connect a voltmeter in a circuit.

Reading Comprehension

Storing Information Magnetically

If you have ever recorded your voice on tape, you have taken advantage of magnetism as a means of storing information. The tape used in audio and video tape records consists of a thin layer of magnetic oxide on a thin plastic tape. When a sound is recorded, the sound is first converted into an electronic current. That current is then sent to the recording head, which acts as a tiny electromagnet.

The electromagnet produces a magnetic field that varies with the electric current. As the tape moves through the recording head, the varying magnetic field magnetizes the tiny section of the tape passing over the narrow gap at each instant. When the tape is played back, the changing magnetism of the tape causes changes in a magnetic field within the player, which then induces a current. This induced current is the output signal that is amplified and sent to a speaker and converted back into sound.

In audio and video recorders, the electronic signals are usually analog. This means that they vary continuously over time. The variation in the degree of magnetization of the tape at any point reflects the variation in amplitude of the audio or video signal. Other devices, such as computers and compact disks, use a digital signal. Unlike an analog signal, a digital signal does not vary continuously, but instead takes on only two values. Combinations of these two values, 0 and 1, can be used to represent words, numbers, and images. The number system that uses only 0 and 1 is known as the binary number system. Each 0 or 1 in the binary system is called a bit, which is short for binary digit. Arrangements of 8 bits are called bytes.

Computer disks, which include hard disks and floppy disks, and magnetic tape are read and written in a similar manner to audiotapes and videotapes. The hard disk inside a computer, for example, is made up of a stack of metal disks that have magnetic particles on one surface. When information is saved to the hard disk, a device changes the orientation of the magnetic particles on the disk's surface. Orientation in one direction represents 0 and orientation in the other direction represents 1. When the disk is read, the 0s and 1s are converted to pulses of electric current. The current is then converted into a visible image that can be observed on a computer screen or printed page.

QUESTIONS

1. What roles do electricity and magnetism play in the recording and playback of a movie on a videotape?

2. How does a digital signal differ from an analog signal?

3. Describe the process in which digital information is stored on a hard disk.

4. Why could bringing a computer disk near a strong magnet destroy the information stored on the disk?

TRANSFER OF CHARGE

Charging by Contact

An exchange of electrons, or transfer of charge, causes the phenomenon associated with the rubber and glass rods and the pith balls.

Electrons are bound more tightly in some materials than in others. Two dissimilar, neutral objects may become charged by rubbing against each other. For example, rubber tends to hold onto electrons more firmly than fur. Hence, when a rubber rod is rubbed against a piece of fur, electrons transfer from the fur to the rubber rod. The fur loses electrons and becomes positively charged. The rubber rod gains electrons and acquires a net negative charge. The magnitudes of the charges on the fur and the rod are equal and their signs are opposite.

If the rubber rod is then brought near a suspended pith ball, the negative charge on the rod repels electrons in the pith ball, forcing them to move to the far side of the ball. As a whole, the ball remains neutral, but the redistribution of electrons causes the ball to become **electrically polarized.** The side of the ball closest to the rod becomes positively charged and the side of the ball farthest from the rod becomes negatively charged (Figure 3-19).

The rod's excess electrons attract the protons on the near side of the ball and repel the electrons on the far side. The force of attraction is stronger (owing to the shorter distance between the rod and the ball's positively charged near side), and so

the balls moves toward the rod. When the ball touches the rod, some of the rod's excess electrons transfer to the pith ball. The ball gains electrons and becomes negatively charged. This method of charge transfer is called **charging by contact.** The ball and the rubber rod are now both negatively charged and they repel each other. The ball moves (and remains) as far away from the rod as possible (Figure 3-20).

When a glass rod is rubbed against a silk cloth, electrons transfer from the glass rod to the silk. The glass rod loses electrons and becomes positively charged. Like the charged rubber rod, the charged glass rod also polarizes a pith ball,

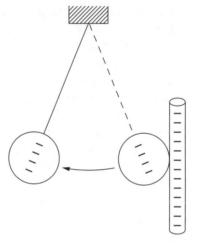

Figure 3-20. When the pith ball touches the rod it becomes negatively charged.

but in the opposite way. The ball's electrons are attracted to the positively charged glass rod and move to the side of the ball closest to it. When the ball touches the rod, some of the ball's electrons transfer to the rod, leaving the ball with more protons than electrons. (The rod remains positively charged because it gains only a few electrons.) At this point, both the ball and the glass rod are positively charged, and the force of repulsion keeps them apart.

Two pith balls that have made contact with a charged rubber rod will repel each other because they have both gained electrons and acquired a negative charge. Two pith balls that have made contact with a charged glass rod will repel each other because they have both lost electrons and become positively charged. Finally, two pith balls that have touched different rods (rubber or glass)

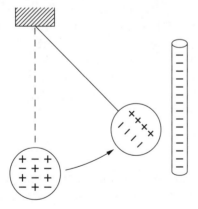

Figure 3-19. A negatively charged rod polarizes the pith ball.

attract each other because they become oppositely charged (Figure 3-21).

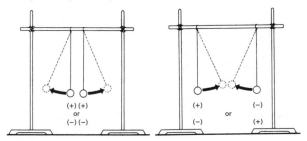

Figure 3-21. Two similarly charged pith balls repel each other and two oppositely charged pith balls attract each other.

Charging by Induction

A charged object may induce an opposite charge in a neutral object without touching it. First, the neutral object must be **grounded**—that is, it must be connected to an object so large that it can either accept or give up a significant number of electrons without becoming noticeably charged. (Earth is often used as a ground.) Once the neutral object is grounded, a charged rod is brought near it without touching it, as in Figure 3-22. If the rod is negatively charged, it repels the electrons of the neutral object, forcing them to transfer to the ground. If the object is then disconnected from the ground while the negatively charged rod is nearby, the object will be left with a net positive charge. On the other hand, if the rod is positively charged, it attracts electrons which transfer from the ground into the neutral object. If the object is then disconnected from the ground while the positively charged rod is nearby, the object is left with a net negative charge. In both cases, the charge acquired by the previously neutral object is *opposite* to that of the rod used to charge it.

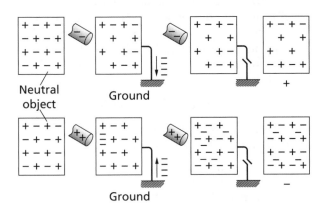

Figure 3-22. Charging by induction.

Detection of Charge The presence of excess charge on an object can be detected by bringing the object near an **electroscope,** a device that consists of a metal knob attached to two light metallic leaves (Figure 3-23). If either a positively

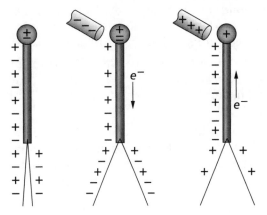

Figure 3-23. Detection of charges using a neutral electroscope.

or a negatively charged object is brought near the knob of the electroscope, the electrons within the electroscope are forced to rearrange themselves, and the electroscope becomes polarized. Each leaf acquires the same type of charge as the charged object, and the leaves diverge.

A neutral electroscope cannot be used to distinguish between a positively charged object and a negatively charged object. However, an electroscope can be charged (either by contact or by induction) and then used to detect both the presence and the type of charge brought near it.

The leaves of a charged electroscope are separated due to the charge on the leaves (Figure 3-24). If an object brought near the knob of the charged electroscope has the same type of charge as the electroscope, the leaves will diverge even more. If the object brought near the charged electroscope is oppositely charged, the leaves will converge to a vertical position.

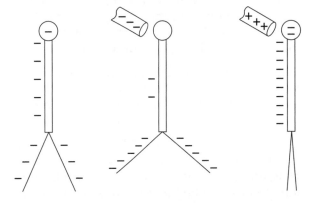

Figure 3-24. Identification of charges using a charged electroscope.

QUESTIONS

123. After two neutral solids, *A* and *B*, were rubbed together, solid *A* acquired a net negative charge. Solid *B*, therefore, experienced a net (1) loss of protons (2) increase of protons (3) loss of electrons (4) increase of electrons

124. A pith ball may become charged by losing or gaining (1) electrons, only (2) protons, only (3) protons and electrons (4) neutrons and protons

125. When a rubber rod is rubbed with fur, the rod becomes negatively charged due to the transfer of (1) electrons to the fur (2) protons to the fur (3) electrons to the rod (4) protons to the rod

126. A neutral atom could be composed of (1) 4 electrons, 5 protons, 6 neutrons (2) 5 electrons, 5 protons, 6 neutrons (3) 6 electrons, 3 protons, 6 neutrons (4) 0 electrons, 5 protons, 5 neutrons

127. The ratio of the magnitude of charge on an electron to the magnitude of charge on a proton is (1) 1:2 (2) 1:1 (3) $1 : 6.25 \times 10^{18}$ (4) 1:1,840

128. How many electrons are contained in a charge of 8.0×10^{-9} coulomb? (1) 5 (2) 2 (3) 8 (4) 4

129. Which is equivalent to three elementary charges? (1) 2.4×10^{-19} C (2) 2.0×10^{-19} C (3) 4.8×10^{-19} C (4) 5.4×10^{-19} C

130. The coulomb is a unit of electrical (1) charge (2) current (3) potential (4) resistance

131. After a neutral object loses 2 electrons, it will have a net charge of (1) −2 elementary charges (2) +2 elementary charges (3) -3.2×10^{-19} elementary charge (4) $+3.2 \times 10^{-19}$ elementary charge

132. Metal sphere *A* has a charge of −2 units and an identical sphere *B* has a charge of −4 units. If the two spheres are brought together and then separated, the charge on sphere *A* will be (1) 0 units (2) −2 units (3) −3 units (4) +4 units

133. If a positively charged rod touches a neutral metal sphere, the number of electrons on the rod will (1) decrease (2) increase (3) remain the same

134. In the charging of a solid, charge transfer is accomplished by the displacement of (1) electrons, only (2) protons, only (3) both electrons and protons (4) neither electrons nor protons

135. Which of the following diagrams shows the leaves of the electroscope charged negatively by induction?

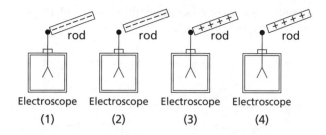

Electroscope (1)   Electroscope (2)   Electroscope (3)   Electroscope (4)

136. An inflated balloon that has been rubbed against a person's hair is touched to a neutral wall and remains attracted to it. Which diagram best represents the charge distribution on the balloon and wall?

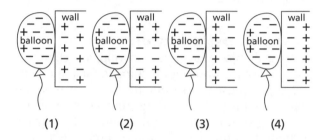

(1)   (2)   (3)   (4)

Thinking and Analyzing

137. A charged rod touches a light suspended ball that hangs from the ceiling by insulating thread. The ball is then visibly repelled from the rod and remains deflected at some angle from the vertical. Explain why this occurred. Specify the various forces acting on the deflected ball. Explain how these forces create a state of equilibrium for the ball.

138. (a) A positively charged rod is brought near a neutral conducting sphere but does not touch the sphere. Describe the balance of charge on the side of the sphere near the charged rod and on the opposite side. Explain why and how this distribution of charge occurred. (b) The charged rod is now allowed to touch the sphere and is then removed. Describe the balance of charge now on both sides of the sphere. Explain your reasoning.

139. Why is Earth used for grounding?

140. Why can't an electroscope be used to determine the type of charge on an object?

Electric Field Diagrams

A representation of the field around a single positive point charge is shown in Figure 3-25. The arrows radiating from the charge are called **field lines.** By convention, field lines always point in the direction of the force that would be exerted by the field on a positive test charge.

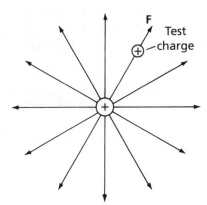

Figure 3-25. The field around a single positive charge.

The concentration of the field lines at any point in a field diagram indicates the intensity of the field. The intensity of an electric field decreases inversely with the square of the distance from a point charge. Thus, the number of field lines per unit area (perpendicular to the field's direction) also decreases inversely with the square of the distance from the point charge in Figure 3-25. At a point twice as far from the charge, the concentration of field lines per unit area is one-fourth as great, as is the intensity of the field.

The field lines in the vicinity of a negative point charge are shown in Figure 3-26. Except for the fact that the field lines are directed radially inward, the figure is the same as that shown for a positive point charge.

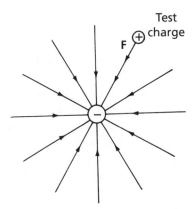

Figure 3-26. The field around a single negative charge.

The electric field in the vicinity of a spherical shell of positive charge is shown in Figure 3-27. At any point inside the shell, the field intensity is zero. The net force on a test charge, found by adding the forces exerted by all the charges on the shell, is zero. Therefore, there is no electric field inside the shell. Outside the shell, the field is the same as though all the charges were concentrated at the center of the shell.

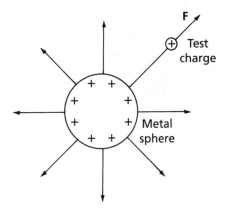

Figure 3-27. The field around a positively charged sphere.

The field created by two equal positive point charges is shown in Figure 3-28. The field around two negative charges is the same as the field around two positive charges, except for the fact that the field lines point toward the charges (Figure 3-29).

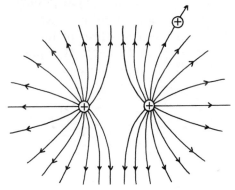

Figure 3-28. The field around two equal positive charges.

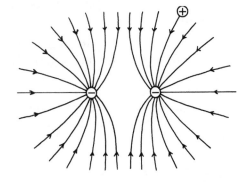

Figure 3-29. The field around two equal negative charges.

The field created by two equal but opposite charges is shown in Figure 3-30. Note that the field lines originate at the positive charge and terminate at the negative charge.

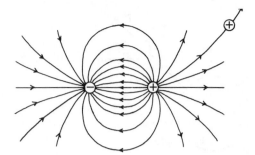

Figure 3-30. The field around equal but opposite charges.

The field between two oppositely charged parallel plates is shown in Figure 3-31. In the case where the distance between the plates is small compared with their size and the charge on the plates is uniformly distributed, the field lines are parallel to one another and perpendicular to the plates (except near the edges). If a positive test charge is released between the plates, it will be pushed in a straight line from the positive to the negative plate. Since the field between the plates is uniformly intense, the magnitude of the force exerted on a test charge is the same everywhere in the region between the plates (except near the edges). Outside the plates, the net force is practically zero, so no field lines appear there.

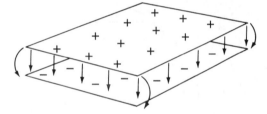

Figure 3-31. The field between oppositely charged parallel plates.

The following features are common to all electric field diagrams:

1. Field lines always begin on positively charged objects and terminate on negatively charged objects.
2. Field lines never intersect each other.
3. Where field lines meet a charged object, they are perpendicular to the surface of the charged object.

Electric Field Intensity and Potential Difference

The electric field intensity **E** at a particular point is given by the relationship

$$E = \frac{F}{q}$$

where F is the force, in newtons, exerted on a test charge q, in coulombs. The unit for electric field intensity is the newton/coulomb (N/C).

If the electric field intensity at a particular point is known, the force exerted on any amount of charge at that point is provided by the formula

$$F = qE$$

Sample Problems

12. What is the intensity of an electric field at a point where a 0.50 C charge experiences a force of 20. N?
Solution:

$$E = \frac{F}{q}$$

$$= \frac{20.\text{N}}{0.50\ \text{C}} = 40.\ \text{N/C}$$

13. If one elementary unit of charge is placed at that point, how strong a force will it experience?
Solution:

$$F = Eq$$

$$= (40.\ \text{N/C})(1.6 \times 10^{-19}\ \text{C})$$

$$= 6.4 \times 10^{-18}\ \text{N}$$

The potential difference V between two points in an electric field of uniform intensity **E,** such as the uniform field between two oppositely charged parallel plates, satisfies the relationship

$$V = Ed$$

where d is the distance in meters between the two points.

Solving for E, we get

$$E = \frac{V}{d}$$

Thus, a uniform electric field intensity can be expressed in volts per meter. Since **E** was defined earlier in terms of newtons per coulomb, we can conclude that 1 V/m is equivalent to 1 N/C.

Sample Problem

14. What is the potential difference between two oppositely charged parallel plates separated by 0.005 m, if the intensity of the electric field between them is 10 N/C?
Solution:

$$V = Ed$$

$$= (10\ \text{N/C})(0.005\ \text{m})$$

$$= (10\ \text{V/m})(0.005\ \text{m})$$

$$= 0.05\ \text{V}$$

QUESTIONS

141. The electric field intensity at a given distance from a point charge is E. If the charge is doubled and the distance remains fixed, the electric field intensity will be (1) $E/2$ (2) $2E$ (3) $E/4$ (4) $4E$

142. Based on the Physics Reference Tables, which equation contains vector quantities? (1) $E = F/q$ (2) $V = W/q$ (3) $V = IR$ (4) $W = Pt$

143. When a charge of 0.04 coulomb is placed at a point in an electric field, the force on the charge is 100 newtons. What is the magnitude of the electric field at that point? (1) 0.00040 N/C (2) 2,500 N/C (3) 100 N/C (4) 4.0 N/C

144. Two charged spheres are shown in the diagram. Which polarities will produce the electric field shown? (1) A and B both negative (2) A and B both positive (3) A positive and B negative (4) A negative and B positive

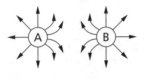

145. Which diagram best represents an electric field?

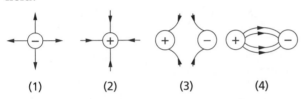

(1)   (2)   (3)   (4)

146. An electron enters the space between two oppositely charged parallel plates as shown in the diagram. What is the direction of the electric force on the electron as it passes between the plates? (1) toward the positive plate (2) toward the negative plate (3) into the page (4) out of the page

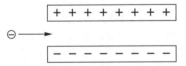

147. Which of the following diagrams best represents the electric field around the two spheres?

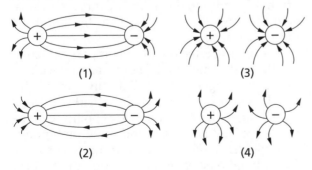

(1)   (3)

(2)   (4)

148. Which diagram best represents the electric field between the two spheres?

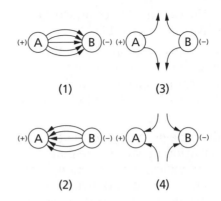

(1)   (3)

(2)   (4)

Base your answers to questions 149 and 150 on the figure and this additional information: A conductor is connected between spheres A and B and then removed after charge has transferred.

+5.00 × 10⁻⁶coulomb   −4.00 × 10⁻⁶coulomb

149. During the period the conductor was attached, what was the direction of the flow of the charged particles? (1) protons flowed from A to B, only (2) electrons flowed from B to A, only (3) protons flowed from A to B as electrons flowed from B to A (4) protons flowed from B to A as electrons flowed from A to B

150. What is the net charge on each sphere? (1) Each has a charge of $+5.0 \times 10^{-7}$ C (2) Each has a charge of -5.0×10^{-7} C (3) Each has a charge of $+4.5 \times 10^{-6}$ C (4) Sphere A has a charge of $+1.0 \times 10^{-6}$ C and B has a charge of -1.0×10^{-6} C

Base your answer to question 151 on the following diagram, which represents an electron projected into the region between two parallel charged plates which are 10^{-3} meter apart. The electric field intensity between the plates is 10^6 newtons per coulomb.

151. In which direction will the electron be deflected? (1) into the page (2) out of the page (3) toward the bottom of the page (4) toward the top of the page

Thinking and Analyzing

152. What is the purpose of drawing electric field lines?

153. How would the field lines around a single positive charge differ from those around a single negative charge? How are field lines drawn to indicate the intensity of an electric field?

154. Compare the concentration of field lines at a point three times as far from the charge as another point. Compare the electric field lines inside and outside of a spherical shell of positive charge.

155. Trace the figure below onto a sheet of paper. Then draw a small arrow at each of the points labeled *A* through *I* to indicate the direction of the electric field at each of these points, which are located in the vicinity of two small, equally and oppositely charged spheres. Draw a larger arrow at the point where the field is most intense. Place an *X* mark over the points where the field is least intense. Explain how you ascertained that the field at these points was the most and least intense.

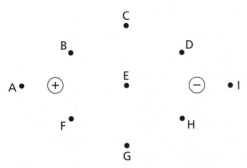

156. If the force exerted on a one-coulomb test charge by a shpere carrying an amount of charge, *Q*, at a distance *d* from the center of the sphere is represented by KQ/d^2, where *K* is the electrostatic constant, how would you represent the force at point *E* in the figure above if each of the two charged spheres carries an amount of charge *Q*, the spheres are separated by distance *d*, and point *E* is midway between the spheres? Provide and explain the steps of your analysis.

157. What happens to the field lines around a positive charge when a second positive charge is brought near it? What happens if instead a negative charge is brought near it?

158. Two oppositely charged plates are arranged so that the distance between them is small when compared with their size. What will happen to a positive test charge released between the plates? Released outside the plates?

Currents Act on Magnets

The magnetic field created by a current is best described by field lines. Magnetic field lines in the vicinity of a straight current-carrying wire can be represented as concentric circles around the wire, with each circle forming a plane perpendicular to the current. The direction of the arrows on these circles is found by applying **left-hand rule #1.** Imagine that you grasp the wire with your left hand, with the thumb pointing in the direction of electron flow. The four fingers wrapped around the wire point in the direction of the arrows to be placed on the circular field lines. (See Figure 3-32.)

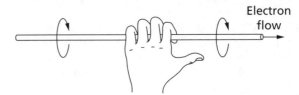

Figure 3-32. Left-hand rule #1.

Inside a solenoid or loop, the field lines are parallel to each other and perpendicular to the circles of current. The direction of the magnetic field lines there is found by applying **left-hand rule #2.** The four fingers of the left hand are made to follow the electron flow; the thumb then points in the direction of the field lines *inside* the coil (Figure 3-33).

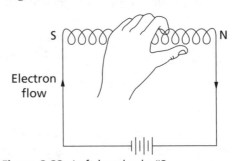

Figure 3-33. Left-hand rule #2.

The magnetic field strength of a solenoid is directly proportional to the number loops, or turns, of wire and to the current.

Magnets Act on Currents

A straight current-carrying wire situated in a magnetic field experiences a force if the charges move perpendicularly to the field, or at least a component of their motion is perpendicular to the field. No force appears if the direction of the current is parallel to the field. The force is greatest when the angle between the field lines and the current is exactly 90°.

The force exerted on the wire is perpendicular to both the direction of the current and the direction of the magnetic field. The direction of this force is found by using **left-hand rule #3.** Hold your left hand flat with the fingers pointing in the direction of the field lines and the thumb pointing in the direction of electron motion. The palm of your hand pushes in the direction of the force on the current-carrying wire. (See Figure 3-34.)

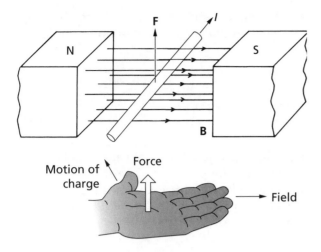

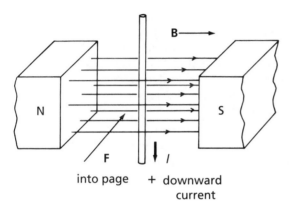

Figure 3-34. Left-hand rule #3.

For example, to find the direction of the force on the downward-moving current between two magnetic poles in Figure 3-35, proceed as follows:

Figure 3-35.

point the thumb of the left hand downward in the direction of electron motion. Then point your fingers in the direction of the magnetic field, to the right. The palm of the hand now indicates that the force is directed into the page, away from the reader.

Sample Problems

15. In what direction will the N-pole of a magnet point if it is placed behind a current moving to the right as shown in Figure 3-36?

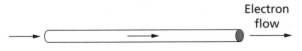

Figure 3-36.

Solution: Using left-hand rule #1, the thumb points to the right and the fingers curve around

the wire such that they point *downward* behind the current.

16. In what direction will the N-pole of a magnet point if it is placed at point *A* in Figure 3-37?

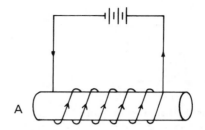

Figure 3-37.

Solution: Using left-hand rule #2, the fingers curve in the direction of the current and the thumb points *to the right.*

17. In what direction will the current-carrying wire in Figure 3-38 be pushed?

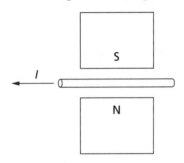

Figure 3-38.

Solution: Using left-hand rule #3, the thumb points to the left, the fingers point up, toward the top of the page, the palm of the hand pushes *out of the page, toward the reader.*

Currents Act on Currents

Since currents create magnetic fields and magnetic fields exert forces on currents, it follows that one current exerts a force on another. (No electric force exists between current-carrying wires, since they are electrically neutral.)

Let us analyze the case of two long parallel wires carrying current to the right, segments of which are shown in Figure 3-39. The magnetic field created by the upper current is found via left-hand rule #1. With the thumb of the left hand pointing to the right, the four fingers wrap around the wire in such a way that they point into the page and away from the reader above the wire, out of the page and toward the reader below the wire.

The lower current is thus situated in a magnetic field that is directed out of the page, toward the reader, as shown in the diagram. Left-hand

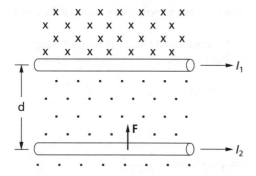

Figure 3-39. The field created by the upper current-carrying wire is into the page (indicated by x's) above the wire and out of the page (indicated by dots) below the wire. Left-hand rule #3 is used to find the direction of the force exerted on the lower wire by this field.

rule #3 provides the direction of the force exerted by the field created by the upper wire on the lower wire. With the thumb pointing to the right and the fingers parallel to the page, pointing toward the reader, the palm of the hand pushes upward, in the plane of the page. The lower current thus experiences a force upward, toward the upper current.

A similar analysis of the force exerted on the upper wire by the magnetic field created by the lower wire would reveal that there is a downward force on the upper wire (toward the lower wire). The net result is that the two wires are attracted to each other.

Each moving charge creates a magnetic field whose direction can be found by applying either left-hand rule #1 or #2, and the field so created exerts a force on the other moving charge. The direction of this force can be found by using left-hand rule #3. The intensity of the field created by a moving charge is proportional to the amount of charge and to the velocity of the charge. Intensity weakens with distance from the moving charge.

QUESTIONS

159. Which diagram best represents the direction of the magnetic field around a wire conductor in which the electrons are moving as indicated? (The *X*'s indicate that the field is directed into the paper and the dots indicate that the field is directed out of the page.)

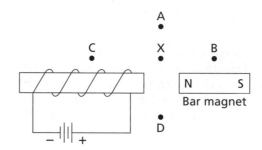

(1)   (2)   (3)   (4)

160. Which diagram best represents the magnetic field around a current-carrying conductor?

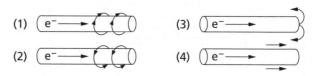

161. The diagram at the right represents a current-carrying loop of wire. The direction of the magnetic field at point *P* is   (1) toward the bottom of the page   (2) to the right   (3) into the page   (4) out of the page

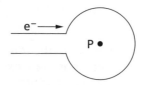

162. Electrons flow in a loop of wire as shown in the diagram. What is the direction of the magnetic field at point *A*?   (1) into the paper   (2) out of the paper   (3) toward the left   (3) toward the right

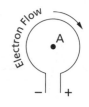

163. In the diagram, in which direction is the magnetic field at point *X*?   (1) toward *A*   (2) toward *B*   (3) toward *C*   (4) toward *D*

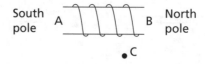

Base your answers to questions 164 through 166 on the following diagram, which represents a cross section of an operating solenoid. A compass is located at point *C*.

164. Which diagram best represents the shape of the magnetic field around the solenoid?

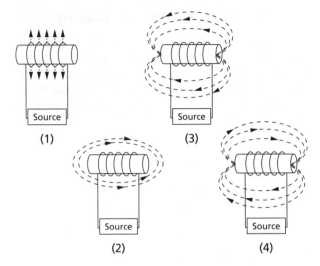

(1) (3)

(2) (4)

165. Which shows the direction of the compass needle at point *C*?

(1) (2) (3) (4)

166. If *B* is the north pole of the solenoid, which diagram best represents the direction of electron flow in one of the wire loops?

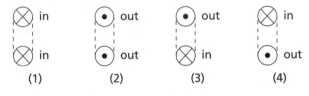

(1) (2) (3) (4)

Base your answers to questions 167 through 170 on the following diagram, which represents a circuit containing a solenoid on a cardboard tube, a variable resistor *R*, and a source of potential difference.

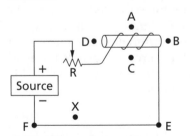

167. The north pole of the solenoid is nearest to point (1) *A* (2) *B* (3) *C* (4) *D*

168. Due to the current in the *FE* section of the circuit, the direction of the magnetic field at point *X* is (1) into the page (2) out of the page (3) to the left (4) to the right

169. If the resistance of resistor *R* is increased, the magnetic field strength of the solenoid will (1) decrease (2) increase (3) remain the same

170. If the number of turns in the solenoid is increased and the current is kept constant, the magnetic field strength of the solenoid will (1) decrease (2) increase (3) remain the same

171. Two long, straight parallel conductors carry equal currents and are spaced 1 meter apart. If the current in each conductor is doubled, the magnitude of the magnetic force acting between the conductors will be (1) unchanged (2) doubled (3) halved (4) quadrupled

172. A rectangular loop of wire is moving perpendicularly to a magnetic field directed out of the page, as illustrated below. For each of the following steps, state whether or not current is induced in the loop and in what direction the current, if any, flows. Explain your reasoning in each case. (a) the loop has not yet entered the field, (b) the loop has partially entered the field, (c) the loop is entirely inside the field, moving across its field lines, (d) the loop has partially exited the field, and (e) the loop has entirely exited the field.

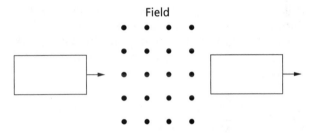

173. The diagram represents a rectangular conducting loop *ABCD* being moved to the right through a magnetic field, which is directed into the page. Which path will the electrons in the induced current follow? (1) *DCBAD* (2) *CBDAC* (3) *BCDAB* (4) *ADBCA*

Base your answers to questions 174 through 178 on the following diagram, which shows a cross section of a wire (*A*) moving down through a uniform magnetic field (*B*). The flux density of the field is 5.0 newtons per ampere-meter. The wire is 1.0 meter long and has a velocity of 2.0 meters per second perpendicular to the magnetic field.

174. What is the direction of the magnetic force on the electrons in the wire?   (1) toward x (2) toward y (3) into the page   (4) out of the page

175. What is the direction of the magnetic force on the wire due to the induced current in the wire?   (1) toward x (2) toward y (3) into the page   (4) out of the page

176. What is the potential difference across the ends of the wire?   (1) 1.6×10^{-18} V   (2) 2.5 V   (3) 70. V   (4) 10. V

177. The maximum potential difference will be induced across the wire when the angle between the direction of the motion of the wire and the direction of the magnetic field is   (1) 0°   (2) 45°   (3) 90°   (4) 180°

178. If the velocity of the wire is increased, the induced potential difference across the wire will   (1) decrease   (2) increase   (3) remain the same

Base your answers to questions 179 through 182 on the following diagram, which represents a U-shaped wire conductor positioned perpendicular to a uniform magnetic field which acts into the page. *AB* represents a second wire which is free to slide among the U-shaped wire. The length of wire *AB* is 1 meter, and the magnitude of the magnetic field is 8.0 webers/meter^2.

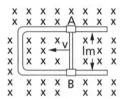

179. If wire *AB* is moved to the left at a constant speed, the direction of the induced electron motion in wire *AB* will be   (1) toward *A*, only   (2) toward *B*, only   (3) first toward *A* and then toward *B*   (4) first toward *B* and then toward *A*

180. If wire *AB* is moved to the left with a constant speed of 10. meters per second, the potential difference induced across wire *AB* will be   (1) 0.8 V   (2) 8.0 V   (3) 10 V   (4) 80 V

181. Wire *AB* is moved at a constant speed to the left. The current induced in the conducting loop will produce a force on wire *AB* which acts   (1) to the right   (2) to the left   (3) into the page   (4) out of the page

182. The resistance of wire *AB* is increased, and the wire is moved to the left at a constant speed of 10 meters per second. Compared to the induced potential difference before the resistance was increased, the new potential difference will be   (1) less   (2) greater   (3) the same

Thinking and Analyzing

183. Trace the figure below onto a sheet of paper. Then draw a small arrow at each of the points labeled *A* through *H* in the vicinity of the current directed into the page at the center of the figure, to indicate the direction of the magnetic field at each location.

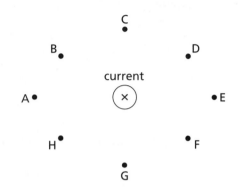

184. Using X's to represent direction into the page and dots to represent direction out of the page, sketch the magnetic field direction at various representative locations inside and outside a circular loop carrying current in the plane of the page, directed counter clockwise, as illustrated below.

Intensity of a Magnetic Field

The magnitude of the force exerted on a straight current-carrying wire situated in a particular magnetic field is proportional to the current in the wire (assuming it is perpendicular to the field lines) and the length of the wire in the field. This is stated mathematically as

$$F = BIL$$

The constant **B** is different for different magnetic fields. Its value is equal to the force that a particular magnetic field exerts on a 1-meter-long wire carrying one amp of current (if the wire is perpendicular to the magnetic field). One magnetic field will exert a stronger force on such a wire than another field only if the field is more intense. Thus the magnitude of **B** represents the intensity of the field. The unit for B, or **magnetic field intensity,** is the newton per ampere-meter (N/A · m).

By convention, the concentration of field lines (the number of lines per unit surface area drawn perpendicularly to the lines) in a region in a magnetic field is made equal to the intensity of the field (the magnitude of **B**) in that region. Magnetic field lines are sometimes called **flux lines** or Webers. The number of flux lines per unit area is the **flux density,** expressed in units of Webers per square meter (Weber/m²). The magnetic field intensity in N/A · m is thus identical to the concentration of field lines in Webers/m². Both units can be used for the magnitude of **B** (1 Weber/m² = 1 N/A · m). Recently the N/A · m and the Weber/m² have been renamed the Tesla, symbolized by T.

Sample Problem

18. An 8 cm segment of a current-carrying wire is situated in a magnetic field that is directed out of the page, toward the reader, as illustrated in Figure 3-40. The direction of the current is to the left and the rate of flow is 20.0 A. A force of 6.4 newtons is found to act on the wire. What is the direction of the force on the wire and the intensity of the magnetic field?

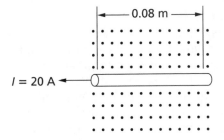

Figure 3-40. The dots indicate that the magnetic field is directed out of the page.

Solution: The direction of the force is found by applying left-hand rule #3. Point the thumb to the left in the direction of the electron motion and the fingers in the direction of the magnetic field, perpendicular to the page and toward you. The palm of the hand then indicates that the force is directed downward, in the plane of the page.

The intensity of the field is found by applying the formula

$$F = BIL$$

change 8 cm to 0.08 m

$$6.4 \text{ N} = (B)(20.0 \text{ A})(0.08 \text{ m})$$

$$B = \frac{6.4 \text{ N}}{(20.0 \text{ A})(0.08 \text{ m})} = 4 \text{ N/A} \cdot \text{m}$$

or 4 Weber/m²

or 4 Tesla

Electromagnetic Waves

The electric and magnetic fields in the vicinity of an accelerating charge change in magnitude and direction as the position and velocity of the charge continue to change. Since a changing magnetic field creates an electric field and a changing electric field creates a magnetic field, an endless chain of fields is generated by the accelerating charge.

The net result is that electric and magnetic fields propagate away from the vicinity of an accelerating charge. This propagation continues even after the charge stops accelerating because the fields continue to generate each other. We refer to this as **electromagnetic radiation.**

If a charge oscillates back and forth between two fixed points (in the process accelerating and decelerating) and the frequency of oscillation is constant, a periodic *electromagnetic wave* of the same frequency is radiated outward from the vicinity of the charge. The magnitude and direction of the electric and magnetic fields vary from point to point in wavelike fashion. At any particular point in the wave, the electric and magnetic fields are perpendicular to each other and to the direction of propagation of the wave. (Figure 3-41).

Electromagnetic waves propagate through empty space at the speed of light, *c*, or 3×10^8 meters per second.

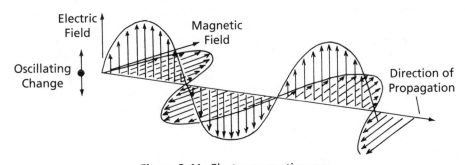

Figure 3-41. Electromagnetic wave.

QUESTIONS

185. Which is the unit of magnetic flux in the MKS system? (1) Weber (2) joule (3) coulomb (4) newton per ampere-meter

186. Magnetic flux density may be measured in (1) N/m^2 (2) $Weber/m^2$ (3) C/m^2 (4) J/m^2

187. If the current in the solenoid is doubled and the number of turns halved, the magnetic field strength of the solenoid will (1) decrease (2) increase (3) remain the same

188. Electromagnetic radiation can be produced by charged particles that are (1) held stationary in a uniform magnetic field (2) held stationary in an electric field (3) moving a constant velocity (4) being accelerated

189. Electromagnetic radiations such as radio, light, and gamma are propagated by the interchange of energy between (1) magnetic fields, only (2) electric fields, only (3) electric and gravitational fields (4) electric and magnetic fields

Thinking and Analyzing

190. On what factors do the magnitude of the force exerted on a straight current-carrying wire in a magnetic field depend?

191. Explain what is meant by the term flux density. What can you conclude about a point at which the flux density is low?

MORE ELECTROMAGNETIC APPLICATIONS

The Galvanometer (-Ⓖ-)

A galvanometer is used to measure small amounts of current. It consists of a coil-shaped wire placed between the opposite poles of permanent magnets. When the current flows through the coil, the field between the poles exerts a torque, forcing the coil to rotate against a spring (see Figure 3-42). If the spring were not there, the coil would rotate until the plane of the wire was perpendicular to the magnetic field. The spring prevents this from happening. It counteracts the torque from the magnetic field with a torque of its own. The coil rotates until the opposing torque exerted by the spring becomes equal to the torque exerted by the field.

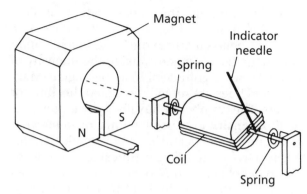

Figure 3-42. A galvanometer.

The resultant deflection of the coil depends on the amount of current; the greater the current in the coil, the greater the deflection. Typically, an indicator needle is attached to the coil. By reading the amount of deflection of the needle one can determine the amount of current in the coil.

When the current ceases to flow, the coil is forced back by the action of the spring to its starting position, with the plane of the coil parallel to the field. The galvanometer is then ready to be used once again.

The Ammeter (-Ⓐ-)

An ammeter is a modified galvanometer and is used to measure larger amounts of current. In an ammeter the coil is connected in parallel with a *shunt*, a material whose resistance is much smaller than that of the galvanometer coil (see Figure 3-43). Most of the current into the ammeter thus bypasses the coil and flows through the shunt. Since the resistance of the coil and shunt are known, the total current through the ammeter can be determined from the current in the coil, which in turn is determined from the deflection of the needle.

To measure current, the ammeter is placed in series with the circuit (or part of the circuit) whose current is to be measured. Since the total resistance of the ammeter is very small, its insertion into the circuit changes the current only negligibly (see Figure 3-44).

Though an ammeter can measure more current than a galvanometer, there is still a limit to the amount of current an ammeter can measure. Once the plane of the galvanometer coil has been twisted 90° and is oriented perpendicularly to the external field, increasing the current no longer produces more rotation. The only way to raise this maximum for any particular ammeter is to decrease the resistance of the shunt. Doing so diverts more of the current to the shunt and away from the coil.

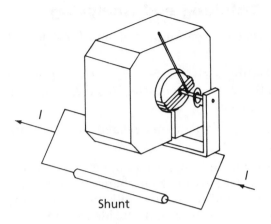

Figure 3-43. An ammeter.

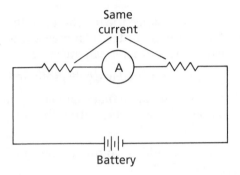

Figure 3-44. Because of its low resistance, the ammeter does not noticeably affect the current in the circuit.

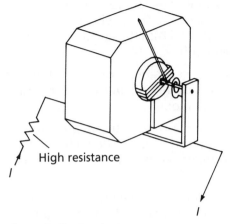

Figure 3-45. A voltmeter.

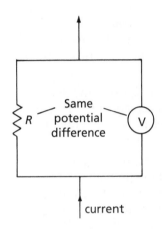

Figure 3-46. Because of its high resistance, the voltmeter does not noticeably affect the current in the circuit.

The Voltmeter (-Ⓥ-)

A voltmeter is also a modified galvanometer and is used to measure potential difference. It consists of a galvanometer coil connected *in series* with a high-resistance material (see Figure 3-45). Since the total resistance of the voltmeter is known, the voltage across voltmeter can be determined from the current through the galvanometer (see "Series Circuits," pp. 67–68), which in turn is determined from the deflection of the needle.

To measure potential difference, a voltmeter is connected in parallel with the part of the circuit whose voltage is to be measured. Since the total resistance of the voltmeter is very high, it draws little current, and its insertion in parallel has a negligible effect on the circuit (see Figure 3-46).

Just as there is a limit to the current an ammeter can read, so every voltmeter has a maximum potential difference it can measure. This maximum can be raised for any particular voltmeter by increasing the resistance of the material in series with the coil. The greater that resistance, the smaller the deflection of the coil in the magnetic field.

QUESTIONS

192. Doubling the current in a loop of wire situated in a magnetic field (1) leaves the torque unchanged (2) halves the torque (3) doubles the torque (4) quadruples the torque

193. A galvanometer measures (1) small amounts of current (2) large amounts of resistance (3) large amounts of current (4) small amounts of power

194. The torque produced by the magnetic field in a galvanometer on the coil is opposed by (1) gravity (2) tension in the spring (3) an electric force (4) another magnet

195. When no current exists in a galvanometer, the plane of the coil should be (1) parallel to the field (2) turned 45 degrees from the field (3) perpendicular to the field (4) any one of the above

196. Ammeters are used to measure (1) small amounts of current (2) large potential differences (3) larger amounts of current (4) small amounts of power

197. To perform its mission, an ammeter is connected (1) in series with the circuit (2) either in series or in parallel with the circuit (3) in parallel with the circuit

198. The total resistance of an ammeter (1) must be very large (2) must be very small (3) could be any amount

199. To raise the maximum current an ammeter can read, the shunt resistance should be (1) decreased (2) made equal to that of the coil (3) increased

200. An ammeter is a galvanometer with a (1) low resistance in series (2) low resistance in parallel (3) high resistance in series (4) high resistance in parallel

201. A voltmeter is a galvanometer with a (1) low resistance in series (2) low resistance in parallel (3) high resistance in series (4) high resistance in parallel

202. When a galvanometer is used, the deflection of the needle occurs as a result of (1) electrostatic force (2) magnetic force (3) gravitational force (4) photoelectric effect

203. The purpose of the shunt in an ammeter is to provide (1) electrostatic deflection of the coil (2) magnetic deflection of the coil (3) resistance to current flow (4) a path for some current to bypass the coil.

204. To function properly, a voltmeter is connected (1) in series with the circuit (2) in parallel with the circuit (3) either in series or in parallel with the circuit

205. The total resistance of a voltmeter (1) must be very large (2) must be very small (3) could be any amount

206. As a torque causes the current-carrying loop in an electric motor to begin rotating, the current in that loop (1) decreases (2) increases (3) remains the same

207. The reading of the ammeter in the diagram at the right should be recorded as (1) 1 A (2) 0.76 A (3) 0.55 A (4) 0.5 A

208. One milliampere produces a full-scale deflection in a galvanometer whose internal resistance is 50 ohms. To convert this instrument into an ammeter whose full-scale deflection is 1 A, it should be shunted with a resistance of approximately (1) 0.005 Ω (2) 0.05 Ω (3) 0.5 Ω (4) 5.0 Ω

Thinking and Analyzing

209. What is a galvanometer and how does it work?

210. During a class experiment, the spring fell out of the class galvanometer. Will the device still work? Explain.

211. How is an ammeter related to a galvanometer?

212. Correct the following statements and explain the reasons for your changes: (a) An ammeter is wired in parallel with the part of the circuit being measured. (b) Inside the ammeter, a galvanometer is connected in series with the shunt.

213. How would you change the resistance of the shunt in an ammeter in order to increase the amount of current the ammeter can measure?

214. How is a voltmeter related to a galvanometer?

215. Why is a high-resistance material used in a voltmeter and how is it connected within the voltmeter?

216. In what way should a voltmeter be connected in a circuit? Why?

217. Is there a way to increase the maximum potential difference that can be measured by a particular voltmeter? Explain.

Motors

Motors operate on the principle that a current-carrying loop in a magnetic field experiences a torque, or turning force. In its most simple form, a motor is composed of a wire loop situated between opposite magnetic poles. One end of the loop is connected to the positive terminal of a battery, and the other end is connected to the negative terminal. (See Figure 3-47.)

Current flows into the page on the right side of the loop and out of the page on the left side. Since the magnetic field lines point to the right, the right side of the loop (segment A) is pushed up and the left side (segment B) is pushed down—as dictated by left-hand rule #3. The loop is thus made to rotate counterclockwise.

To keep the loop rotating in one direction, the current must be reversed every half-turn. Otherwise, the current in segment A would continue to flow into the page and the force exerted on it would continue to act in the upward direction. When segment A arrives on the left side, this force would act to reverse the rotation of the loop by turning it clockwise.

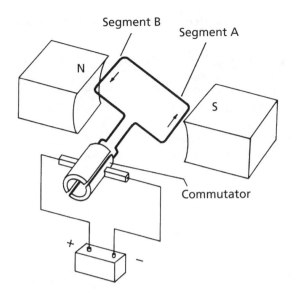

Segment B   Segment A

N   S

Commutator

+   −

Figure 3-47.

To prevent this from happening, each end of the wire loop is connected to a conducting material in the shape of a half-ring. Each half-ring makes contact with a wire leading to one of the battery's terminals by rubbing against a brush. This way, when wire segment A gets to the left side, its half-ring makes contact with the other brush, the one that leads to the opposite terminal of the battery. As a result, the current through segment A is reversed and now flows out of the page. The force on it now points downward, and the rotation of the loop continues to be counterclockwise. A similar reversal in the current's direction occurs in wire segment B when it gets to the right side. This arrangement is known as a **split-ring commutator.**

Motors usually contain many wire loops that together constitute the **armature** of the motor. Typically, the wire loops are wrapped around a "permeable" material, such as soft iron, that becomes magnetized when current flows around it. The magnetic field of the magnetized iron adds to the flux density (or intensity) of the external field. This strengthens the torque acting to rotate the coils.

Back EMF   Once the current flows through the armature of a motor and the coil begins rotating, the motion of the wires across the field lines leads to an induced current. (Recall electromagnetic induction, page 76). This induced current is opposite in direction to the current that makes the armature rotate in the first place.

For example, consider wire segment A in Figure 3-47 as it pushed upward because the current through it is directed into the page. As soon as it

starts moving upward, a magnetic force appears that acts to push the electrons *out of the page*. To see why this is so, use left-hand rule #3. Point the fingers to the right, in the direction of the field, and the thumb upward, in the direction of the moving electrons as they are carried upward by a moving wire. The palm of the hand then pushes out of the page, indicating the direction of the force exerted on the electrons by the field as a result of the wire's motion.

The force responsible for this oppositely directed induced current is referred to as **back EMF.** It is an example of *Lenz's Law* which states that *all magnetic effects lead to forces that oppose the change that produced the effect.* You will learn more about Lenz's law in the next section. The magnetic effect in this case is the rotation of the wire loop. The magnetically-produced rotation leads to a force that opposes the current, the "change" that led to the rotation. As a result of the oppositely-directed induced current, the actual rate of flow of electrons in the wire (the net current) is reduced.

The existence of the back EMF also guarantees that the Law of Conservation of Energy is obeyed. Had there been no back EMF, the rotational kinetic energy of the rotating armature would have been "free"—there would have been no equivalent loss of energy elsewhere in the system. Once the current is reduced as a result of the motion of the armature, less heat is generated in the coils. Less of the battery's chemical energy is converted into heat, and more is converted into rotational kinetic energy. The gain in kinetic energy is balanced by a reduction in heat energy generated by the current.

QUESTIONS

218. A current-carrying loop of wire in a magnetic field is forced to   (1) move perpendicularly to the field   (2) rotate   (3) move parallel to the field

219. The current in the armature of a dc motor (1) flows steadily in one direction   (2) varies in magnitude in one direction   (3) alternates in direction

220. The current in the armature of an electric motor switches direction with each rotation. Which motor part produces this phenomenon? (1) magnet   (2) split-ring commutator   (3) armature   (4) stator

221. The coil is an electric motor is made to rotate by (1) gravity (2) a nuclear force (3) an electric force (4) a magnetic force

222. The wire loops in a motor are wrapped around soft iron to (1) increase the intensity of the magnetic field (2) increase the current in the loops (3) decrease the intensity of the magnetic field (4) decrease the current in the loops

223. If the rotation of the coil in an electric motor is stopped while the motor is still connected to the battery, the current in the coil will (1) decrease (2) increase (3) remain the same

224. The back EMF in an electric motor guarantees that which of the following laws is not violated by the operation of the motor? (1) action-reaction (2) conservation of momentum (3) universal gravitation (4) conservation of energy

Thinking and Analyzing

225. Describe two methods of increasing the strength of the torque experienced by a loop of wire placed in a magnetic field.

226. In a motor, current flowing through the right side of the loop flows out of the page and current flowing through the left side of the loop flows into the page. In what direction will the loop begin rotating if the magnetic field lines point to the right? Explain.

227. Explain the purpose of a split-ring commutator.

Charged Particles in Magnetic Fields

If instead of a long train of electrons, a single charged particle moves across a magnetic field, the field exerts a force on the particle if its motion, or at least a component of its motion, is perpendicular to the field lines. No force is exerted if the particle travels parallel to the field. Left-hand rule #3 is applicable, provided that the thumb points in the direction of the motion of the particle. However, if the particle is positively charged, as in the case of a proton or alpha particle, the direction of the force is opposite that indicated by the palm of the hand.

The magnitude of the force on an individual charged particle is provided by the formula

$$F = qvB$$

where F is the force, in newtons; q is the amount of charge in coulombs; v is the component of the velocity of the particle perpendicular to the magnetic field, in meters per second; and B is the intensity of the field in N/A $\cdot$ m, Webers/m², or Tesla.

Sample Problems

19. What is the direction and magnitude of the force exerted on a proton that moves to the left at the rate of 2×10^4 m/s across a 4.0 Tesla magnetic field whose lines are perpendicular to the page and point away from the reader? (See Figure 3-48.)

Figure 3-48. A proton moving at 2×10^4 m/s to the left across a magnetic field with intensity 4.0 Tesla. The field is directed into the page.

Solution: The direction of the force is found by applying left-hand rule #3 and *reversing* the palm of the hand (because the charge on the proton is positive). Point the thumb to the left and the fingers perpendicularly to the page, away from you. The palm of the hand now pushes upward, in the plane of the page. But since the charge on the particle is positive, the force acts in the *opposite* direction, downward, in the plane of the page.

The magnitude of the force is found by applying the formula

$$F = qvB$$
$$= (1.6 \times 10^{-19}\,\text{C})(2 \times 10^4\,\text{m/s})(4.0\,\text{T})$$
$$= 1.28 \times 10^{-14}\,\text{N}$$

20. What is the magnitude and direction of the force exerted by the same magnetic field on an electron that travels perpendicularly to the page, toward the reader, at the same speed?

Solution: No force is exerted, since the charged particle is moving parallel to the field.

Thermionic Emission

When metallic substances are heated to incandescence, they emit electrons. This happens because, at high temperatures, the atoms are too energetic to be able to hold on to their outermost electrons. We refer to this phenomenon as **thermionic emission**—*therm* for heat, *ionic* for charged. It is also known as the "Edison Effect" after its discoverer, Thomas Edison. As the temperature is increased, the rate of electron emission increases.

As electrons are emitted, however, there is a buildup of negative charge in the space around the incandescent material. This growing negative "space charge" makes it increasingly difficult for other electrons to escape from the material, since they are repelled back into the material. This places a limit on the number of electrons that can be emitted.

Electron Beams The limit can be overcome by placing a positively charged plate, or **anode,** near the negatively charged electron emitter (known as the **cathode**). The positive anode acts to pull emitted electrons toward itself and away from the cathode, thereby eliminating the building of negative charge and enabling other electrons to leave the cathode without difficulty. This results in a continuous beam of electrons traveling from the cathode to the anode.

As the electrons in the beam travel from the cathode to the anode, the electric field between the plates causes them to accelerate. The greater the potential difference between the cathode and anode, the greater the acceleration rate of the electrons toward the anode. Vacuum tubes in electronic devices usually consist of such cathode-anode arrangements.

The cathode-anode arrangement is but one of many devices used in laboratories today to accelerate charged particles to speeds approaching that of light. Such devices are called **particle accelerators.** The fast-moving particles are then aimed at various targets, and they bombard the target nuclei with great force. A great deal of information about the atomic and subatomic worlds has been obtained in this way.

Control of Electron Beams The path of an electron beam can be manipulated by placing an electric or magnetic field in the vicinity of the beam. In an electric field the beam is deflected by a force that is directed *parallel* to the field lines; in a magnetic field the beam is deflected by a force that is directed *perpendicularly* to the field lines and to the beam (as dictated by left-hand rule #3). The magnitude of the force exerted on each electron by an electric field is provided by the formula $F = Eq$, and that exerted by a magnetic field is provided by $F = qvB$.

Cathode Ray Tubes An evacuated tube that contains a source of electrons at one end (the cathode) and a fluorescent screen (coated with material that glows when electrons strike it) at the other end is referred to as a **cathode ray tube.** The "ray" emitted by the cathode is, of course, a beam of electrons. Between the ends of the tube are placed one or more pairs of plates arranged parallel to each other (see Figure 3-49). The plates are

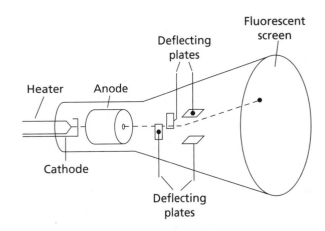

Figure 3-49. Cathode-ray tube.

connected to an outside source of charge, and varying amounts of charge can be imparted to them.

As the electrons in the beam pass through the field between the plates, they are deflected. By varying the charge on the plates, the shape of the path of the beam can be manipulated and the glowing spot on the fluorescent screen (where the electrons strike) can be moved up, down, or sideways. The brightness of the spot can be varied by controlling the intensity of the electron beam (the rate of emission of electrons from the cathode). The television picture tube and the oscilloscope tube are advanced forms of the cathode ray tube.

Mass Spectroscopy If a beam of electrons is aimed at a gas, the ensuing collisions between the electrons and the molecules of the gas sometimes cause electrons to be knocked out of the gas molecules. The molecules thereby lose their electric neutrality and acquire a positive charge. When the positive ions are then subjected to electric and magnetic fields that act on them and the resultant deflections in their paths are measured, their charge-to-mass ratios can be determined. If the charge on the ions is known (they can only be some whole number multiple of the elementary unit of charge), their masses can be calculated from the charge-to-mass ratios. In this manner, the masses of many different atomic species have been determined. The device used in this process is known as a **mass spectrometer.**

This procedure is also used to separate atoms of the same element with different mass (called "isotopes"). Their differing masses make them take divergent paths when charged and placed in electric and magnetic fields.

Mass of the Electron If a beam of electrons is accelerated by an electric field of known intensity, the kinetic energy of the electrons in the beam can be determined. If such a beam is then passed through a magnetic field of known intensity and the deflection of the beam is measured, the charge-to-mass ratio of the electrons can be determined.

Since the charge on an electron is known (1.6×10^{-9} C), knowing the electron's charge-to-mass ratio leads to knowledge of its mass. In this way it was determined that the mass of an electron is 9.1×10^{-31} kg.

The Laser If electrons accelerated by a large potential difference are made to collide with certain types of atoms, the electron-atom collisions stimulate the atoms to emit light. Light produced this way is of one color and usually very intense. A device that emits this kind of light is referred to as a **laser,** an acronym for Light Amplification by Stimulated Emission of Radiation.

In the helium-neon laser most commonly found in classrooms, the electrons are made to collide with helium atoms, and the excited helium atoms then collide with neon atoms. The neon atoms respond by emitting red light.

Induced Voltage

We already know that when a wire is moved perpendicularly across magnetic field lines, the field exerts a force on the electrons in the wire, and if the conductor is part of a complete circuit, a current is induced in the wire as a result.

Since this force pushes the electrons through a distance (the length of the wire), the field does work on the electrons. The amount of work done, in joules, on every coulomb of charge between the ends of the wire segment in the field (the only place work is done) is known as the **induced potential difference,** or the **induced voltage** of the circuit. Sometimes it is referred to as the induced EMF (for electromotive force, though it represents work, not force). The symbol for induced potential difference is V.

The induced voltage, V, is provided by the formula

$$V = BLv$$

where B is the **magnetic field intensity,** in Tesla, L is the length of the wire segment in the field, in meters, and v is the velocity of the wire (perpendicular to the field), in meters per second. The units for V are joules/coulomb, or volts.

If the wire is part of a closed circuit, the induced current is related to the induced voltage by Ohm's Law, $V = IR$, where R is the resistance, in ohms, of the *entire* circuit. The power of the circuit in watts, is provided by the relationship $P = VI$.

21. What is the voltage and current induced in a 4.0 ohm circuit if a 0.5 meter segment of the circuit is moved perpendicularly to a 2 N/A · m field at the rate of 8 m/sec.
Solution:

$$V = BLv$$

$$V = \left(2.0 \frac{N}{A \cdot m}\right)(0.5 \text{ m})\left(8.0 \frac{m}{sec}\right)$$

$$V = \frac{8.0 \text{ N} \cdot m}{A \cdot sec} = \frac{8.0 \text{ N} \cdot m}{\frac{C}{sec}} \cdot sec = \frac{8.0 \text{ N} \cdot m}{C}$$

$$V = 8.0 \frac{joules}{coulomb} \text{ or 8.0 volts}$$

$$V = IR$$

$$8.0 \text{ volts} = (I)(4.0 \text{ ohms})$$

$$I = 2.0 \frac{volts}{ohms} = 2.0 \text{ amperes}$$

22. What is the power of the circuit?
Solution:

$$P = VI$$

$$P = \left(8.0 \frac{J}{C}\right)\left(2.0 \frac{C}{sec}\right) = 16 \text{ Watts}$$

Generator

A sample generator consists of a wire loop that rotates between the two opposite poles of a magnet. As the loop of wire rotates, the induced current and voltage vary. Twice during every rotation of the loop, the induced voltage and current are zero; this happens when the plane of the loop is *perpendicular* to the field lines. At those two points, the wire segments are moving parallel to the field, and no force is exerted on the electrons. Also, twice during every rotation, the plane of the loop is *parallel* to the field. At these two points the motion of the wire is perpendicular to the field lines and the induced current and voltage are at a maximum.

In between the perpendicular and parallel orientations, the induced current and voltage are greater than zero but less than the maximum, since only a component of the motion of the wire is then perpendicular to the field. In addition, the direction of the induced voltage and current in the loop is reversed every half turn, since the wire's direction of motion is reversed. The wire segment that is on the right side and moving downward in Figure 3-50 will be moving upward when it gets to the left side after one half of a rotation.

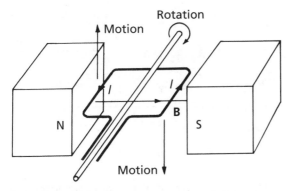

Figure 3-50. Loop of wire rotating in a magnetic field.

The rotating loop is connected to an external circuit that carries the current to a variety of appliances. As the loop rotates, the current and potential difference generated vary in magnitude and alternate in direction. This is referred to as **alternating current** (ac). The maximum current and voltage values are proportional to the intensity of the magnetic field and to the rotational speed of the loop.

Lenz's Law

All magnetic effects lead to forces that oppose the change that produced the effect. We saw earlier how this rule is applied to motors (p. 95). The current induced in a wire as it moves across magnetic field lines and in the ac generator is also a magnetic effect. As such, it is also subject to the rule known as Lenz's Law.

The magnetic effect in this case is the induced current. The "change" that produces it is the motion of the wire across the field lines. As soon as the induced current appears, a force (recall that magnetic fields act on currents) manifests itself to oppose the motion of the wire. For example, the current (directed into the page) induced by the downward motion of the wire in Figure 3-51 leads to an upward-acting force that resists the wire's motion. This can be verified by left-hand rule #3: the thumb points in the direction of electron flow, into the page; the fingers in the direction of the magnetic field, to the right; and the palm of the

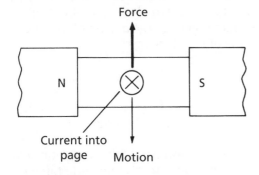

Figure 3-51.

hand pushes (representing the force) upward, parallel to the page.

Since an induced current can exist only as long as the wire moves across the field, and a force opposing the motion of the wire appears at the same time as the current, the only way the current can be maintained is by forcing the wire to continue to move against this opposing force. The work done to keep the wire moving is equal to the energy provided by the current. The energy created by the induced current is therefore not "free." Lenz's Law, thus, provides yet another example of the Law of Conservation of Energy.

In the case of the ac generator, work must be done to keep the wire loop rotating. This is usually accomplished by a steam turbine that derives its energy from the heat produced by burning coal, oil, or from nuclear reactions.

The "change" that induces the current in the second case of electromagnetic induction (see p. 77) is the change over time in the number of flux lines enclosed by a wire loop. In this case Lenz's Law operates as follows: when the number of external field lines increases, the magnetic field created by the induced current opposes the external field. This causes the number of flux lines through the loops to decrease. When the number of external field lines decreases, the magnetic field created by the induced current supplements the external field. This causes the number of field lines through the loops to increase.

Sample Problem

23. The plane of a loop of wire is oriented perpendicularly to a magnetic field whose flux lines point into the page, away from the reader (see Figure 3-52). The intensity of the field weakens over time, and the number of flux lines enclosed by the loop decreases. How will the current induced in the loop be directed?

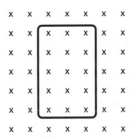

Figure 3-52.

Solution: According to Lenz's Law, the induced current creates a magnetic field that *increases* the number of flux lines enclosed by the loop. This means that the field lines created by the current inside the loop point in the *same direction* as the external field, in this case into the page and away from the reader. Use of left-hand rule #2 shows that the induced current has to move counterclockwise. (Start with the thumb pointing into the page, in the direction of the magnetic field. The four fingers then point in the direction of the induced current, counterclockwise.)

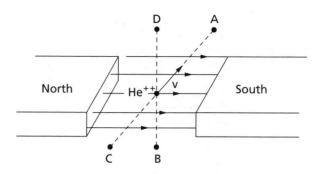

QUESTIONS

228. The space charge near an incandescent cathode is   (1) negatively charged   (2) positively charged   (3) either positively or negatively charged

229. The cathode-anode arrangement is designed to   (1) decelerate electrons   (2) accelerate protons   (3) accelerate electrons   (4) maintain constant speed of the electrons

230. An electron traveling at a speed v in the plane of this paper enters a uniform magnetic field. Which diagram best represents the condition under which the electron will experience the greatest magnitude force as it enters the magnetic field?

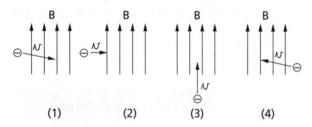

231. If a charged particle moving through a magnetic field experiences a magnetic force, the angle between the magnetic field and the force exerted on the particle is   (1) 0°   (2) 45°   (3) 90°   (4) 180°

232. If a charged particle moving perpendicularly to a uniform magnetic field increases in velocity, the magnetic force on the charge   (1) decreases   (2) increases   (3) remains the same

Base your answers to questions 233 through 237 on the following diagram, which represents a helium ion with a charge of +2 elementary charges moving toward point A with a constant speed v of 2.0 meters per second perpendicular to a uniform magnetic field between the poles of a magnet. The strength of the magnetic field is 0.10 weber per square meter.

233. The direction of the magnetic force on the helium ion is toward point   (1) A (2) B (3) C (4) D

234. The magnitude of the magnetic force exerted on the helium ion is   (1) 3.2×10^{-20} N   (2) 6.4×10^{-20} N   (3) 0.10 N   (4) 0.20 N

235. If the strength of the magnetic field and the speed of the helium ion are both doubled, the force on the helium ion will be   (1) halved   (2) doubled   (3) the same   (4) quadrupled

236. If the polarity of the magnet is reversed, the magnitude of the magnetic force on the helium ion will   (1) decrease   (2) increase   (3) remain the same

237. The helium ion is replaced by an electron moving at the same speed. Compared to the magnitude of the force on the helium ion, the magnitude of the force on the electron is   (1) less   (2) greater   (3) the same

Base your answers to questions 238 through 241 on the following diagram, which represents an electron beam entering the space between two parallel, oppositely charged plates. A uniform magnetic field, directed out of the page, exists between the plates.

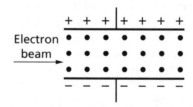

238. If the magnitude of the electric force on each electron and the magnetic force on each electron are the same, which diagram best represents the direction of the *vector sum* of the forces acting on one of the electrons?

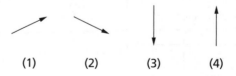

239. In which direction would the magnetic field have to point in order for the magnetic force on

the electrons to be opposite in direction from the electric force on the electrons? (1) toward the bottom of the page (2) toward the top of the page (3) out of the page (4) into the page

240. If the electric force were equal and opposite to the magnetic force on the electrons, which diagram would best represent the path of the electrons as they travel in the space between the plates?

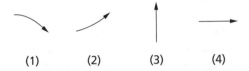

(1)   (2)   (3)   (4)

241. If only the potential difference between the plates is increased, the force on the electron will (1) decrease (2) increase (3) remain the same

Base your answers to questions 242 through 246 on the following diagram, which represents an electron moving at 2.0×10^6 meters per second into a magnetic field which is directed into the paper. The magnetic field has a strength of 2.0 newtons per ampere meter.

$$\begin{array}{cccc} & & & B \\ X & X & X & X \\ X & X & X & X \\ X & X & X & X \\ X & X & X & X \end{array}$$

e⁻ ———→

242. Which vector best indicates the direction of the force on the electron?

———→   ←———   ↑   ↓

(1)   (2)   (3)   (4)

243. What is the magnitude of the force on the electron? (1) 6.4×10^{-13} N (2) 4.0×10^6 N (3) 6.4×10^6 N (4) 8.0×10^6 N

244. If the strength of the magnetic field were increased, the force on the electron would (1) decrease (2) increase (3) remain the same

245. If the velocity of the electron were increased, the force on the electron would (1) decrease (2) increase (3) remain the same

246. The electron is replaced with a proton moving with the same velocity. Compared to the magnitude of the force on the electron, the magnitude of the force on the proton would be (1) less (2) greater (3) the same

Base your answers to questions 247 through 250 on the following diagram, which represents an electron beam in a vacuum. The beam is emitted by the cathode C, accelerated by anode A, and passes through electric and magnetic fields.

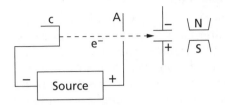

247. If an electron in the beam is accelerated to a kinetic energy of 4.8×10^{-16} joule, the potential difference between the cathode and the anode is (1) 7.7×10^3 V (2) 4.8×10^{-3} V (3) 3.0×10^3 V (4) 3.0×10^{-3} V

248. In which direction will the electron beam be deflected by the electric field? (1) into the page (2) out of the page (3) toward the top of the page (4) toward the bottom of the page

249. In which direction will the force of the magnetic field act on the electron beam? (1) into the page (2) out of the page (3) toward the top of the page (4) toward the bottom of the page

250. If an electron in the beam moves at 2.0×10^8 meters per second between the magnetic poles where the flux density is 0.20 weber per square meter, the force on the electron is (1) 6.4×10^{-12} N (2) 6.4×10^{-10} N (3) 4.0×10^7 N (4) 4.0×10^9 N

Thinking and Analyzing

251. One charged particle moves parallel to a magnetic field. A second charged particle moves perpendicular to the magnetic field. A third charged particle moves diagonally across the magnetic field. Discuss any forces exerted by the field on each particle.

252. How does the force exerted by a magnetic field on a charged particle moving through the field depend on the intensity of the field and the velocity of the particle?

253. What is the Edison Effect and how is it dependent on temperature?

254. Why is there a limit on the number of electrons that can be emitted during thermionic emission? How can the limit be overcome?

255. What is a particle accelerator and what is its purpose?

256. How is the picture on a conventional television screen produced?

257. What makes laser light different from the light produced in an ordinary light bulb?

Transformers (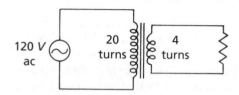)

A typical transformer is constructed as follows: wire carrying alternating current, usually powered by a generator, is wound around one arm of a rectangular-shaped "core" made of soft iron (see Figure 3-53). This coil is referred to as the **primary coil.** Another wire is wound around a second arm of the core and is known as the **secondary coil.** The secondary coil leads to the appliance we wish to operate, but it is *not* connected to any power source nor to the primary coil. Indeed the two coils usually consist of insulated wires that cannot make contact with each other.

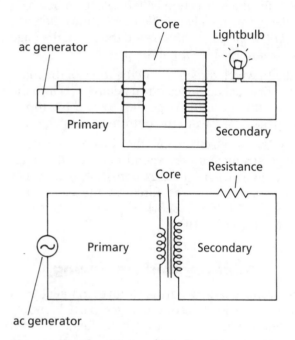

Figure 3-53. Transformer and schematic equivalent.

As the current in the primary coil continues to alternate in magnitude and direction, it creates a magnetic field that alternates in intensity and direction (recall "Currents Act on Magnets," pp. 74 and 86). The highly permeable soft iron core becomes alternately magnetized and demagnetized. Consequently, the intensity and direction of the magnetic field created by the core in the region of the secondary coil also alternates. The changing magnetic field induces current (ac) and EMF in the secondary circuit (see page 77). This induced current powers the appliance connected to that coil.

The voltage induced in the secondary coil is usually different from that in the primary coil.

The ratio of the voltage in the primary, V_p to the voltage in the secondary, V_s, is equal to the ratio of the number of loops of wire around the primary arm, N_p, to the number of loops around the secondary arm, N_s. This is stated mathematically as

$$\frac{V_p}{V_s} = \frac{N_p}{N_s}$$

If the secondary arm contains more loops than the primary, the voltage induced in the secondary coil is greater and the transformer is called a **step-up transformer.** If the secondary arm contains fewer loops than the primary, its voltage is smaller and the transformer is referred to as a **step-down transformer** (Figure 3-54).

Figure 3-54. Step-down transformer.

However, as a consequence of the Law of Conservation of Energy, the power output from the secondary (to the appliances connected to it) cannot exceed the power input of the primary (supplied by the generator). At best, the power output of the secondary will equal the power input to the primary and

$$V_p I_p = V_s I_s$$

Such transformers are said to be 100% efficient; no heat energy is lost between the primary and the secondary.

Most transformers are not 100% efficient, and the power output from the secondary is usually less than the power input to the primary. The efficiency of a transformer is defined as the ratio of the two rates of doing work, expressed in percentage form:

$$\% \text{ Efficiency} = \frac{V_s I_s}{V_p I_p} \times 100\%$$

Sample Problems

24. A step-down transformer consists of a primary coil containing 20 turns and a secondary coil with 4 turns. The generator provides the primary with 120 volts of potential difference. What is the voltage induced in the secondary?

Solution:

$$\frac{V_p}{V_s} = \frac{N_p}{N_s}$$

$$\frac{120}{V_s} = \frac{20}{4}$$

$$V_s = \frac{(4)(120)}{20} = 24.0 \text{ volts}$$

25. If the transformer is 80% efficient and 1000 watts of power are supplied to the primary, how much current flows through the secondary?
Solution:

$$\% \text{ Efficiency} = \frac{V_s I_s}{V_p I_p} \times 100$$

$$80 = \frac{V_s I_s}{1000} \times 100$$

$$V_s I_s = 800$$

$$(24)I_s = 800$$

$$I_s = 33.3 \text{ amps}$$

QUESTIONS

258. Compared with the voltage in the coil of a transformer with more turns of wire, the voltage in the coil with fewer turns is (1) smaller (2) greater (3) the same

259. An ideal transformer cannot (1) increase the current (2) increase the voltage (3) increase the power (4) decrease the current

260. A transformer is connected to a source of alternating current. The only factor always common to both primary and secondary windings is the (1) current (2) voltage (3) frequency (4) resistance

261. The current flowing in the primary of a transformer depends upon (1) the resistance of the secondary coil (2) the resistance of the primary coil (3) the current taken by the secondary (4) the resistance between the primary and secondary coils

262. A transformer has 50 turns on the primary and 100 turns on the secondary. If the primary is connected to a 6-volt battery the voltage on the secondary will be (1) zero (2) less than zero (3) twice the voltage on the primary (4) half the voltage on the primary

263. A transformer changes (1) electrical energy into mechanical energy (2) mechanical energy into electrical energy (3) high voltage dc to low voltage dc (4) low voltage ac to high voltage ac

Base your answers to questions 264 through 267 on the following information: A transformer consists of a primary connected to a 120-volt ac source that drives 4 A of current through the primary, and a secondary that contains one-third as many turns of wire as the primary. The transformer's efficiency is 80 percent.

264. The voltage of the secondary is (1) 360 V (2) 90 V (3) 40 V (4) 480 V

265. The current through the secondary is closest to (1) 80 A (2) 8 A (3) 3 A (4) 10 A

266. The current in the secondary (1) is of the ac type (2) could be either ac or dc (3) is of the dc type (4) is of the rectified ac type

267. The power output of the secondary is (1) equal to the power input to the primary (2) greater than the power input to the primary (3) less than the power input to the primary.

268. To step up 6 V to 30 V with a transformer whose primary contains 10 coils of wire, the secondary should consist of (1) 5 coils (2) 3 coils (3) 50 coils (4) 15 coils

269. What is the power output of a transformer whose efficiency is 60 percent, if the power input to the primary is 240 W? (1) 144 W (2) 300 W (3) 400 W (4) 180 W

Thinking and Analyzing

270. Is work done when a current is induced in a wire? Explain.

271. How is the induced voltage, V, in a wire moved through a magnetic field related to the length of the wire in the magnetic field and the intensity of the field?

272. What is a generator?

273. At what point during the rotation of a loop of a wire in a generator is the induced current zero? When is it at its maximum?

274. What is alternating current and how is it produced in a generator?

275. In what way does Lenz's Law and the Law of Conservation of Energy relate to electric generators?

276. A local electric company transmits electricity over wires at 10,000 volts. How does a transformer enable you to receive that same electricity at the 120 volts required by many of your household appliances?

277. How are step-up and step-down transformers used?

CHAPTER 4

Wave Phenomena

INTRODUCTION TO WAVES

Traveling Disturbances A disturbance is a change in a body of matter that is opposed by a force of nature; the body becomes the **medium** through which the disturbance travels. Traveling disturbances have a point of origin and contain energy that is transmitted through the medium. They can propagate through such material media as solids, liquids, and gases.

Disturbances in Solids When a person holds one end of a rope (the other end attached to, say, a door knob) and flicks his wrist upward, a crest is formed. From its point of origin at one end, the crest moves toward the other end of the rope (Figure 4-1). The force of tension in the rope acts to pull the crest down; as the crest comes down in response to these forces, it pushes against the adjacent part of the rope, causing the crest to reappear farther down along the rope. This happens repeatedly as the crest travels the length of the rope.

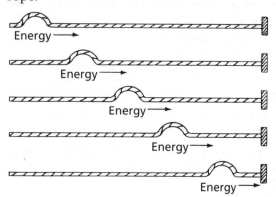

Figure 4-1. Disturbance traveling in a rope.

Disturbances in Liquids The circular ripples formed by a pebble dropped into a pond are disturbances traveling in the body of water. First a crest is formed by the downward thrust of the pebble into the water (similar to the flick of the wrist with the rope). The forces of tension and gravity then pull this circular crest down. As the crest collapses in one spot, it reemerges farther away from the point of origin, turning the ripple into an ever-expanding circle whose center is the point where the pebble entered the water.

Disturbances in Gases When a tuning fork is struck, it oscillates back and forth. As one prong of the fork swings in one direction, it pushes air molecules in that same direction, creating a pocket of compressed air (Figure 4-2). As this compressed air expands and returns to normal, it pushes against the adjacent volume of air, compressing it. As with the crest on the rope and the ripple in the pond, the disturbance (compressed air) travels through a medium (air), away from its source (the tuning fork).

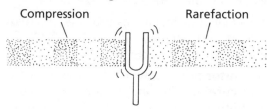

Figure 4-2. A series of compressions and rarefactions form a sound wave.

Pulses

A single vibratory disturbance is called a **pulse.** One example of a pulse is a traveling crest of water. When the disturbance reaches a particular part of the pool, the water molecules there are pushed upward, forming a crest. When the disturbance passes that point, the water molecules come down. In this way, the up-and-down vibration travels from place to place.

Periodic Waves

A regularly repeating series of pulses is called a **periodic wave.** Here the vibratory disturbances are evenly spaced, one pulse following the other like cars in a train—thus the term **wave train.** Periodic waves are usually referred to simply as *waves.* Returning to the rope example: to form periodic waves, the wrist at one end of the rope is flicked up and down continuously at a regular rate; each upward flick sends a crest across the rope, and each downward flick sends a trough (Figure 4-3).

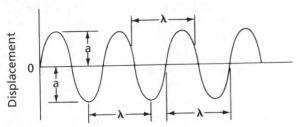

Figure 4-3. Amplitude (a) and wavelength (λ).

The same effect can be produced in water by successively inserting a finger into the water and pulling it out. Each time the finger is inserted, a circular crest is formed. Each time the finger is pulled out, a circular trough is formed. A regularly repeating pattern of crests following troughs travels across the water.

Likewise, the vibration of the tuning fork sends out a series of pulses. As the tuning fork oscillates back and forth, compressions and **rarefactions** (pockets of expanded air) follow each other into the surrounding air (Figure 4-2).

One complete repetition of the pattern in a periodic wave is referred to as a **cycle**. For example, a crest followed by a trough, or a compression followed by a rarefaction, constitute one cycle.

Sound and light are two special types of waves. Sound waves consist of compression-rarefaction cycles produced by an oscillating material. Light waves consist of electromagnetic disturbances that need no material medium to propagate from place to place; light can travel in a vacuum.

Transverse Waves   Waves in which the disturbances are *perpendicular* to the direction of wave motion are called **transverse waves.** The vertical disturbances in a rope or body of water produce waves that move horizontally, and so are examples of transverse waves. Light is also a transverse wave.

Longitudinal Waves   Waves in which disturbances are *parallel* to the direction of wave motion are called **longitudinal waves.** The compressions and rarefactions of sound waves, for example, consist of molecules vibrating parallel to the motion of the wave. Sound waves, therefore, are longitudinal waves.

Some waves, such as large ocean waves, consist of combinations of longitudinal and transverse vibrations.

Wave Characteristics

Waves cause the particles of a medium to vibrate about their rest position; but it is the energy of the wave, not the particles of the medium, that travels through the medium. When a crest, for example, moves over the surface of water, no water is actually moving with the crest. The water moves vertically (up and down) but not horizontally. Only the energy needed to cause the up-and-down vibration moves through the water.

Frequency   The number of cycles produced by a vibrating source per second is the **frequency** of the wave, symbolized by the letter f. Frequency also represents the number of cycles that pass by a fixed point per second. "Cycles per second" are expressed in **hertz** (Hz), a derived unit. A radio station that transmits at 600 kilohertz (kHz) sends 600,000 cycles per second past a receiving antenna.

The frequency of a wave is determined by its source. The nature of the medium through which the wave travels does not affect its frequency. For example, the frequency of a sound wave produced by a tuning fork is determined by how many times per second the tuning fork oscillates and does not depend upon the temperature or quality of the surrounding air. If the tuning fork completes five full oscillations every second, it produces five compression-rarefaction cycles per second, and five such cycles per second will be seen following each other past any fixed point in the path of the wave.

Period   The time required for a complete cycle to be produced or to pass a given point is the **period** of the wave, symbolized by T. Like frequency, period is determined by the source of the wave.

The period of a wave is the reciprocal of its frequency. If the frequency is 10 Hz, the period is $\frac{1}{10}$ second. The relationship between period and frequency can be summarized by the formulas

$$T = \frac{1}{f} \quad \text{and} \quad f = \frac{1}{T}$$

Sample Problem

1. If the time necessary for one cycle of a wave to pass a given point is $\frac{1}{3}$ second, what is the frequency of the wave?
   Solution:
   $$f = \frac{1}{T} = \frac{1}{\frac{1}{3}\,\text{s}} = 3\,\text{Hz}$$

Wavelength   The length of one complete cycle is called the **wavelength** of the wave, symbolized by the Greek letter lambda [λ] Wavelength can be measured from crest to crest, trough to trough, or between corresponding points on adjacent pulses. (Figure 4-3). Both the source and the medium affect the wavelength.

Speed   The **speed** of a wave is the distance traveled per unit time by any part of the wave. Speed is generally expressed in meters per second and is symbolized by v. The speed of a wave depends on the nature of the medium through which it travels. Sound waves, for example, travel faster in warm air than in cold air. The relationship between the speed of sound and the temperature of the air is provided by the formula $v = 331 + 0.6T$, where v is the speed of sound in meters/second and T is the temperature in °C.

Some materials allow waves of different frequencies to travel through them at different speeds. Such media are called **dispersive.** Glass is a dispersive medium for light waves.

The speed of a wave is also equal to the product of its frequency and wavelength.

$$v = f\lambda$$

If 5 cycles pass a given point in one second and each cycle is 2 meters long, then 10 meters of "wave" pass the point per second. The frequency (f) is 5 Hz, the wavelength (λ) is 2 meters, and the speed ($f\lambda$) is 10 meters per second.

Sample Problem

2. The speed of a radio wave is 3×10^8 m/s. What is the wavelength of a radio wave whose frequency is 600 kHz?
  Solution:

$$v = f\lambda$$

$$\lambda = v/f$$

$$= \frac{3 \times 10^8 \text{ m/s}}{6 \times 10^5 \text{ s}^{-1}} = 5 \times 10^2 \text{ m}$$

(*Note:* Hz represents cycles/second but a "cycle" is not a unit since it is not a measured quantity. The unit for frequency is therefore 1/sec, or sec^{-1}.)

Amplitude   The maximum disturbance in each cycle is known as the **amplitude** of the wave. The amplitude of a wave traveling through a material is equal to the maximum displacement of particles of the medium from their rest, or equilibrium, position. For waves in water, the amplitude is the maximum height of a crest or the maximum depth of a trough (Figure 4-3). For the compressions and rarefactions of sound waves, the amplitude is the greatest deviation in density or pressure from the norm of the surrounding air.

The amplitude of a wave is determined by its source. A tuning fork that goes through wider oscillations produces more compressed compressions and more rarefied rarefactions. A larger pebble dropped into water pushes up taller crests. The greater the amplitude of a wave, the more energy it carries. As the amplitude of a sound wave increases, the loudness of the sound increases. Similarly, as the amplitude of a light wave increases, the brightness of the light increases.

Phase   Points on a periodic wave that are identically displaced from the equilibrium position and are moving in the same direction away from the equilibrium position are said to be **in phase.** In other words, the phase difference between them is 0°. Points that are in phase are always a whole number of wavelengths apart. Points A, I, and Q in Figure 4-4 meet all of these conditions and are therefore in phase. The same is true of points B, J, and R and E and M. Points A and B, B and D, or B and H, on the other hand, do not meet all of these requirements, and are said to be **out of phase.**

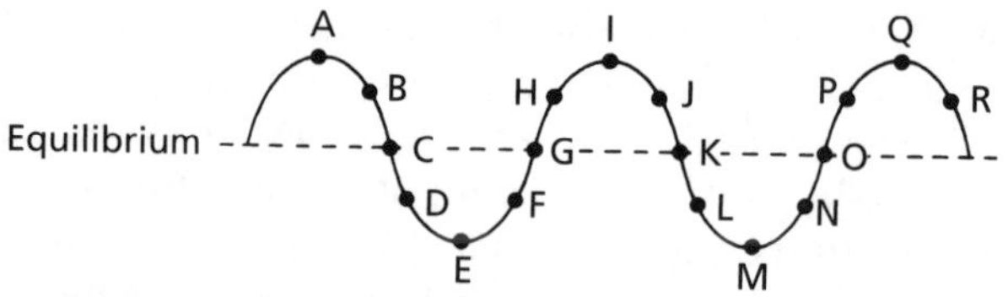

Figure 4-4.

Points on a periodic wave that are equally displaced from the equilibrium position but are moving in opposite directions are said to be 180° out of phase. Points that are 180° out of phase are always an odd number of half wavelengths apart. Points A and E, B and F, and F and J (Figure 4-4) are all pairs of points with a phase difference of 180° between them.

Boundary Behavior   When a wave encounters a boundary between two different media, part of the wave is reflected back into the first medium and part is transmitted into the second medium. The fraction of the wave's energy that is reflected and the fraction transmitted depend on the type of wave and on the nature of the two media. For example, when a light wave traveling through the air hits glass, most of the wave's energy is transmitted through the glass and only a small fraction is reflected. On the other hand, when a water wave reaches the end of a pool or lake, or when a sound wave encounters a smooth rigid wall, most of the wave's energy is reflected back into the first medium.

The part of the wave that is reflected at the boundary between two media retains the same speed, frequency, and wavelength as the original wave. The part of the wave that is transmitted into the second medium, however, experiences a change in speed, since the speed of a wave is determined by the medium. The transmitted wave's frequency, on the other hand, is determined by its source and does not change. Since wavelength, frequency, and speed are interrelated ($v = f\lambda$), a change in speed must result in a change in at least one of the other two factors. If the frequency remains constant there must be a change in wavelength when the wave enters the second medium. For example, the speed of light in glass is less than it is in air; this means that the wavelength of light becomes shorter as it passes from air to glass.

The Doppler Effect

Although it is generally true that the number of cycles passing by a given point per second (the **observed frequency** of a wave) is equal to the number of cycles produced by the source per second (the **transmitted frequency**), this is not the case if the source and the observer are moving relative to each other.

When the source and the observer approach each other, the number of cycles observed passing by per second is greater than would have been the case had the source and observer been at rest. In this case, the observed frequency is greater than the transmitted frequency.

When the source and observer move away from each other, the number of cycles observed passing by per second is less than would have been the case had the source and observer been at rest. In this case, the observed frequency is less than the transmitted frequency.

These phenomena are known as the **Doppler effect,** and important consequences result from them. The pitch of a sound wave, a quality that is related to frequency, changes noticeably as the source of a sound, such as a siren or radio, first approaches the observer, passes by, then recedes. In the case of light waves, the Doppler effect leads to changes in color. White light from an approaching source, for example, takes on a bluish appearance. From a receding source, the light shifts toward the red.

The amount of increase or decrease in frequency that results from relative motion between a source and an observer is dependent upon the speed of the source or the observer or both. Indeed, it is possible to determine the unknown speed of a source of sound or light, toward or away from the observer, from the change in pitch of the sound or change in color of the light.

QUESTIONS

1. Wave motion in a medium transfers   (1) energy, only   (2) mass, only   (3) both mass and energy   (4) neither mass nor energy

2. A single vibratory disturbance that moves from point to point in a material medium is known as a   (1) phase   (2) pulse   (3) distortion   (4) wavelet

3. A transverse wave moves to the right through a medium. Which diagram best represents the motion of the molecules of the medium due to the wave motion?

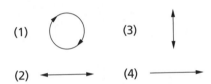

4. In which type of wave is the disturbance parallel to the direction of wave travel?   (1) torsional   (2) longitudinal   (3) transverse   (4) circular

5. Longitudinal waves are involved in the transmission of   (1) light   (2) radar   (3) sound   (4) photons

6. If the frequency of a sound wave in air remains constant, its energy can be varied by changing its   (1) amplitude   (2) speed   (3) wavelength   (4) period

7. The amplitude of the wave shown below is represented by the distance between points   (1) A and B (2) A and C (3) A and D (4) E and D

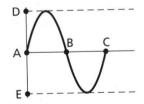

8. In the diagram below, a wave of 1.00-meter amplitude is moving from left to right in an elastic cord. The displacement of point A after the wave has passed point B will be   (1) 1.00 meter up   (2) 1.00 meter down   (3) 0.500 meter up or down   (4) 0.00 meter

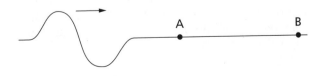

9. In the diagram below, a train of waves is moving along a string. What is the wavelength?
(1) 1 m   (2) 2 m   (3) 3 m   (4) 6 m

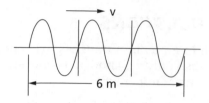

Base your answers to questions 10 through 12 on the following diagram which represents a segment of a periodic wave traveling to the right in a steel spring.

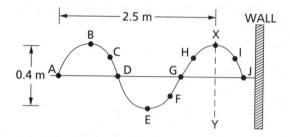

10. What is the amplitude of the wave?   (1) 2.5 m   (2) 2.0 m   (3) 0.2 m   (4) 0.4 m

11. What is the wavelength of the wave?   (1) 1.0 m   (2) 2.0 m   (3) 2.5 m   (4) 0.4 m

12. If a wave crest passes line *XY* every 0.40 second, the frequency of the wave is   (1) 1.0 Hz   (2) 2.5 Hz   (3) 5.0 Hz   (4) 0.4 Hz

13. The reciprocal of the frequency of a periodic wave is the wave's   (1) period   (2) amplitude   (3) propagation   (4) velocity

14. As the frequency of the wave generated by a radio transmitter is increased, the wavelength   (1) decreases   (2) increases   (3) remains the same

15. If the period of a wave is doubled, its wavelength will be   (1) halved   (2) doubled   (3) unchanged   (4) quartered

16. As the frequency of a wave increases, the period of that wave   (1) decreases   (2) increases   (3) remains the same

17. Periodic waves are produced by a wave generator at the rate of one wave every 0.50 second. The period of the wave is   (1) 1.0 s   (2) 2.0 s   (3) 0.25 s   (4) 0.50 s

Base your answers to questions 18 and 19 on the following information.

The frequency of a wave is 2.0 cycles per second, and its speed is 0.04 meter per second.

18. The period of the wave is   (1) 0.005 sec   (2) 2.0 sec   (3) 0.50 sec   (4) 0.02 sec

19. The wavelength of the wave is   (1) 1.0 m   (2) 0.02 m   (3) 0.08 m   (4) 4.0 m

20. If the frequency of a sound wave is 440. cycles per second its period is closest to   (1) 2.27×10^{-3} second/cycle   (2) 0.75 second/ cycle   (3) 1.33 seconds/cycle   (4) 3.31×10^2 seconds/cycle

21. A wave traveling at 5.0×10^4 meters per second has a wavelength of 2.5×10^1 meters. What is the frequency of the wave?   (1) 1.25×10^6 Hz   (2) 2.0×10^3 Hz   (3) 5.0×10^{-4} Hz   (4) 5.0×10^3 Hz

22. As a wave enters a medium, there may be a change in the wave's   (1) frequency   (2) speed   (3) period   (4) phase

23. As light passes from air into glass, its speed   (1) decreases   (2) increases   (3) remains the same

24. Periodic waves with a wavelength of 0.05 meter move with a speed of 0.30 meter per second. When the waves enter a dispersive medium, they travel at 0.15 meter per second. What is the wavelength of the waves in the dispersive medium?   (1) 20. m   (2) 1.8 m   (3) 0.05 m   (4) 0.025 m

25. Which will generally occur when a pulse reaches a boundary between two different media?   (1) The entire pulse will be reflected.   (2) The entire pulse will be absorbed?   (3) The entire pulse will be transmitted.   (4) Part of the pulse will be transmitted and part will be reflected.

26. A car's horn is blowing as the car moves at constant speed toward an observer. Compared with the frequency of the sound wave emitted by the horn, the observed frequency is   (1) constant, and lower   (2) constant, and higher   (3) the same   (4) varying, and lower

Base your answers to questions 27 through 29 on the following diagram which represents waves around a sound source that is moving with a constant velocity through air. The source produces waves of a constant frequency.

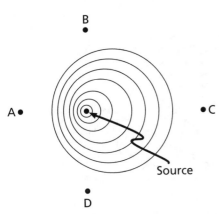

27. The diagram illustrates (1) interference (2) diffraction (3) reflection (4) the Doppler effect

28. The source is moving toward point (1) *A* (2) *B* (3) *C* (4) *D*

29. Compared with the frequency of the waves observed at *C*, the frequency of the waves observed at *A* is (1) less (2) greater (3) the same

Thinking and Analyzing

30. What is the medium of a wave?

31. Define the term *wave train*.

32. How do transverse waves differ from longitudinal waves?

33. What does it mean to say that a wave has a frequency of 200 Hz?

34. What determines the frequency of a wave?

35. What is the period of a wave that has a frequency of 50 Hz?

36. If the time necessary for one cycle of a wave to pass a given point is 1/5 second, what is the frequency of the wave?

37. What is the wavelength of the wave shown in the diagram?

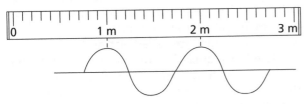

38. Which of the following factors are affected by the nature of the medium—frequency, period, wavelength, and speed, amplitude? Explain.

39. What is a dispersive medium?

40. If 4 cycles pass a given point in one second and each cycle is 3 meters long, what is the speed of the wave?

41. The speed of a wave is 300 m/s. What is the wavelength of the wave if its frequency is 10 kHz?

42. What is the amplitude of the wave shown in the diagram?

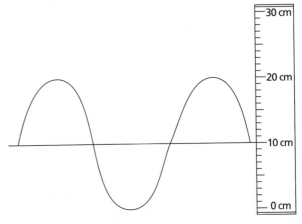

43. What happens to the loudness of a sound as its amplitude increases?

44. How are the speed, frequency, and wavelength of a reflected wave related to the original wave?

45. Explain why the motion of a source of sound away from an observer leads to the observer receiving a sound of longer wavelength and lower frequency than if the source were at rest (Doppler effect).

When Waves Meet

Two or more waves may pass through a medium at the same time. When this occurs two rules apply. First, the total displacement experienced at any point where waves meet is equal to the sum of the displacements of the individual waves at that point. This is known as the **principle of superposition.** Second, waves pass through each other, with each wave unaffected by the passage of the others. After meeting, the individual waves continue traveling in their original directions and with the same characteristics as before.

Constructive Interference As an example, consider two crests traveling toward each other in a rope. Assume one is 3 cm tall and the other is 2 cm tall before they meet. At the moment they meet, the rope is displaced 5 cm upward from its normal (equilibrium) position. Then the 3-cm and 2-cm-tall crests reappear and continue onward, one to the right and the other to the left, in the same directions they were traveling before they met (Figure 4-5 on page 110).

Since these two crests "interfered" with each other when they met and the result was a larger

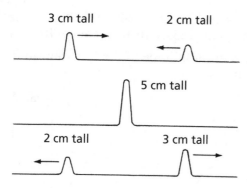

Figure 4-5. Constructive interference.

disturbance, we call this **constructive interference.**

Destructive Interference   As another example, consider a crest and a trough heading toward each other in a rope. The crest is 2 cm tall (displacement of $+2$) and the trough is 2 cm deep (displacement of -2). When they meet, the net displacement is zero and the rope straightens out. Then the crest and trough reappear, with the crest continuing on its way to the left and the trough continuing on its way to the right. In effect, they passed through each other (Figure 4-6).

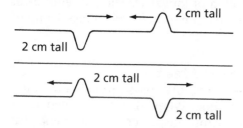

Figure 4-6. Destructive interference.

Since these two pulses interfered with each other only to negate each other's disturbances, this is an example of **destructive interference.**

Maximum constructive interference occurs at points where the phase difference between the waves that meet is 0° and maximum destructive interference occurs where the waves are 180° out of phase. The total destruction of two overlapping periodic waves occurs if they have equal amplitudes and frequencies and are everywhere 180° out of phase.

Two Sources in Phase   Two wave sources vibrating at the same frequency and producing waves of equal amplitude are said to be **sources in phase.** In Figure 4-7, two such sources, located at s_1 and s_2, are operating in the same medium, such as a body of water. Each source produces crests and troughs that propagate outward in all

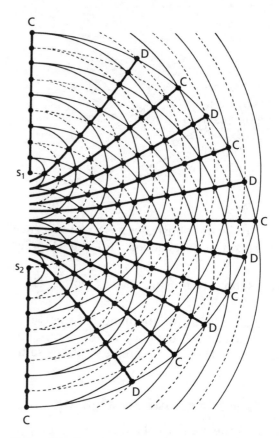

Figure 4-7. Two sources in phase and their interference pattern.

directions. The solid semicircles in the figure represent the crests and the dotted semicircles represent the troughs. The lines labeled C connect points of constructive interference—along these lines the crests of one wave meet the crests of the other wave (solid semicircles meet solid semicircles) and the troughs meet troughs (dotted semicircles meet dotted semicircles). The path distances from any point on these lines to the two sources are either equal or differ by an *even* number of half-wavelengths (the same as a whole number of wavelengths). The waves meet in phase and constructive interference occurs. Points of constructive interference are called **antinodes** and lines that connect them, along which the water is wavy, are called **antinodal lines.**

The lines labeled D, on the other hand, connect points of destructive interference. Along these lines the crests of one wave meet the troughs of the other (solid semicircles meet dotted semicircles). The path distances from any point on these lines to the two sources differ by an *odd* number of half-wavelengths ($\frac{1}{2}\lambda, \frac{3}{2}\lambda, \frac{5}{2}\lambda, \ldots$). The waves meet out of phase and destroy each other. These points are called **nodes** and the lines that connect them, along which the water is calm, are called **nodal lines.**

Standing Waves Another example of interference is the guitar string that is fixed at both ends and plucked in the middle. Two waves travel from the point where the string is plucked, in opposite directions, towards the ends of the string. At the ends of the string the waves are reflected and they pass through each other as they travel to the opposite ends. Then they are reflected again, pass through each other again, and so on until the waves die out. For certain combinations of string length and wavelength, the waves repeatedly pass through each other in such a way that at some points on the string they always meet to interfere constructively, while at other points they always interfere destructively. At points where a crest of one wave always meets a crest of the other and a trough always meets a trough (constructive interference), antinodes are formed and the string vibrates visibly. At points where a crest of one wave always meets a trough of the other (destructive interference), nodes are formed and the string remains motionless.

This leads to the familiar appearance of plucked guitar strings (Figure 4-8). Since the eye sees no horizontal movement of crests or troughs along the string, only up-and-down vibrations in place, we call these **standing waves.** Actually, two interfering waves are continuously moving across the string; it is only the locations of the nodes and antinodes that remain stationary.

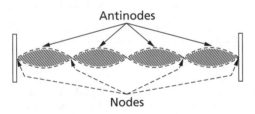

Figure 4-8. A plucked guitar string showing standing waves.

Standing waves are produced whenever two waves of the same frequency and amplitude travel in opposite directions in the same medium. As in the case of the guitar string, they are most often produced by the reflection of a wave at a fixed boundary.

Resonance Most objects have a natural frequency of vibration. If struck, they respond by vibrating at a particular frequency. When an object is disturbed by a wave whose frequency is the same as its natural vibration frequency, the amplitude of vibration of the object continues to increase. This phenomena is called **resonance.** For

example, a tuning fork vibrating at its natural frequency in the vicinity of an *identical* tuning fork induces the second tuning fork to vibrate and produce sound waves of the same frequency. The amplitude of the induced sound waves increases until the waves from both tuning forks have equal amplitudes.

QUESTIONS

46. Which point on the wave shown in the diagram is 180° out of phase with point *P*? (1) 1 (2) 2 (3) 3 (4) 4

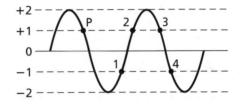

47. Which two points on the wave diagram are in phase? (1) *A* and *E* (2) *D* and *F* (3) *C* and *E* (4) *B* and *F*

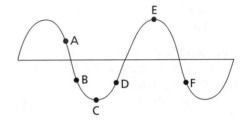

Base your answers to questions 48 through 52 on the following diagram which represents a transverse wave.

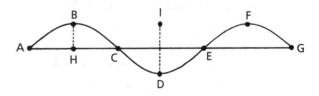

48. Which two points are in phase? (1) *A* and *C* (2) *B* and *D* (3) *C* and *E* (4) *B* and *F*

49. The amplitude of the wave is the distance between points (1) *A* and *C* (2) *A* and *E* (3) *B* and *H* (4) *I* and *D*

50. How many cycles are shown in the diagram? (1) 1 (2) 2 (3) 3 (4) 1.5

51. A wavelength is the distance between points (1) *A* and *C* (2) *A* and *E* (3) *B* and *H* (4) *I* and *D*

52. If the period of the wave is 2 seconds, its frequency is (1) 0.5 cycle/sec (2) 2.5 cycles/sec (3) 3.0 cycles/sec (4) 1.5 cycles/sec

53. As the phase difference between two interfering waves changes from 0° to 180°, the amplitude of the resultant wave (1) decreases (2) increases (3) remains the same

Base your answers to questions 54 through 58 on the following diagram which represents a vibrating string with a periodic wave originating at *A* and moving to *G*, a distance of 6.0 meters.

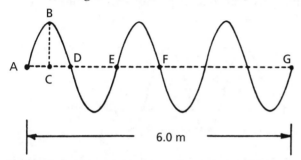

54. What type of wave is represented by the diagram? (1) elliptical (2) longitudinal (3) torsional (4) transverse

55. What is the wavelength of this wave? (1) 1.0 m (2) 2.0 m (3) 3.0 m (4) 6.0 m

56. Which phenomenon would occur if the waves were reflected at *G* and returned back to *A* through the oncoming waves? (1) diffraction (2) dispersion (3) standing waves (4) Doppler effect

57. As the wave moves toward *G*, point *E* on the string will move (1) to the left and then to the right (2) vertically down and then vertically up (3) diagonally down and then diagonally up (4) diagonally up and then diagonally down

58. If the waves were produced at a faster rate, the distance between points *D* and *E* would (1) decrease (2) increase (3) remain the same

59. Which pair of moving pulses in a rope will produce destructive interference?

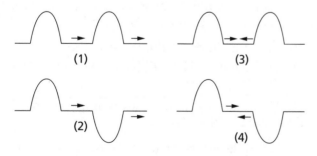

60. Which pair of waves will produce a resultant wave with the smallest amplitude?

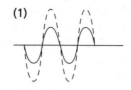

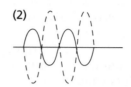

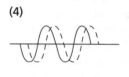

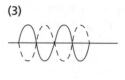

61. The diagram at the right shows a rope with two waves moving along it in the directions shown. What will be the resultant wave pattern at the instant when the maximum displacement of both pulses is at point *O* on the rope?

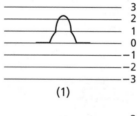

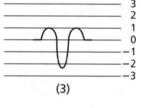

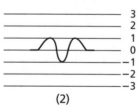

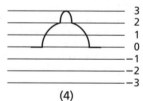

62. The diagram at the right shows two pulses traveling in opposite directions through a transmitting medium. Which diagram best represents the resulting pulse when the pulses combine at point *P*?

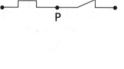

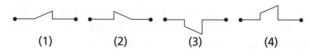

63. The following diagrams show four waves that pass simultaneously through a region. Which two waves will produce maximum constructive interference if they are combined? (1) *A* and *C* (2) *A* and *B* (3) *B* and *C* (4) *C* and *D*

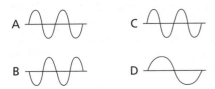

64. Standing waves may be produced in the same medium if (1) the wavelength of one wave is half that of the other (2) two waves travel in the same direction (3) two waves travel in opposite directions and then back toward each other (4) the frequency of one wave is three times that of the other

65. A tuning fork that vibrates at a frequency of 100 Hz can produce resonance in a fork having which of the following frequencies? (1) 100 Hz (2) 200 Hz (3) 300 Hz (4) all of these

Thinking and Analyzing

66. Describe the principle of superposition in your own words.

67. Two waves traveling parallel to each other overlap in a body of water, in phase with each other. The amplitude of one wave is 3.0 cm, the amplitude of the other is 1.0 cm. Both have a wavelength of 2.0 cm. Construct to scale two complete cycles of the resultant wave in the water. Do the same for the case where two waves overlap in opposite phases.

68. The figure below illustrates two overlapping coherent waves in a body of water. Their sources S_1 and S_2 are at the locations shown. The semicircular lines in the figure are the crests; midway between these lines are the troughs. Point A is equidistant from both sources, located at a distance of three wavelengths from each source.

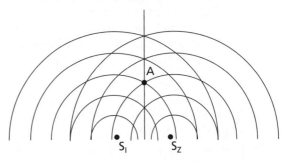

Trace the figure onto a sheet of paper. Then locate and label the following points: (B) on the central maximum, 5 wavelengths from each source, (C) a point of maximum destructive interference on the first nodal line, (D) a point of maximum constructive interference on the second antinodal line, (E) a point where crest meets crest and the difference in distance to the two sources is one wavelength, (F) a point where crest meets trough and the difference in distance to the two sources is two and a half wavelengths.

69. What conditions lead to the production of standing waves?

70. Explain the phenomena of resonance.

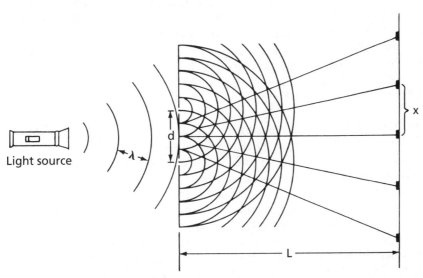

Figure 4-9. Interference pattern generated by light passing through two narrow slits.

The Wave Nature of Light

Light is an electromagnetic radiation that can produce the sensation of sight. Much of the behavior of light can be interpreted in terms of wave phenomena.

The Double-Slit Experiment

In a famous experiment, Thomas Young passed light through two slits cut into an opaque screen (Figure 4-9, p. 113). The light produced a pattern of many bright bands, separated by dark bands, on another screen behind the slits. How could as many as twenty bands of light result from only two slits?

Interference Pattern

Young explained this phenomenon by postulating that light is a wave. When the light wave arrives at the wall with the slits, the part of every successive wave front that passes through the slits act as a new source of waves. This produces a whole set of semicircles of crests and troughs that spread out behind each slit (Figure 4-9). This behavior is characteristic of waves of all types and is summarized by *Huygen's Principle—every point on a wave front acts as a source of waves with the same speed*. A water wave passing through a slit in a wall, for example, also produces a set of crests and troughs that expand in all directions behind the slit.

Since the light that approaches the two slits comes from one source, the slits act as sources of **coherent light waves**—waves of the same frequency that are produced by sources in phase. When a crest arrives at one slit, a crest arrives at the other. Thus, behind the wall with the slits, there are two overlapping coherent waves. This leads to the alternating columns of constructive and destructive interference we described earlier for two overlapping water waves. Where a column of constructive interference meets the screen, a band of light appears. Where a column of destructive interference meets the screen a dark spot appears because the two light waves destroy each other.

The pattern of bright and dark bands on the screen reveals the arrangement of the alternating lines of constructive and destructive interference. It is thus referred to as an **interference pattern.** The bands are of equal width and are equally spaced apart from each other.

The distance between two neighboring bands of light, x, and the distance between the wall and the screen, L, are related to the distance between the slits, d, and the wavelength of the light, λ, by the formula

$$\frac{\lambda}{d} = \frac{x}{L}$$

Speed of Light

Experiments have shown that the speed of light in a vacuum is 3.00×10^8 meters per second. This number is an important physical constant and is used in a wide variety of applications. It is the speed of all colors of light in a vacuum irrespective of brightness or source. The speed of light is equal to the product of frequency and wavelength (as is the speed of any periodic wave). This relationship is represented by the formula $c = f\lambda$, where the letter c represents the speed of light, 3.00×10^8 m/s.

The speed of light in a material medium is dependent upon the frequency of the light and the nature of the medium. In media other than a vacuum, light travels at speeds slower than 3.00×10^8 m/s. The exact value of the speed of light differs from material to material, and within the same material it may be different for different colors. In glass, light travels at a rate equal to about two thirds its speed in a vacuum (with slight variations from color to color). Through air, on the other hand, the speed of light is only slightly slower than through a vacuum.

The Electromagnetic Spectrum

Light is but one member of a large family of waves that are electromagnetic in nature. Other members of the family (in order of increasing wavelength) include: gamma rays, X rays, ultraviolet, infrared, radar, and radio waves. All consist of electric and magnetic fields that propagate from place to place, with the strength and direction of these fields alternating in wavelike fashion. All electromagnetic waves are generated by accelerated charged particles.

The different types of electromagnetic waves make up the **electromagnetic spectrum.** They all travel through empty space at the speed of light (3.00×10^8 meters per second). They differ, however, in frequency and wavelength. As all waves must, they obey the formula $\lambda f = v$. Since they all travel at the same rate, we know that their wavelengths (λ) and frequencies (f) are inversely proportional.

Figure 4-10 shows the different types of electromagnetic waves, in order of decreasing wavelength and increasing frequency. Each wave type represents a range of frequencies and wavelengths.

The pure colors of light—red, orange, yellow, green, blue, and violet—differ from each other in frequency and wavelength, with red having the longest wavelength and smallest frequency and violet the shortest wavelength and greatest frequency. Wavelengths shorter than that of violet and longer than that of red cannot be sensed by the human eye and are invisible. This is why we cannot see X rays or radio waves. Colors other

Frequency (cyc es per second)

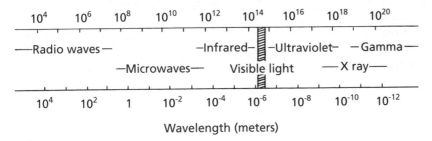

Figure 4-10. The electromagnetic spectrum.

than those listed (including white) are produced by mixtures of light waves of different wavelengths (the pure colors), with each mixture producing a unique sensation in the eye and a unique color.

Polarization of Light   Transverse waves, whose disturbances are perpendicular to the direction of motion of the wave, can be **polarized.** That is, a particular plane may be selected for the back-and-forth vibration, to the exclusion of all other possible planes. The crests and troughs in a rope, for example, can be made to point "up and down" in the plane of this page, "in or out" perpendicularly to the page, or in some in-between plane. Longitudinal waves, on the other hand, cannot be polarized since their disturbances are parallel to the direction of wave motion.

Experiments have determined that light can be polarized. Certain filters (**polaroids**) allow only waves vibrating in one particular plane to pass through them; all others are blocked. This could occur only if light were a transverse wave.

Diffraction   Light passing through a single slit produces a pattern of bright and dark bands on a screen behind the slit. This pattern, however, is different from that produced by two slits. Directly opposite the slit appears a wide, bright band known as the **central maximum.** On either side of this dominant band of light appear much narrower and fainter bands separated by areas of darkness (Figure 4-11). This is known as a **diffraction** pattern. A graph of the light intensity versus position on the screen is also shown.

Diffraction results from interference. Since the slit opening must have some size, the part of the wave front that passes through the slit is not a single point but a collection of points. Each point in this collection acts as a source of expanding waves, in accordance with Huygen's Principle. We thus have, behind the slit, many overlapping waves that interfere with each other, in some places constructively, in others destructively. The

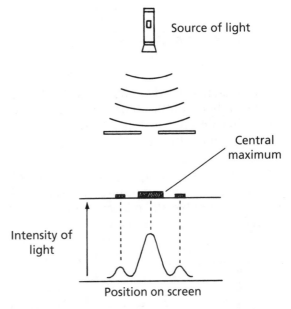

Figure 4-11. Diffraction pattern with graph of light intensity versus position.

bright and dark bands on the screen reveal the arrangement of the areas of constructive and destructive interference.

With the unaided eye, the fainter and narrower bands on either side of the central maximum cannot be detected. Instead, we see the dominant central maximum with what appears to be fuzzy boundaries. Since the width of the central maximum grows with distance from the slit, it appears as if light spreads out upon passing through an opening or behind an obstruction. Thus diffraction is also defined as the spreading of light behind an obstacle.

QUESTIONS

71. The pattern of bright and dark bands observed when monochromatic light passes though two narrow slits is due to (1) polarization (2) reflection (3) refraction (4) interference

Base your answer to question 72 on the following diagram. The diagram represents two parallel slits 2.0×10^{-4} meter apart which are illuminated by parallel rays of monochromatic light of wavelength 6.0×10^{-7} meter. The interference pattern is formed on a screen 2.0 meters from the slits.

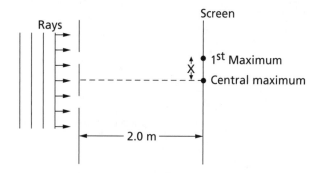

72. If the distance between the slits is decreased, the distance between the central maximum and the first maximum will (1) decrease (2) increase (3) remain the same

Base your answer to question 73 on the following diagram which represents red light incident upon a double-slit barrier, producing an interference pattern on a screen.

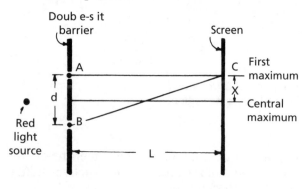

73. Which diagram best describes the pattern observed on the screen?

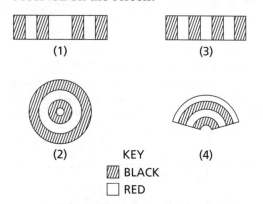

Base your answers to questions 74 through 76 on the following diagram. An interference pattern is produced on screen B when light passes through the double slit in barrier A.

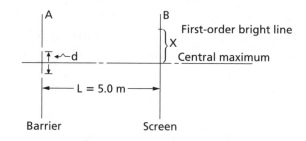

74. The pattern produced on the screen is the result of interference and (1) reflection (2) refraction (3) diffraction (4) polarization

75. Compared with the value of distance x for yellow light, the value of distance x for blue light will be (1) less (2) greater (3) the same

76. As the screen is brought closer to the double slit, the value of distance x will (1) decrease (2) increase (3) remain the same

77. Which formula represents a constant for light waves of different frequencies in a vacuum? (1) $f\lambda$ (2) f/λ (3) λ/f (4) $f + \lambda$

78. All electromagnetic waves have the same speed in (1) water (2) flint glass (3) alcohol (4) a vacuum

79. Compared with the speed of light in a material medium, the speed of light in a vacuum is (1) less (2) greater (3) the same

80. Which is *not* in the electromagnetic spectrum? (1) light waves (2) radio waves (3) sound waves (4) X-rays

81. In a vacuum, all electromagnetic waves have the same (1) frequency (2) wavelength (3) speed (4) energy

82. Which characterizes a polarized wave? (1) transverse and vibrating in one plane (2) transverse and vibrating in all directions (3) circular and vibrating at random (4) longitudinal and vibrating at random

83. Whether or not a wave is longitudinal or transverse may be determined by its ability to be (1) diffracted (2) reflected (3) polarized (4) refracted

84. Which diagram best illustrates the diffraction of waves?

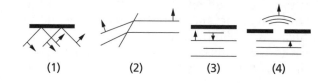

Base your answer to question 85 on the following information. Monochromatic light passes through a single narrow slit forming a diffraction pattern on a screen.

85. Which graph best represents the light intensity of the single-slit diffraction pattern for monochromatic light?

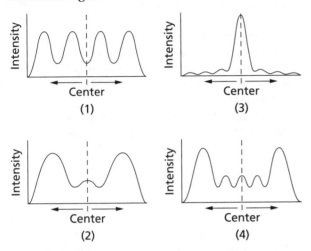

(1)   (3)

(2)   (4)

86. Which wave phenomenon is represented by the diagram?   (1) Doppler effect   (2) dispersion   (3) diffraction   (4) refraction

87. A wave spreads into the region behind a barrier. This phenomenon is called   (1) diffraction   (2) reflection   (3) refraction   (4) interference

Thinking and Analyzing

88. Describe two phenomena that would encourage you to adopt the wave view of light. Explain why the particulate view is inadequate to account for the data provided by these phenomena.

89. What causes a pattern of bright and dark bands to appear when light passes through a narrow slit?

90. How far will light travel in a vacuum in 10. s?

91. List the groups of waves in the electromagnetic spectrum in order of increasing frequency.

92. A microwave has a wavelength of 2.0 m. What is the frequency of the wave?

93. Is the pattern of light produced by double slits the same as that produced by a single slit? Explain.

94. How does the width of the central maximum change if the distance from the slit is decreased?

THE BEHAVIOR OF LIGHT

Reflection

The Law of Reflection   Light that is reflected off a surface obeys the *Law of Reflection: the angle of incidence is equal to the angle of reflection.* The **angle of incidence,** θ_i, is defined as the angle between the incident ray and a line normal (perpendicular) to the surface (Figure 4-12). The **angle of reflection,** θ_r, is defined as the angle between the normal and the reflected ray. The Law of Reflection says that $\theta_i = \theta_r$. If a ray of light strikes a surface at an angle of 40° from the normal, it will be reflected at an angle of 40° from the normal on the opposite side. The incident ray, the reflected ray, and the normal all lie in the same plane.

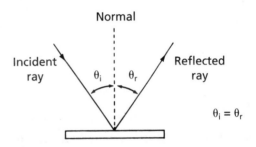

Figure 4-12. The Law of Reflection.

Regular Reflection   In real life a light source typically emits a multitude of rays in different directions. The law of reflection applies to every individual pencil-thin ray of light that strikes a surface (Figure 4-13). If the surface is smooth, all the reflected rays can be extended to one point

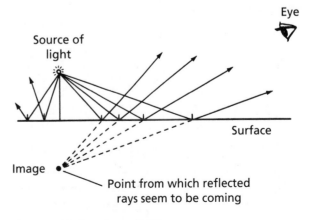

Figure 4-13. Regular reflection.

behind the surface as illustrated in Figure 4-13. To an eye intercepting a batch of these reflected rays, they all appear to emanate from that point. The point looks like the source of light. We say that the eye sees an image of the source behind the surface at that point.

Diffuse Reflection   If the rays emitted by a light source encounter a rough, irregular surface, the reflected rays are scattered in different directions, as shown in Figure 4-14. The reflected rays do not seem to be emanating from any one point and no image appears.

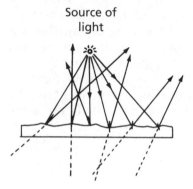

Figure 4-14. Diffuse reflection.

Refraction

The Law of Refraction   When light passes obliquely from one medium into another, it is **refracted,** or bent, at the boundary between the two media. The direction of this bending depends on the change in speed experienced by the light as it went from the first medium into the second medium. If the speed of light is slower in the second medium, as is the case when light passes from air into glass, the light bends toward the normal. In this case, the angle between the refracted ray and the normal (the **angle of refraction**) is smaller than the angle of incidence (Figure 4-15a). On the other hand, if the speed of

light is greater in the second medium, as is the case when light passes from water to air, the light bends away from the normal. In this case, the angle of refraction is greater than the angle of incidence (Figure 4-15b). If light strikes a boundary between two media perpendicularly, that is, along the normal, no bending takes place and the light passes straight through.

The Absolute Index of Refraction   The amount of bending of light, whether toward or away from the normal, depends on the ratio of the speed of light in the first medium to that in the second medium.

The **absolute index of refraction,** n, of a medium is defined as the ratio of the speed of light in vacuum (c) to the speed of light in the medium (v). This is expressed by the equation

$$n = \frac{c}{v}$$

Since the speed of light varies in different media, it follows that different substances have different absolute indices of refraction. The absolute index of refraction of vacuum is 1.00. Since light travels slower in all material media than it does through vacuum, all substances have absolute indices of refraction greater than 1.00. The absolute index of refraction of air is only slightly greater than 1.00, since the speed of light in air is only slightly less than in vacuum. A table of n values for several substances appear in an appendix to this book.

Sample Problem

3. The speed of yellow light in crown glass is 1.97×10^8 m/s. What is the absolute index of refraction of crown glass?
Solution:

$$n = \frac{c}{v}$$

$$= \frac{3.0 \times 10^8 \text{ m/s}}{1.97 \times 10^8 \text{ m/s}} = 1.52$$

Snell's Law   The angle of refraction for any given angle of incidence is found by using *Snell's Law:*

$$n_1 \sin \theta_1 = n_2 \sin \theta_2$$

where θ_1 is the angle of incidence, θ_2 is the angle of refraction, n_1 is the absolute index of refraction of the first medium, and n_2 is the absolute index of refraction of the second medium.

Snell's law can also be expressed in terms of the velocities of light in the two media, as follows:

$$\frac{\sin \theta_1}{\sin \theta_2} = \frac{v_1}{v_2}$$

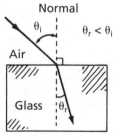

a. Light traveling from air into glass

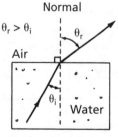

b. Light traveling from water into air

Figure 4-15. Laws of refraction.

where v_1 is the speed of light in the first medium and v_2 is the speed of light in the second medium.

Note that for any two substances, the ratio n_2/n_1 is equal to v_1/v_2. This ratio is referred to as the **relative index of refraction** of the particular pair and order of media. Also note that

$$\frac{n_2}{n_1} = \frac{v_1}{v_2} = \frac{\lambda_1}{\lambda_2}$$

Sample Problem

4. A ray of light strikes crown glass at an angle of 30° from the normal. The absolute index of refraction of crown glass is 1.52, and the speed of light in the glass is 1.97×10^8 m/s. What is the angle of refraction?

Solution:

Method 1

$$n_1 \sin \theta_1 = n_2 \sin \theta_2$$

$$(1.00)(\sin 30°) = (1.52)(\sin \theta_2)$$

$$\sin \theta_2 = \frac{.50}{1.52} = .33$$

$$\theta_2 = 19°$$

Method 2

$$\frac{\sin \theta_1}{\sin \theta_2} = \frac{v_1}{v_2}$$

$$\frac{\sin 30°}{\sin \theta_2} = \frac{3.00 \times 10^8 \text{ m/s}}{1.97 \times 10^8 \text{ m/s}}$$

$$\frac{.50}{\sin \theta_2} = 1.52$$

$$\sin \theta_2 = .33$$

$$\theta_2 = 19°$$

Critical Angle When light crosses a boundary and its speed is greater in the second medium, the Law of Refraction states that it bends away from the normal. The angle of refraction is then greater than the angle of incidence. Therefore, at such boundaries, there exists an angle of incidence for which the corresponding angle of refraction is 90°. At this angle of incidence, called the **critical angle,** θ_c, the ray emerges parallel to the boundary (Figure 4-16).

Critical angles do not exist when the speed of light is slower in the second medium. The light then bends toward the normal and away from the boundary.

Total Internal Reflection The critical angle is the largest angle of incidence for which Snell's law

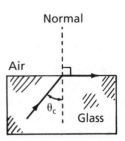

Figure 4-16. Critical angle.

works when light crosses a boundary where its speed is greater in the second medium. For all angles of incidence greater than the critical angle, no refraction occurs and the light does not enter the second medium. Instead, the rays are reflected back into the first medium, obeying the Law of Reflection (Figure 4-17). This phenomenon is known as **total internal reflection.**

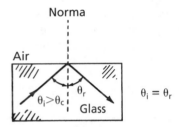

Figure 4-17. Total internal reflection.

For example, consider a ray of light that strikes perpendicularly into a 45°-45°-90° glass prism (Figure 4-18). No refraction occurs at the first boundary (into the glass) since the light strikes that boundary perpendicularly. The light continues straight into the glass and approaches the opposite boundary, on the way out of the glass, with an angle of incidence of 45 degrees. This is larger than the critical angle of glass-to-air which is 42 degrees. The light does not leave the prism but is internally reflected. The angle of reflection is equal to the angle of incidence, and the

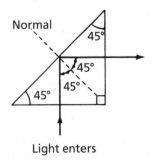

Figure 4-18. A ray of light strikes a 45°-45°-90° prism perpendicularly.

light is reflected 45 degrees from, and on the other side of, the normal.

Dispersion White light is **polychromatic.** It consists of waves of different colors and frequencies. In some media, called **dispersive media,** waves of different frequency travel at different speeds. Since the amount of refraction at a boundary depends on the ratio of the speed of light in the first medium to that in the second medium, it follows that at some boundaries different colors undergo different amounts of bending and have different absolute indices of refraction. When white light passes obliquely into a dispersive medium, each of the different colors and frequencies in the mixture undergoes a different amount of bending. The net result is that the colors are separated, or **dispersed,** by the dispersive medium.

Both glass and water are dispersive media for light. A ray of white light passing through glass emerges not as a single ray of white, but as separate rays of red, orange, yellow, green, blue, and violet. The red is refracted the least while the violet is refracted the most (Figure 4-19).

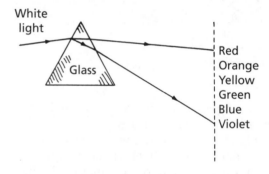

Figure 4-19. Dispersion.

A **nondispersive medium** is one in which the speed of the wave does not depend on the frequency. A vacuum is nondispersive for light.

QUESTIONS

95. Which phenomenon of light is illustrated by the diagram below? (1) regular reflection (2) diffuse reflection (3) diffraction (4) refraction

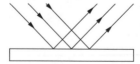

96. Which of the diagrams representing light rays reflecting from a surface illustrates diffuse reflection?

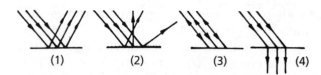

97. The change in the direction of a wave when it passes obliquely from one medium to another is called (1) diffraction (2) interference (3) refraction (4) superposition

98. When a light ray passes from medium 1 to medium 2, its speed decreases. Which arrow best represents the path of the ray in medium 2? (1) 1 (2) 2 (3) 3 (4) 4

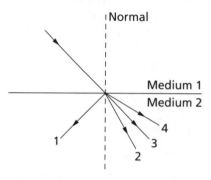

99. Which arrow best represents the path that a monochromatic ray of light will travel as it passes through air, corn oil, glycerol, and back to air?

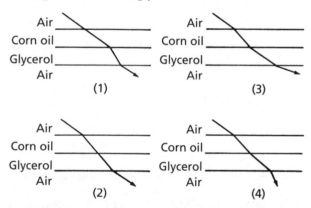

100. The diagram at the right represents a wave traveling from medium 1 to medium 2. The relative index of refraction may be determined by calculating the ratio of

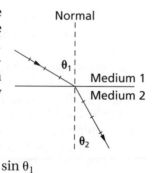

(1) $\dfrac{\theta_1}{\theta_2}$ (3) $\dfrac{\sin \theta_1}{\sin \theta_2}$

(2) $\dfrac{\sin \theta_2}{\sin \theta_1}$ (4) $\dfrac{n_1}{n_2}$

Base your answers to questions 101 through 103 on the following diagram which represents a ray of monochromatic light incident upon the surface of plate X. The values of n in the diagram represent absolute indices of refraction.

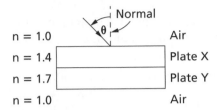

101. The speed of the light ray in plate X is approximately (1) 1.8×10^8 m/sec (2) 2.1×10^8 m/sec (3) 2.5×10^8 m/sec (4) 2.9×10^8 m/sec

102. Compared with angle θ, the angle of refraction of the light ray in plate X is (1) smaller (2) greater (3) the same

103. Compared with angle θ, the angle of refraction of the ray emerging from plate Y into the air will be (1) smaller (2) greater (3) the same

104. Which wave phenomenon could *not* be demonstrated with a single wave pulse? (1) a standing wave (2) diffraction (3) reflection (4) refraction

105. In the following diagram, ray AB is incident on surface XY at point B. If medium 2 has a lower index of refraction than medium 1, through which point will the ray most likely pass? (1) E (2) F (3) C (4) D

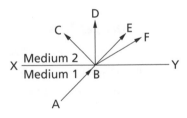

106. For a given angle of incidence, the greatest change in the direction of a light ray will be produced when the light ray passes obliquely from air into (1) Lucite (2) glycerol (3) alcohol (4) flint glass

107. When a wave enters a medium of higher refractive index, its velocity (1) decreases (2) increases (3) remains the same

108. A ray of light traveling through water strikes a water-air surface with an angle of incidence equal to the critical angle. What will be the angle of refraction? (1) 180° (2) 90° (3) 45° (4) 30°

Base your answers to questions 109 through 113 on the following diagram which represents a ray of monochromate violet light waves ($\lambda = 4.0 \times 10^{-7}$ m) passing from air through Lucite and then into air again.

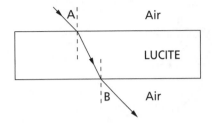

109. The frequency of these light waves in air, in hertz (cycles per second), is (1) 7.5×10^{14} (2) 1.3×10^{-14} (3) 7.5×10^{-14} (4) 1.3×10^{-14}

110. The apparent wavelength of these light waves in Lucite is (1) 6.0×10^{-7} m (2) 2.7×10^{-7} m (3) 6.4×10^{-7} m (4) 4.0×10^{-7} m

111. Compared with the speed of the violet light in air, the speed of the violet light in Lucite is (1) less (2) greater (3) the same

112. Compared with the frequency of waves of violet light in air, the frequency of waves of violet light in Lucite is (1) less (2) greater (3) the same

113. Compared with angle A, angle B is (1) smaller (2) larger (3) the same

114. The speed of light in corn oil is the same as the speed of light in (1) diamond (2) flint glass (3) air (4) glycerol

115. If the speed of light in a medium is 2.0×10^8 meters per second, the index of refraction for the medium is (1) 1.0 (2) 2.0 (3) 1.5 (4) 0.67

116. The diagram at the right shows a light ray incident on the boundary between two media. Total internal reflection may occur when the index of refraction of medium Y is (1) less than the index of refraction of X

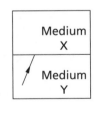

(2) greater than the index of refraction of X (3) equal to the index of refraction of X

117. In which diagram is angle θ a critical angle?

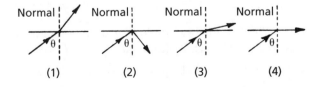

118. The following diagram shows a ray of light (*R*) incident upon a surface at an angle greater than the critical angle. Through which point is the ray most likely to pass? (1) *A* (2) *B* (3) *C* (4) *D*

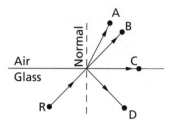

119. The following diagram represents a light ray traveling from crown glass into air. The position of the light source is changed to vary the angle θ. As θ approaches the critical angle, the angle of refraction approaches (1) 0° (2) 41° (3) 90° (4) 55°

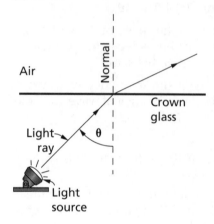

Base your answers to questions 120 through 125 on the following diagram. The diagram shows two light rays originating from source *S* in medium *y*. The dashed line represents a normal to each surface.

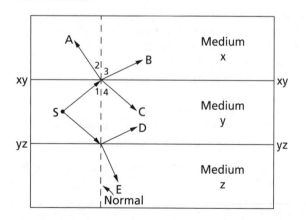

120. Which light ray would *not* be produced in this situation? (1) *A* (2) *B* (3) *C* (4) *E*

121. A reflected light ray is ray (1) *A* (2) *B* (3) *C* (4) *E*

122. Which two angles must be equal? (1) 1 and 2 (2) 2 and 3 (3) 3 and 4 (4) 1 and 4

123. Light originating from source *S* could produce total internal reflection at (1) surface *yz*, only (2) surface *xy*, only (3) neither surface *xy* nor *yz*

124. Compared with the speed of light in medium *x*, the speed of light in medium *z* is (1) less (2) greater (3) the same

125. Which phrase best describes the phenomenon illustrated by the following diagram? (1) scattering and diffraction (2) reflection and interference (3) transmission and Doppler effect (4) refraction and dispersion

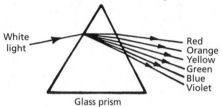

Glass prism

126. The separating of polychromatic light into its component frequencies as it passes through a prism is called (1) interference (2) diffraction (3) diffusion (4) dispersion

127. A medium in which waves of different frequencies travel at different speeds and may be separated is called (1) a dispersive medium (2) a nondispersive medium (3) an inelastic medium (4) a coherent medium

128. Compared with the speed of light in a vacuum, the speed of light in a dispersive medium is (1) less (2) greater (3) the same

Thinking and Analyzing

129. Why does an image of the source appear behind the surface in regular reflection?

130. Does diffuse reflection produce an image? Explain.

131. Trace the figure below onto a sheet of paper. Then draw the image of triangle ABC as seen by the observer on the opposite side of the XY line, which corresponds to the reflecting surface.

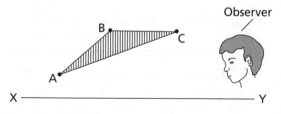

132. Sketch a diagram to illustrate, via the reflection, that a full-length plane mirror need be only

one half as tall as the object in front of it. Show that this is true for any distance between the object and the plane mirror.

133. A ray of light strikes the midpoint of one of the legs of a 45-45-90 degree triangular prism made of crown glass, as illustrated below. The ray strikes along the normal to the surface. Accurately sketch the path of the ray all the way through the prism. Provide the values of all angles formed between the ray and the surfaces it encounters.

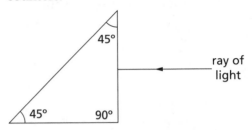

134. Repeat question 133 for a ray of light that strikes a semicircular slab of crown glass, as illustrated below. The ray strikes at the center of the circle, at an angle of 30 degrees from the surface of the glass.

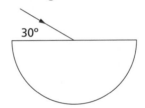

135. Under what conditions will a ray of light pass straight through the boundary between two media?

136. Draw the path of a ray of light striking an air-glass boundary at an angle of 40 degrees from the surface of the glass. Then draw the reflected ray and the transmitted ray in the appropriate direction.

137. Determine the index of refraction of medium (2) in the diagram below if medium (1) is air.

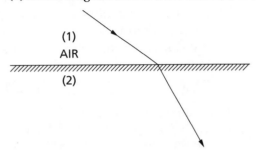

138. Given what you know about refraction, explain the phenomenon of dispersion. Why and under what circumstances does it occur? What characteristic of a medium determines whether it is dispersive or nondispersive?

Reading Comprehension

Seismic Waves

When you think of waves you might think of waves on a rope or waves in a body of water. You may even imagine sound or light waves. But there are other types of waves that can travel through Earth and eventually cause changes on Earth's surface. These waves are called seismic waves, and they are produced by earthquakes.

An earthquake occurs when layers of rock beneath Earth's surface move as a result of built-up stress. The disturbance during this motion travels in the form of waves that spread out in every direction from the point where the earthquake occurs, known as the focus.

There are three general types of seismic waves: primary waves, secondary waves, and surface waves. Primary waves, or P waves, are longitudinal waves.

(continued)

P waves travel faster than secondary or surface waves and are therefore detected before the others. The medium for these waves is rock, which experiences compressions and rarefactions much like air does as a sound wave travels through it.

Secondary, or S waves, are transverse waves. S waves vibrate from side to side and push the ground back and forth or up and down. As a result, they shake structures on Earth's surface. Unlike P waves, S waves cannot travel through liquids. Therefore, S waves cannot travel through Earth's liquid core to the opposite side of the planet.

Surface waves are sometimes formed when P waves and S waves reach Earth's surface. These waves are a combination of longitudinal and transverse waves. They move in an almost circular pattern along the surface. Although surface waves travel more slowly than either P waves or S waves, they are responsible for the most severe ground movements during an earthquake.

QUESTIONS

1. Compare and contrast primary, secondary, and seismic waves.
2. A seismograph is a device that detects seismic waves. Explain what characteristic of the waves is related to the amount of energy carried by the wave.
3. Which is the only type of seismic wave that can travel through Earth's core? Explain.
4. In what order do the three different types of earthquake waves arrive at any point removed some distance from the center of the quake?
5. Which type of wave is the cause of the most severe shaking of buildings during an earthquake?

Enrichment   Wave Phenomena

DOUBLE-SLIT INTERFERENCE PATTERN

When coherent light waves pass through two slits in a barrier on their way to a screen, a pattern of bright and dark bands forms on the screen. The bands are equally spaced and of the same width. This pattern is the result of alternating lines of constructive and destructive interference.

The distance between two adjacent bands of light, x, and the distance between the barrier and the screen, L, are related to the distance between the slits, d, and the wavelength of the light, λ by the formula

$$\frac{\lambda}{d} = \frac{x}{L}$$

When using this relationship, you must take care to express all distances in the same unit of length, for example, the meter. (See Figure 4-9 on page 113.)

Sample Problem

5. A beam of red light is made to pass through two slits that are 4.0×10^{-3} m apart. On a screen 1.0 meter distant from the slits an interference pattern appears with bands of light separated by 1.8×10^{-4} m. What is the wavelength of the light?

Solution:

$$\frac{\lambda}{d} = \frac{x}{L}$$

$$\frac{\lambda}{4.0 \times 10^{-3}\,\text{m}} = \frac{1.8 \times 10^{-4}\,\text{m}}{1.0\,\text{m}}$$

$$\lambda = 7.2 \times 10^{-7}\,\text{m}$$

In doing this experiment it has been found that the spacing between the bands, x, is different for different colors of light. This can only mean that the wavelength, λ, is different for different colors.

Calculating the Critical Angle

Calculating the Critical Angle When light crosses a boundary and its speed is greater in the second medium, the Law of Refraction states that it bends away from the normal. The angle of refraction is then greater than the angle of incidence. Therefore, at such boundaries, there exists an angle of incidence for which the corresponding angle of refraction is 90°. At this angle of incidence, called the **critical angle**, θ_c, the ray emerges parallel to the boundary (Figure 4-16 on page 119). The value of θ_c depends on the absolute indices of refraction of the two media and is therefore different for different media. If the first medium is some material and the second is vacuum (or air), the value of θ_c is given by the formula

$$\sin \theta_c = \frac{1}{n}$$

where n is the absolute index of refraction of the first medium.

Sample Problem

6. What is the critical angle when light passes from diamond to air? (The absolute index of refraction of diamond is 2.42.)

Solution:

$$\sin \theta_c = \frac{1}{n} = \frac{1}{2.42} = .41$$

$$\theta_c = 24°$$

QUESTIONS

Base your answer to question 139 on the following diagram which shows light from a monochromatic source incident on a screen after passing through a double slit.

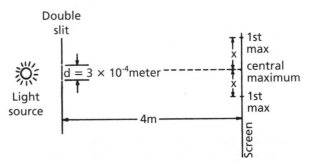

139. What is the wavelength of the light source if the distance between the central light band and the next light band is 0.01 meter? (1) 6.7×10^5 m (2) 8.3 m (3) 3.3×10^{-1} m (4) 7.5×10^{-7} m

Base your answers to questions 140 through 144 on the following diagram. The diagram represents two parallel slits 2.0×10^{-4} meter apart which are illuminated by parallel rays of monochromatic light of wavelength 6.0×10^{-7} meter. The interference pattern is formed on a screen 2.0 meters from the slits.

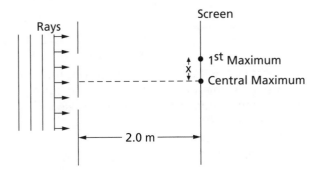

140. Distance x is (1) 6.0×10^{-3} m (2) 6.0×10^{-7} m (3) 3.0×10^{-3} m (4) 3.0 m

141. The difference in path length for the light from each of the two slits to the first maximum is (1) λ (2) 2λ (3) $\lambda/2$ (4) 0

142. If the wavelength of the light passing through the slits is doubled, the distance from the central maximum to the first maximum will (1) decrease (2) increase (3) remain the same

143. If the screen is moved closer to the slits, the distance between the central maximum and the first maximum will (1) decrease (2) increase (3) remain the same

144. If the distance between the slits is decreased, the distance between the central maximum and the first maximum will (1) decrease (2) increase (3) remain the same

Base your answer to question 145 on the following diagram which represents monochromatic light incident upon a double slit in barrier A, producing an interference pattern on screen B.

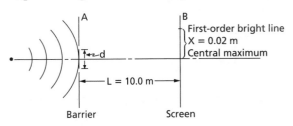

145. If $x = 0.02$ meter, $L = 10.0$ meters, and the wavelength of the incident light is 5.0×10^{-7} meter, the distance d between the slits is (1) 2.5×10^{-4} m (2) 2.0×10^{-2} m (3) 2.5×10^{-2} m (4) 4.0×10^{-5} m

146. What is the sine of the critical angle for the light ray at the boundary between plate Y and the air? (1) 1.0 (2) 0.83 (3) 0.71 (4) 0.59

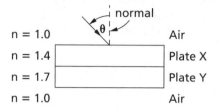

147. Light ($\lambda = 5.9 \times 10^{-7}$ meter) travels through a solution. If the absolute index of refraction of the solution is increased, the critical angle will

(1) decrease
(2) increase
(3) remain the same

GEOMETRIC OPTICS

Plane Surfaces

We learned earlier (p. 117) that rays of light from a point-source that are reflected off a smooth surface appear to emanate from a single point behind the surface. As a result, the eye is led to see an image of the source behind the surface. Since the image is not produced by rays of light actually coming to a point, but merely seem to be coming from a point, we label it a **virtual image.**

Careful study of Figure 4-20 reveals that the distance between the source of light and the surface (the **object distance, d_o**) is equal to the distance between the surface and the image (the **image distance, d_i**). These distances are measured along the line that connects the object (the source) and the image. That line is perpendicular to the surface.

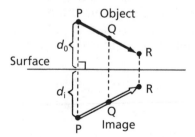

Figure 4-20. Reflection from a plane surface creates a virtual image.

If the source is not a mere point of light but an extended object, an image is formed of the entire object. The image is erect, reversed, equal in size to that of the object, and appears as far behind the surface as the corresponding part of the object is in front of the surface (Figure 4-20). We see this every time we look at ourselves in a plane mirror.

Converging Lenses

A lens that is thicker in the middle than at the edges is said to be **convex** in shape. A line drawn perpendicularly to the plane of such a lens and through its center is referred to as the **principal axis** of the lens (Figure 4-21). A ray of light traveling along the principal axis is not refracted, because it enters and leaves the lens perpendicularly to its surfaces. Rays of light that pass through the center of the lens not along the principal axis are refracted, but emerge parallel to their original direction. If the lens is thin, however, these rays emerge, for all practical purposes, lined up with their original direction.

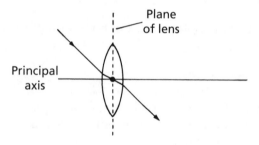

Figure 4-21. A convex lens.

If we apply the law of refraction to each of a group of rays that strike the lens parallel to the principal axis, we find that the lens acts to bring these rays together, to a point, on the other side of the lens. Convex lenses are therefore referred to as **converging lenses,** and the point where the incoming parallel rays meet is known as the **focal point** or **principal focus** of the lens. The focal point is situated on the principal axis (Figure 4-22). The distance between the center of the lens

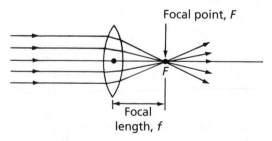

Figure 4-22. Light rays striking a convex lens parallel to the principal axis converge at the focal point.

and the focal point, called the **focal length** of the lens, depends upon the material the lens is made of, its size and curvature. It is, therefore, different for different lenses.

Real Images Rays of light that come from an object situated on one side of a convex lens and not too distant from it, do not, however, approach the lens parallel to each other. Ray 1 from the top of the object-source of light in Figure 4-23 happens to be traveling parallel to the principal axis and is refracted in such a way that it passes through the focal point, f, on the opposite side of the lens. But rays 2 and 3 that emanate from the same point are not parallel to the principal axis. They, too, are refracted by the lens, on their way in and again on the way out, but these refractions do not direct them to the focal point.

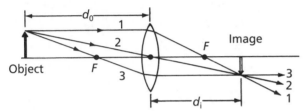

Figure 4-23. A convex lens with the object distance greater than the focal length.

Instead, all the rays coming from the top of the object-source are made to come together, by the action of the lens, at some point other than the focal point. The same happens to the rays that come from every other part of the object-source.

The points of convergence of rays from different parts of the object-source are arranged, near each other, in the same way that the object parts are arranged in the object. The net result is that a screen placed at the appropriate distance from the lens reveals a clear image of the entire object.

This phenomenon occurs when the object distance (the distance between the object and the center of the lens) is greater than the focal length. Since this image is created by the actual convergence of rays of light (unlike the image formed by plane mirrors) we call it a **real image.** Real images are always inverted.

Virtual Images When the object distance is less than the focal length, the refracted rays of light do not come together and cannot form a real image. Instead, they diverge as they emerge from the other side of the lens. However, to the eye it seems as if those rays are coming from one point. As a result, the eye sees a virtual image of the object on the same side of the lens as the object (Figure 4-24). Virtual images are always upright.

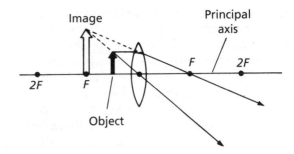

Figure 4-24. A convex lens with the object distance less than the focal length.

In the case of an object distance equal to the focal length, no image of any type is formed. Just as incoming parallel rays meet at the focal point, so rays coming from the focal point emerge from the lens parallel to each other. They neither converge to form a real image nor diverge to form a virtual image (Figure 4-25).

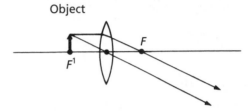

Figure 4-25.

Size and Location of Image The location of an image produced by a convex lens can be determined from the formula

$$\frac{1}{d_o} + \frac{1}{d_i} = \frac{1}{f}$$

where d_o is the object distance, d_i is the distance between the lens and the image (known as the image distance) and f is the focal length. All of these distances are measured from the center of the lens, along the principal axis. (Figure 4-23)

Once the position of the image is known, its size (length or width) can be determined from the formula

$$\frac{s_o}{s_i} = \frac{d_o}{d_i}$$

where s_o is the size of the object-source and s_i is the size of the image.

Alternatively, the size and location of the image can be determined by drawing a ray diagram. We start by placing the object-source on the principal axis. One ray is drawn from the top of the object parallel to the principal axis, and another from the top of the object through the center of the lens. The first ray emerges from the lens to pass through the focal point; the second goes straight through the lens. If the rays converge, the image is real and the top of the inverted image coincides with the point where the drawn rays meet (on the side of the lens opposite that of the object). If the rays diverge, the image is virtual and the top of the upright image coincides with the point where the divergent rays seem to be coming from (on the same side of the lens as the object). The image distance and size can then be determined by measurement. If the rays neither converge nor diverge, no image of any type is formed.

Sample Problems

7. An 8 cm tall object is situated 30 cm from a convex lens whose focal length is 10 cm. How far from the lens does an image of the object appear? How tall is the image?

Solution:

a. Formula method

Image distance

$$\frac{1}{d_o} + \frac{1}{d_i} = \frac{1}{f}$$

$$\frac{1}{30 \text{ cm}} + \frac{1}{d_i} = \frac{1}{10 \text{ cm}}$$

$$\frac{1}{d_i} = \frac{1}{10} - \frac{1}{30} = \frac{2}{30}$$

$$d_i = 15 \text{ cm}$$

Image size

$$\frac{s_o}{s_i} = \frac{d_o}{d_i}$$

$$\frac{8 \text{ cm}}{s_i} = \frac{30 \text{ cm}}{15 \text{ cm}}$$

$$s_i = 4 \text{ cm}$$

b. Ray diagram method (see Figure 4-26)

8. What is the **magnification** (ratio of image size to object size) of a magnifying glass (convex lens) whose focal length is 6 cm if an object is placed 2 cm behind it?

Solution:

$$\frac{1}{d_o} + \frac{1}{d_i} = \frac{1}{f}$$

$$\frac{1}{2}\text{cm} + \frac{1}{d_i} = \frac{1}{6}\text{cm}$$

$$\frac{1}{d_i} = \frac{1}{6} - \frac{1}{2} = \frac{-2}{6}$$

$$\frac{1}{d_i} = \frac{-1}{3}$$

$$d_i = -3 \text{ cm}$$

$$\frac{s_o}{s_i} = \frac{d_o}{|d_i|}$$

$$\frac{s_o}{s_i} = \frac{2}{|-3|} = \frac{2}{3}$$

$$\frac{s_i}{s_o} = \frac{3}{2} = 1.5$$

magnification is 1.5

Note: When the image distance is a negative number, a virtual image is formed. The absolute value of the image distance is then used in the formula

$$\frac{s_o}{s_i} = \frac{d_o}{d_i}.$$

The eye, camera, telescope, microscope, projector, and magnifying glass all make use of convex lenses.

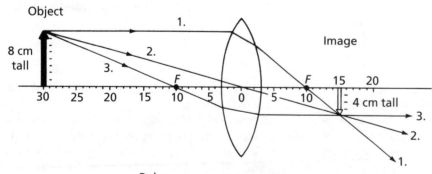

Rules
1. In parallel, out through *F*
2. In through center, out straight
3. In through *F*, out parallel

Figure 4-26.

Diverging Lenses

A lens that is thinner in the middle than at the edges is said to be **concave** in shape. If we apply the law of refraction to each of a group of rays that strike such a lens parallel to its principal axis, we find that the lens acts to separate the rays (Figure 4-27). Such lenses are therefore referred to as **diverging lenses.**

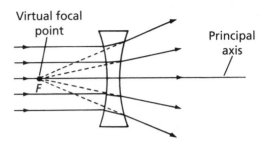

Figure 4-27. A concave lens.

The point where incident rays parallel to the principal axis appear to be coming from after they are refracted by a diverging lens is referred to as the **virtual focal point** of the lens. The distance between the virtual focal point and the center of the lens is the focal length. The formulas, definitions, and symbols introduced above for converging lenses are also applicable to diverging lenses. The only exception is that the focal length, f, of a concave lens is assigned a negative value. The procedures for drawing ray diagrams are analogous to those used with converging lenses.

Since diverging lenses do not bring rays of light together, they cannot form real images. However, an eye that intercepts the diverging rays sees them as coming from one point behind the lens. In this way, diverging lenses produce virtual images on the same side of the lens as the object. These images are erect and smaller than the object (Figure 4-28). Table 4-1 summarizes the information about lenses.

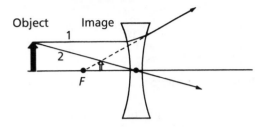

Rules
1. In parallel, out from F
2. In through center, out straight

Figure 4-28. Diverging lenses produce virtual images on the same side as the object.

Concave Mirrors

A small segment of a sphere with a reflecting surface on the inside of the sphere is called a **concave mirror.** The point that corresponds to the center of the sphere is called the **center of curvature** of the mirror. The distance between the center of curvature, C, and the mirror is known as the **radius of curvature,** R. The line that connects the center of curvature to the geometric center of the mirror is known as the **principal axis** of the mirror (Figure 4-29). Rays of light that pass through the center of curvature from any direction, including that of the principal axis, strike the mirror perpendicularly and are reflected perpendicularly back onto themselves (as dictated by the Law of Reflection).

Table 4-1. Summary Table of Lenses

	Object Distance	Real (inverted) Virtual (erect)	Image Size	Position of Image	Image Distance
Converging Lenses	Infinity	Real	much smaller	opposite	$d_i = f$
	$d_o > 2f$	Real	smaller	opposite	$d_i > f$ $d_i < 2f$
	$d_o = 2f$	Real	same	opposite	$d_i = 2f$
	d_o between f & $2f$	Real	larger	opposite	$d_i > 2f$
	$d_o = f$	no image	—	—	—
	$d_o < f$	Virtual	larger	same	d_i negative & $|d_i| > d_o$
Diverging Lenses	Any value	Virtual	smaller	same	d_i negative $|d_i| < d_o$ $|d_i| < |f|$

Note: when d_i is positive, image is on opposite side of lens and real; when d_i is negative, image is on the same side of the lens as the object and virtual.

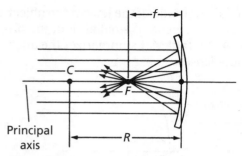

Figure 4-29. A concave mirror.

If we apply the Law of Reflection to each of a group of rays that strike the mirror parallel to the principal axis, we find that the mirror acts to converge those rays to a point. Concave mirrors are therefore called **converging mirrors,** and the point where the incident parallel rays meet is called the **focal point** or **principal focus** of the mirror. The focal point and the center of curvature are situated on the principal axis.

The distance between the focal point and the mirror (measured along the principal axis) is the **focal length**, f, of the mirror. This distance is different for different mirrors but is always equal to half the radius of curvature of the mirror ($f = \frac{1}{2} R$). The focal point is always found midway between the mirror and the center of curvature.

Images by Concave Mirrors

Rays of light that come from an object situated on the reflecting side of a concave mirror at distances greater than the focal length are made to converge at a point on the same side of the mirror as the object. That point is *not* the focal point, however, since these rays do not strike the mirror parallel to the principal axis. A real, inverted image of the object appears on a screen placed at the point of convergence (Figure 4-30).

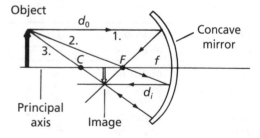

Rules
1. In parallel, out through F
2. In through F, out parallel
3. In through C, out through C

Figure 4-30. A real image produced by a concave mirror.

As in the case of lenses, the distance between the mirror and the image, d_i, is related to the distance between the mirror and the object, d_o, and the focal length, f, by the formula

$$\frac{1}{d_o} + \frac{1}{d_i} = \frac{1}{f}$$

The focal length is positive and can be replaced by $f = (\frac{1}{2})R$. Thus we obtain

$$\frac{1}{d_o} + \frac{1}{d_i} = \frac{2}{R}$$

The size of the image is related to the size of the object by the formula

$$\frac{s_o}{s_i} = \frac{d_o}{d_i}$$

All these distances are measured along the principal axis to the center of the reflecting surface. As in the case for lenses, the size and location of the image created by a mirror can also be found by drawing an appropriate ray diagram (Figure 4-30).

If the object-source of light is placed at the focal point ($d_o = f$), the reflected rays emerge parallel to each other, and no image is created; the formula yields no solution for d_i (Figure 4-31). This provides a mechanism for focusing all the rays of light emitted by a source in one direction, a technique that is widely used in searchlights and headlights.

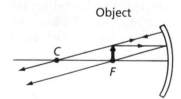

Figure 4-31.

If the object is placed closer to the mirror than the focal point ($d_o < f$), the reflected rays diverge, and no real image is created. Instead, the eye sees the diverging rays as coming from one point on the opposite side of the mirror. A virtual, upright image appears on the side of the mirror opposite that of the object. This is indicated by the negative value for d_i obtained by applying the formula

$$\frac{1}{d_o} + \frac{1}{d_i} = \frac{1}{f}$$

in such situations (Figure 4-32).

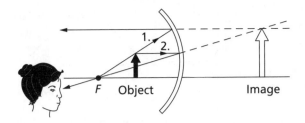

Rules
1. In from *F*, out parallel
2. In parallel, out through *F*

Figure 4-32. A virtual image formed by a concave mirror.

Convex Mirrors

A small segment of a sphere with a reflecting surface on the outside is called a **convex mirror.** If we apply the Law of Reflection to each of a group of rays that strike the mirror parallel to the principal axis, we find that the mirror acts to separate the rays. Convex mirrors are therefore called **diverging mirrors** (Figure 4-33).

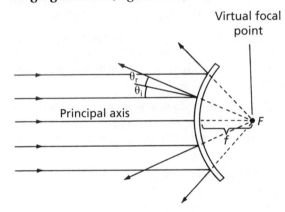

Figure 4-33. A convex mirror.

The point where the incident rays parallel to the principal axis seem to be coming from after being reflected by the mirror is the **virtual focal point** of the mirror. The distance between this point and the center of the diverging mirror is the **focal length** of the mirror. The formulas, definitions, and symbols described earlier for converging mirrors are also applicable to diverging mirrors, as are the procedures for drawing ray diagrams. The only exception is that the focal length, *f*, is negative for diverging mirrors.

Since diverging mirrors do not bring rays of light together, they cannot form real images. Instead, diverging mirrors create virtual images on the side of the mirror opposite that of the object. These images are erect and smaller than the object (Figure 4-34).

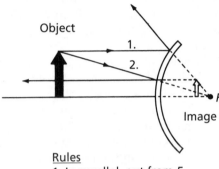

Rules
1. In parallel, out from *F*
2. In toward *F*, out parallel

Figure 4-34. Diverging mirrors create virtual images.

Diverging mirrors are widely used as outside rear-view mirrors for cars and as security mirrors in stores, where a wide field of view is desirable.

Table 4-2 summarizes the information about mirrors.

Table 4-2. Summary Table of Mirrors

	Object Distance	Real (inverted) Virtual (erect)	Image Size	Position of Image	Image Distance
Converging Mirrors	Infinity	Real	much smaller	same	$d_i = f$
	$d_o > 2f$	Real	smaller	same	$d_i > f$ $d_i < 2f$
	$d_o = 2f$	Real	same	same	$d_i = 2f$
	d_o between f & $2f$	Real	larger	same	$d_i > 2f$
	$d_o = f$	no image	—	—	—
	$d_o < f$	Virtual	larger	opposite	d_i negative & $|d_i| > d_o$
Diverging Mirrors	Any value	Virtual	smaller	opposite	d_i negative $|d_i| < d_o$ $|d_i| < |f|$

Note: when d_i is positive, image is real and on the same side of the mirror as the object; when d_i is negative, image is virtual and on the opposite side of the mirror.

Defects in Lenses and Mirrors

Since different colors of light undergo different amounts of refraction when entering and leaving a dispersive medium such as a lens (p. 120), it follows that rays of light of different color do not converge at the same point after passing through a lens. Violet light, whose wavelength is the shortest, converges closest to the lens; red light, whose wavelength is the largest, converges farthest from the lens. Different colors, as a result, have different focal lengths even when passing through the same lens.

This fact must be taken into account when images are made with an instrument, such as a camera, whose operation is based on refraction. If the light is monochromatic, the image distance (distance between lens and film) can be adjusted from color to color. In the case of infrared cameras, however, this would necessitate a rather large adjustment. Instead, the lens is changed to one with a different focal length.

If the light consists of a mixture of colors, as in the case of sunlight and incandescent bulbs, the various colors form separate images near one another. This results in a blurred image—a defect known as **chromatic aberration.** The problem can be rectified by joining the converging lens to a diverging one made of a different material.

Another defect, one that affects both lenses and mirrors, is known as **spherical aberration.** Rays of light that pass through the edges of a lens, or that are reflected near the edges of a mirror, do not meet all the other rays at the focal point or in the image. This problem is corrected by covering the edges of the lens with a diaphragm, or by making the mirror parabolic instead of spherical in shape.

QUESTIONS

148. As an object is moved closer to a plane mirror, the distance between the image and the mirror will (1) decrease (2) increase (3) remain the same

149. Which diagram best represents the reflection of an object O by plane mirror M?

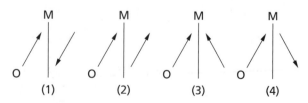

150. Which graph best represents the relationship between the image size and the object size for an object reflected in a plane mirror?

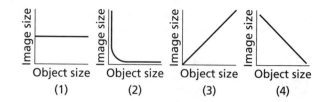

Base your answers to questions 151 through 155 on the following diagram which represents an object placed 0.20 meter from a converging lens with a focal length of 0.15 meter.

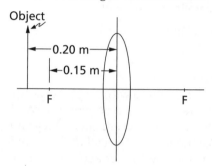

151. Which phenomenon best describes the image formation by the lens? (1) diffraction (2) dispersion (3) polarization (4) refraction

152. The image produced by the lens is (1) enlarged and real (2) enlarged and erect (3) diminished and virtual (4) diminished and inverted

153. If the object distance were increased, the image would become (1) larger and erect (2) smaller and virtual (3) smaller, only (4) larger, only

154. If the object were placed 0.10 meter from the lens, the image would be (1) enlarged and inverted (2) real and inverted (3) reduced and real (4) virtual and erect

155. Which monochromatic light, when used to illuminate the object, would produce the *smallest* image distance? (1) red (2) yellow (3) green (4) blue

156. In which direction does most of the light in ray R pass? (1) A (2) B (3) C (4) D

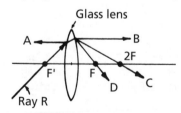

Base your answers to questions 157 through 161 on the following diagram which represents an object that is 0.2 meter high. The object is located 0.5 meter from a converging lens with a focal length of 1.0 meter.

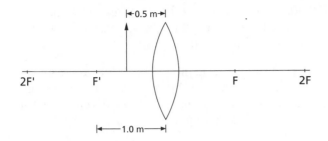

157. How far from the lens is the image? (1) 1.0 m (2) 0.2 m (3) 0.5 m (4) 0.01 m

158. The image would be described as (1) real and inverted (2) real and erect (3) virtual and inverted (4) virtual and erect

159. The smallest image of the object would be produced by the lens when the object is located at (1) 0.5F (2) 2F (3) 3F (4) 4F

160. If the object were moved toward the lens from the position shown in the diagram, the distance from the lens to the image would (1) decrease (2) increase (3) remain the same

161. If the object were moved toward the lens from the position shown in the diagram, the size of the image would (1) decrease (2) increase (3) remain the same

Base your answers to questions 162 through 166 on the following information and diagram. The diagram represents a converging lens made of Lucite, which is used to focus the parallel monochromatic yellow light rays shown. F and F' are the principal foci.

162. The rays will pass through point (1) A (2) B (3) F (4) 2F

163. If an object is placed between F' and the lens, the image formed would be (1) real and smaller (2) real and larger (3) virtual and smaller (4) virtual and larger

164. If an object that is placed 0.04 meter to the left of the lens will produce a real image at a distance of 0.08 meter to the right of the lens, the focal length of the lens is approximately (1) 0.015 m (2) 0.027 m (3) 0.040 m (4) 0.080 m

165. As the light emerges from the lens, its speed will (1) decrease (2) increase (3) remain the same

166. The Lucite lens is replaced by a flint glass lens of identical shape. Compared with the focal length of the Lucite lens, the focal length of the flint glass lens will be (1) smaller (2) larger (3) the same

167. The diagram at the right represents light rays approaching a diverging lens parallel to the principal axis. Which of the following diagrams best represents the light rays after they have passed through the diverging lens?

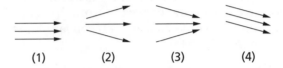

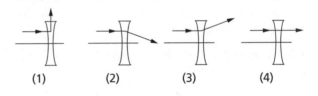

168. A light ray is incident upon a diverging lens as shown in the diagram at the right. Which of the following diagrams best represents the path of the ray after it enters the lens?

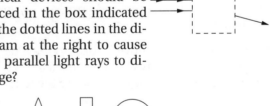

169. Which of the following optical devices should be placed in the box indicated by the dotted lines in the diagram at the right to cause the parallel light rays to diverge?

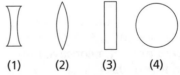

170. In the following diagram of a concave mirror, which point represents the center of curvature? (1) A (2) B (3) B' (4) A'

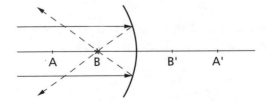

171. The following diagram represents a spherical mirror with three parallel light rays approaching. Which light ray will be reflected normal to the surface of the mirror?   (1) *A*, only   (2) *B*, only   (3) *C*, only   (4) all of the rays

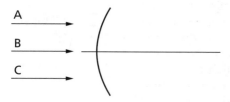

172. Which of the following are diverging instruments?   (1) concave lenses and concave mirrors   (2) concave lenses and convex mirrors   (3) convex mirrors and convex lenses   (4) convex lenses and concave mirrors

173. The image created by a concave lens   (1) can appear on either side of the lens   (2) is always on the same side of the lens as the object   (3) is always on the opposite side of the lens as the object

Base your answers to questions 174 through 177 on the following information. A 10-centimeter tall arrow is situated 12 cm from a concave lens whose focal length is 6 cm.

174. The image distance is closest to   (1) 6 cm   (2) 18 cm   (3) 4 cm   (4) 2 cm

175. The image length is closest to   (1) 30 cm   (2) 1.2 cm   (3) 2.5 cm   (4) 3.33 cm

176. The image is   (1) real and inverted   (2) virtual and upright   (3) real and upright   (4) virtual and inverted

177. If the object is moved closer to the lens, the image   (1) moves away from the lens   (2) remains in place   (3) moves closer to the lens

Base your answers to questions 178 through 183 on the following information. A 10-centimeter tall arrow is situated in front of a concave mirror at the center of curvature of the mirror.

178. The image distance will be   (1) equal to the focal length   (2) equal to the object distance   (3) twice the object distance   (4) equal to one-half the focal length

179. The height of the image will be closest to   (1) 10 cm   (2) 5 cm   (3) 20 cm   (4) 15 cm

180. The image will be   (1) real and upright   (2) virtual and upright   (3) virtual and inverted   (4) real and inverted

181. If the arrow is moved farther away from the mirror, the image   (1) moves away from the mirror   (2) remains in place   (3) moves closer to the mirror   (4) disappears

182. A source of light is placed at the focal point in front of a concave mirror. The reflected rays   (1) are parallel to one another   (2) meet at the center of curvature   (3) diverge   (4) meet at the focal point

183. An object is placed closer to a concave mirror than is the focal point. The image   (1) appears on the same side of the mirror as the object   (2) appears on the opposite side of the mirror as the object   (3) does not appear anywhere

Thinking and Analyzing

184. Why is the focal length different for converging lenses of different shape and composition?

185. Under what circumstances does a converging lens produce a real image? A virtual image?

186. An 8 cm tall object is situated 20 cm from a convex lens whose focal length is 4 cm. How far from the lens does an image of the object appear? How tall is the image?

187. Describe the image formed by a diverging lens.

188. Trace the diagram below onto a sheet of paper. The diagram illustrates three rays reflected off a concave mirror. For each reflected ray, sketch the corresponding incident ray in the correct position and orientation.

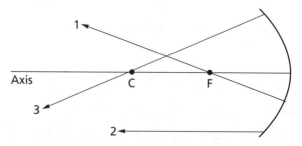

189. Trace the diagram below onto a sheet of paper. The diagram illustrates three rays reflected off a convex mirror. For each reflected ray, sketch the corresponding incident ray in the correct position and orientation.

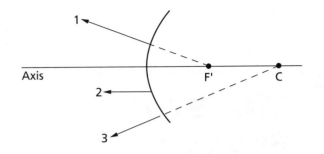

Axis   F'   C

190. A 1.0 cm tall candle flame is situated 2.0 cm from a concave mirror. The focal length of the

mirror is 4.0 cm. Construct a ray diagram to ascertain the location, orientation, and size of the image of the flame.

191. A 1.0 cm tall object is situated 3.0 cm from a convex mirror. The virtual focal point of the mirror is located 5.0 cm from the mirror. Construct a ray diagram to ascertain the location, orientation, and size of the image of the object.

192. How does chromatic aberration and spherical aberration affect mirrors and lenses? How can these defects be corrected?

CHAPTER 5

Modern Physics

THE DUAL NATURE OF LIGHT

Two Models of Light

In the mid 1800s, scientists were convinced that the age-old question, "What is light?" had been answered conclusively. Light, they said, is an electromagnetic wave. Polarization, diffraction, and interference offered proof of the wave nature of light. In addition, the speed of light was the same as that of electromagnetic waves. By the late 1800s, however, certain experiments showed that light behaved as though it consisted of particles. These apparently contradictory models of light, wave and particle, took decades to resolve.

The Photoelectric Effect

When electromagnetic radiation strikes certain materials, particularly metals, electrons are ejected from them and escape into the space around the materials. This phenomenon is known as the **photoelectric effect.** Materials that behave in this manner are said to be **photoemissive,** and the emitted electrons are referred to as **photoelectrons.**

The more intense the electromagnetic radiation that strikes a photoemissive material, the more photoelectrons are ejected per second. A brighter beam of light, for example, causes more photoelectrons to be emitted per second than a dimmer one. Increasing the intensity of the radiation, however, does not result in more energetic photoelectrons. Instead, the kinetic energy of the emitted electrons depends on the frequency of the incident radiation and on the type of photoemissive material. The higher the frequency, the greater the energy of the photoelectrons.

For each photoemissive material there is a **threshold frequency**—a frequency below which no photoelectrons will be emitted, no matter how intense the radiation. For example, a material whose threshold frequency is that of yellow light emits no electrons when bombarded by red light

or radio waves, no matter how intense the radiation. But this material will emit many electrons when bombarded by even the faintest green light or by X rays.

Figure 5-1 shows the relationship between the maximum kinetic energy of photoelectrons, KE_{max}, and the frequency of the incident radiation, f, for two different photoemissive materials, A and B. For every photoemissive material, the maximum kinetic energy of photoelectrons varies linearly with the frequency of the incident radiation. The slope of the graph is the same for all photoemissive materials and is equal to **Planck's constant,** h (6.6×10^{-34} J $\cdot$ s). The point at which the graph intercepts the x axis is different for different photoemissive materials and represents the threshold frequency, f_o of the material.

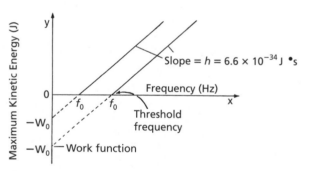

Figure 5-1.

The relationship between KE_{max} and f can also be expressed mathematically as

$$KE_{max} = hf - W_o$$

where h is Planck's constant and W_o is the absolute value of the y-intercept of the graph. This y-intercept is different for different photoemissive materials and is known as the **work function** of the material.

If light and the other EM radiations were just electromagnetic waves, the kinetic energy of the ejected electrons should depend on the intensity of the radiation, rather than the frequency, and

136

no threshold frequency should exist. More intense radiation (brighter light) then means waves with greater amplitude that exert stronger electric and magnetic forces. As a result, the electrons should emerge with more kinetic energy when the radiation is more intense. But since frequency, not intensity, is the sole determining factor of the kinetic energy of emitted photoelectrons, to the point that a "threshold" for frequency exists, a new and improved model of light had to be devised.

The Quantum Theory

The photoelectric effect was explained by Albert Einstein in 1905. He proposed that light and all forms of electromagnetic radiation consisted of particles called **photons.** This proposal was based on Max Planck's **quantum theory** which states that electromagnetic radiation is emitted in discrete amounts, or **quanta,** of energy. Einstein extended this idea: not only was electromagnetic radiation *emitted* in discrete amounts of energy, it was also *absorbed* in discrete amounts, because electromagnetic radiation consists of particles, each carrying a discrete amount of energy.

The energy of each particle, or photon, of light or any type of electromagnetic radiation is directly proportional to the frequency of the radiation. It is found, according to Einstein, by using the formula

$$E = hf$$

where E is the energy, in joules, h is Planck's constant, $(6.6 \times 10^{-34} \text{ J} \cdot \text{sec})$ and f is the frequency of the radiation, in hertz. This formula indicates that photons of higher frequency have more energy than those of lower frequency.

Since all forms of electromagnetic radiation travel at the speed of light and satisfy the relationship $c = \lambda f$, the energy of a photon can also be expressed as

$$E = \frac{hc}{\lambda}$$

where λ is the wavelength, and c is the speed of light. Thus, the energy of a photon is inversely proportional to its wavelength.

In the photoelectric effect, each photon acts individually on one electron. A photon gives either all of its energy, equal to hf, to the electron it interacts with, or none. An electron that gains no energy remains in the material. One that absorbs all of the energy of the photon may or may not escape from the particular material, depending on how much energy it absorbed and how much it needs to escape.

The minimum amount of energy an electron needs to be able to escape from a photoemissive material is the work function, W_o, of that material. This is also the minimum amount of energy an electron loses as it escapes. Thus, if hf (photon energy) is greater than W_o, the electron picks up more than enough energy to escape. After absorbing hf joules of energy, the escaping electron loses a minimum of W_o joules on the way out and emerges with, at most, $(hf - W_o)$ joules of kinetic energy. This is why the maximum kinetic energy of photoelectrons satisfies the relationship

$$\text{KE}_{\text{max}} = hf - W_o$$

Below the threshold frequency, hf is less than W_o. An electron hit by such a photon cannot escape from the material, even though it absorbs all the energy of the photon. Increasing the intensity of radiation does not help, because that only increases the number of photons hitting the material per second, not the amount of energy per photon. Each photon must still act individually on one electron and can only impart hf joules of energy—not enough to eject the electron. Very rarely do two photons strike the same electron in quick succession so that the electron absorbs a second dosage of energy before the first dosage is dissipated through the material.

The threshold frequency f_o of a photoemissive material is thus the frequency at which the quantity hf is equal to the work function W_o. This leads to the equation

$$W_o = hf_o$$

a formula that is confirmed by the KE_{max} versus f graph for any photoemissive material (such as the graph in Figure 5-1). If we use the dotted portion of the graph between the x and y intercepts to calculate the slope, which we know is equal to h, Planck's constant, we get

$$\text{slope} = \frac{\Delta y}{\Delta x} = \frac{W_o}{f_o} = h \qquad \text{or} \qquad W_o = hf_o$$

Increasing the intensity of radiation increases the rate of emission of photoelectrons because more photons then strike the photoemissive material per second. If the photons are energetic enough to eject electrons (above the threshold), the more of them that hit the material per second, the greater the number of electrons emitted per second.

1. The threshold frequency of a photoemissive material is 2×10^{15} Hz. What is the work function of the material?

Solution:

$W_o = hf_o$

$\quad = (6.6 \times 10^{-34}\,\text{J} \cdot \text{s})(2.0 \times 10^{15}\,\text{Hz})$

$\quad = 1.3 \times 10^{-18}\,\text{J}$

2. If radiation with frequency of $3.0 \times 10^{15}\,\text{Hz}$ strikes the material, what is the maximum kinetic energy of the emitted photoelectrons?

Solution:

$\text{KE}_{\text{max}} = hf - W_o$

$\quad = (6.6 \times 10^{-34}\,\text{J} \cdot \text{s})(3.0 \times 10^{15}\,\text{Hz})$

$\quad\quad - (1.3 \times 10^{-18}\,\text{J})$

$\quad = 2.0 \times 10^{-18}\,\text{J} - 1.3 \times 10^{-18}\,\text{J}$

$\quad = 7.0 \times 10^{-19}\,\text{J}$

3. What is the energy of each incident photon?

Solution:

$E = hf$

$\quad = (6.6 \times 10^{-34}\,\text{J} \cdot \text{s})(3.0 \times 10^{15}\,\text{Hz})$

$\quad = 2.0 \times 10^{-18}\,\text{J}$

Photon Momentum

The idea that light and other electromagnetic radiation consist of particles was enhanced by experiments conducted by Arthur Compton in 1922. Compton aimed beams of X rays at electrons and showed that both energy and momentum are conserved in photon-particle collisions, just as they are in collisions between ordinary particles. Whatever energy and momentum is lost by the photons is picked up by the electrons they collide with. This implies that photons are like particles in every way—they have momentum and mass and exert force when they collide with other particles. The only difference between photons and ordinary particles is that photons have no rest mass—they cannot exist in a state of rest.

The momentum, **p,** of a photon was shown by Compton to satisfy the relationship

$$p = \frac{h}{\lambda}$$

where h is Planck's constant and λ is the wavelength in meters. Combining this formula with $c = \lambda f$, yields

$$p = \frac{hf}{c} \quad \text{and} \quad p = \frac{E}{c}$$

4. What is the momentum of a photon of orange light (wavelength of 6.0×10^{-7} meters)?

Solution:

$p = \dfrac{h}{\lambda}$

$p = \dfrac{6.6 \times 10^{-34}\,\text{J} \cdot \text{s}}{6.0 \times 10^{-7}\,\text{m}}$

$p = 1.1 \times 10^{-27} \dfrac{\dfrac{\text{kg} \cdot \text{m}}{\text{s}^2} \cdot \text{m} \cdot \text{s}}{\text{m}}$

$\quad = 1.1 \times 10^{-27} \dfrac{\text{kg} \cdot \text{m}}{\text{s}}$

Matter Waves

In 1924, Louis de Broglie proposed that if electromagnetic waves have particle properties, then moving particles should have wave properties. He based this idea on his belief that nature is symmetrical. Experimental evidence soon confirmed his ideas. Two American physicists C. J. Davisson and L. H. Germer found that beams of electrons produce interference patterns, just as waves do. This was later found to be true for protons and neutrons as well. The waves associated with moving particles are known as **matter waves.**

For subatomic particles with extremely small mass, the wavelength of the matter wave is large enough to be observed and measured. For objects of greater mass, however, the de Broglie wavelength is negligibly small, cannot be detected, and, for all practical purposes, can be ignored.

QUESTIONS

1. Which two characteristics of light can best be explained by the wave theory of light? (1) reflection and refraction (2) reflection and interference (3) refraction and diffraction (4) interference and diffraction

2. Which phenomenon can be explained *only* in terms of the particle model of light? (1) reflection (2) refraction (3) photoelectric effect (4) diffraction

3. A monochromatic light incident upon a photoemissive surface emits electrons. If the intensity of the incident light is increased, the rate of electron emission will (1) decrease (2) increase (3) remain the same

4. When incident on a given photoemissive surface, which color of light will produce photoelectrons with the greatest energy? (1) red (2) orange (3) violet (4) green

5. The threshold frequency of a metal surface is in the violet light region. What type of radiation will cause photoelectrons to be emitted from the metal's surface? (1) infrared light (2) red light (3) ultraviolet light (4) radio waves

6. The work function of a photoelectric material can be found by determining the minimum frequency of light that will cause electron emission and then (1) adding it to the velocity of light (2) multiplying it by the velocity of light (3) adding it to Planck's constant (4) multiplying it by Planck's constant

7. The work function of a metal is 4.2 eV. If photons with an energy of 5.0 eV strike the metal, the maximum kinetic energy of the emitted photoelectrons will be (1) 0 eV (2) 0.80 eV (3) 3.8 eV (4) 9.2 eV

8. The threshold frequency for a photoemissive surface is 6.4×10^{14} Hz. Which color light, if incident upon the surface, may produce photoelectrons? (1) blue (2) green (3) yellow (4) red

Base your answers to questions 9 through 13 on the following information.

Photons with an energy of 3.0 eV strike a metal surface and eject electrons with a maximum kinetic energy of 2.0 eV.

9. The work function of the metal is (1) 1.0 eV (2) 2.0 eV (3) 3.0 eV (4) 5.0 eV

10. If the photons had a higher frequency, what would remain constant? (1) the energy of the photons (2) the speed of the photons (3) the kinetic energy of the electrons (4) the speed of the electrons

11. If the photon intensity were decreased, there would be (1) an increase in the energy of the photons (2) a decrease in the energy of the photons (3) an increase in the rate of electron emission (4) a decrease in the rate of electron emission

12. Compared with the frequency of the 3.0-eV photons, the threshold frequency for the metal is (1) lower (2) higher (3) the same

13. If a metal with a greater work function were used and the photon energy remained constant, the maximum energy of the ejected electrons would (1) decrease (2) increase (3) remain the same

Base your answers to questions 14 through 18 on the following information.

Photons of wavelength 2×10^{-7} meter are incident upon a photoemissive surface whose work function is 6.6×10^{-19} joule.

14. The speed of the incident photons is approximately (1) 2.0×10^{-7} m/s (2) 6.6×10^{-19} m/s (3) 1.3×10^{-25} m/s (4) 3.0×10^{8} m/s

15. The maximum kinetic energy of the photoelectrons is approximately (1) 0 J (2) 3.3×10^{-19} J (3) 6.6×10^{-19} J (4) 9.9×10^{-19} J

16. If the frequency of the incident photons is increased, the kinetic energy of the emitted photoelectrons will (1) decrease (2) increase (3) remain the same

17. If the intensity of the incident photons is decreased, the rate of emission of photoelectrons will (1) decrease (2) increase (3) remain the same

18. Photons of the same wavelength are incident upon a photoemissive surface with a lower work function. Compared with the original situation, the maximum kinetic energy of the photoelectrons emitted from the new surface would be (1) less (2) greater (3) the same

Base your answers to questions 19 through 23 on the following graph which represents the maximum kinetic energy of photoelectrons as a function of incident electromagnetic frequencies for two different photoemissive metals, A and B.

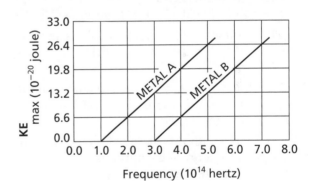

Frequency (10^{14} hertz)
Note: 1 hertz = 1 cycle / second

19. The slope of each line is equal to (1) Bohr's constant (2) the photoelectric constant (3) Compton's constant (4) Planck's constant

20. The threshold frequency for metal A is (1) 1.0×10^{14} Hz (2) 2.0×10^{14} Hz (3) 3.0×10^{14} Hz (4) 0.0 Hz

21. The work function for metal B is closest to (1) 0.0 J (2) 2.0×10^{-19} J (3) 3.0×10^{-19} J (4) 1.5×10^{-14} J

22. Compared with the work function for metal B, the work function for metal A is (1) less (2) greater (3) the same

23. Monochromatic light with a period of 2.0×10^{-15} second is incident on both of the metals. Compared with the energy of the photoelectrons emitted by metal A, the energy of the photoelectrons emitted by metal B is   (1) less   (2) greater   (3) the same

Base your answers to questions 24 through 26 on the following diagram which represents monochromatic light incident upon photoemissive surface A. Each photon has 8.0×10^{-19} joule of energy. B represents the particle emitted when a photon strikes surface A.

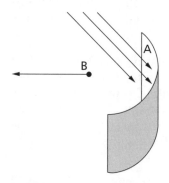

24. What is particle B?   (1) an alpha particle   (2) an electron   (3) a neutron   (4) a proton

25. If the work function of metal A is 3.2×10^{-19} J, the energy of particle B is   (1) 3.0×10^{-19} J   (2) 4.8×10^{-19} J   (3) 8.0×10^{-19} J   (4) 11×10^{-19} J

26. The frequency of the incident light is approximately   (1) 1.2×10^{15} Hz   (2) 5.3×10^{-15} Hz   (3) 3.7×10^{-15} Hz   (4) 8.3×10^{-16} Hz

27. Which formula may be used to compute the energy of a photon?   (1) $E = hf$ (2) $E = mg\Delta h$ (3) $E = \frac{1}{2}mv^2$ (4) $E = Fd$

28. Compared with the energy of the photons of blue light, the energy of the photons of red light is   (1) less   (2) greater   (3) the same

29. The energy of a photon varies   (1) directly as the wavelength   (2) directly as the frequency   (3) inversely as the frequency   (4) inversely as the square of the frequency

30. All of the following particles are traveling at the same speed. Which has the greatest wavelength?   (1) proton   (2) alpha particle   (3) neutron   (4) electron

31. If the wave properties of a particle are difficult to observe, it is probably due to the particle's   (1) small size   (2) large mass   (3) low momentum   (4) high charge

32. Which graph best represents the relationship between the energy of a photon and its wavelength?

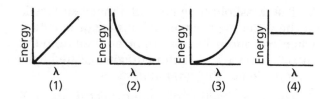

33. As the wavelength of a ray of light increases, the momentum of the photons   (1) decreases   (2) increases   (3) remains the same

34. Compared with the photon momentum of blue light, the photon momentum of red light is   (1) less   (2) greater   (3) the same

35. Which is conserved when a photon collides with an electron?   (1) velocity   (2) momentum, only   (3) energy, only   (4) momentum and energy

Thinking and Analyzing

36. Describe the photoelectric effect.

37. Describe two features of the photoelectric effect that could not be explained on the basis of the wave model of light.

38. Sketch the shape of the graph of the maximum kinetic energy of electrons ejected from a photomaterial vs the frequency of the radiation incident upon it. Identify on the graph the location of the work function and the threshold frequency.

39. Explain why it is not precisely correct to describe some things, such as electrons and atoms, as particles while describing other things, such as light and X rays, as waves. In what way are electrons and X rays similar to each other and in what way are they different from each other?

40. Sketch the shape of a graph of the maximum kinetic energy of electrons ejected from a photomaterial vs the brightness (intensity) of the radiation incident upon it.

MODELS OF THE ATOM

With the discovery of electrons and protons, scientists turned their attention to the arrangement of these particles within the fundamental unit of matter—the atom. In the simplest model, which came to be known as the "plum pudding" model, the protons and electrons are mixed together and uniformly distributed within the entire atom. The mutual attraction between the unlike charges overcomes the repulsion between the like charges, forming a tightly bound and cohesive unit. This occurs because the distances between the unlike charges is smaller (they are arranged one beside the other) than the distances between the like charges (they are arranged diagonally across from each other). In this model, no location within the atom is favored to occupy more of one type of charge than the other.

The Rutherford Experiment

In order to further probe into the structure of the atom, Ernest Rutherford conducted a series of experiments in which he aimed a beam of alpha (α) particles at thin sheets of metal foil. Alpha particles, emitted by radioactive substances, consist of two protons and two neutrons and are therefore positively charged. They are identical to the nuclei of helium atoms. Rutherford found that most of the alpha particles passed through the metal foil without being deflected. A small percentage, however, were deflected, or scattered, through angles ranging from 0° to 180°. Some even reversed course and bounced back.

The Nuclear Shell Model

To explain his results, Rutherford proposed that an atom is a sphere of mostly empty space with a tiny heavy core, or **nucleus,** at the center, where most of the atom's mass and all of its positive charge are located. The negative charges of the atom make up the outer shell. To prevent this model of the atom from collapsing onto itself under the influence of the electric attraction between the protons in the nucleus and the electrons in the shell, the electrons must be assumed to be in motion around the nucleus. The electric attraction provides the centripetal force necessary to keep the electrons orbiting.

Since α particles are positively charged, they must be fragments of the nuclei of the atoms that emit them. The reason most of the α particles go straight through the foil is that most of the space occupied by each atom in the foil is empty. The electrons in the shells are unable to deflect the alpha particles, because α particles are much heavier than electrons. To the extent that a nucleus in the foil exerts a repulsive electric force on an alpha particle, another nucleus in a neighboring atom exerts a force in the opposite direction. These forces cancel each other.

However, a small percentage of the alpha particles in the beam get close enough to the heavier nuclei in the foil to experience a repulsive force that deflects the lighter α particles. An α particle headed straight into a nucleus is stopped by the repulsive force before it collides head-on and is turned back. An α particle that, while coming close to a nucleus, is not quite aiming for a head-on collision, is forced into a hyperbolic path away

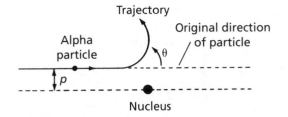

Figure 5-2. Alpha-particle trajectory.

from the nucleus (Figure 5-2). Such alpha particles emerge deflected from their original path through some number of degrees between zero and 180.

The amount of deflection, or the **scattering angle,** θ, depends on how close the α particle gets to the nucleus and on the KE of the particle. The closer it gets, the greater the repulsive force, and the greater the scattering angle. The distance between an α particle's original path and the direction that leads to a head-on collision is called the **impact parameter** and is labeled p. The smaller the impact parameter, p, the greater the scattering angle, θ. When $p = 0$, the alpha particle is headed straight into the nucleus, and the scattering angle will be 180 degrees.

In assuming the nuclear-shell model and its associated details, Rutherford obtained excellent agreement between theory and experiment. The number of α particles deflected through different scattering angles matched the theoretically predicted results in every case.

Rutherford's experiments yielded a good "order of magnitude" estimate for the size of the nucleus. The radius of a typical nucleus is of the order of 10^{-14} meters. This is one ten-thousandth the radius of a typical atom, which is about 10^{-10} meters.

Emission Spectra The nuclear-shell model of the atom, while successful in explaining scattering phenomena, does not resolve all the mysteries of atomic behavior. One such unresolved mystery is that of **emission spectra.** Gases under low pressure, when heated to incandescence, emit electromagnetic radiation of only certain wavelengths and frequencies and no others. The radiation in the visible light range, for example, can be separated and identified by passing the light through a prism (Figure 5-3 on page 142). Lines of specific colors (wavelengths) appear, separated by gaps of darkness that correspond to missing colors. The same is true of the radiation outside the visible light range, such as radio, infrared, ultraviolet, and X ray emissions. Specific wavelengths are emitted; wavelengths in between are not.

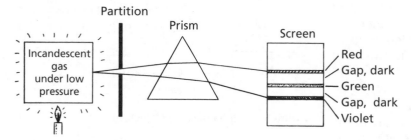

Figure 5-3. Emission spectrum.

Even more curious is the fact that no two elements emit the same set of wavelengths. Each emits a unique combination, called the **emission spectrum** of that element. Unknown gases can be identified by their emission spectra, much as people can be identified by their fingerprints.

The radiation emitted by hydrogen consists of wavelengths that have been grouped into "series" named after their discoverers. The Balmer series is one such group; it includes the visible light wavelengths in the hydrogen spectrum (lines of red, green, and violet).

Rutherford's model does not explain why only certain wavelengths are emitted and not others and why every element emits a different set of wavelengths.

Bohr Model of the Atom

To explain such mysteries as the emission spectra of the elements, Niels Bohr proposed a modified nuclear-shell model for the atom. According to Bohr, the electrons in the shell of an atom are not free to be at any distance from the nucleus, nor are they allowed to have any amount of energy. Instead, they are restricted to certain distances and energy values. Every type of atom has a unique set of allowed orbits, each at a certain distance from the nucleus, and the electrons are confined to those orbits. The total energy of an electron, kinetic plus potential, is determined by the orbit it is in and no other amounts of energy are permitted to the electrons.

As an electron circles around the nucleus in one of its allowed orbits, it neither loses nor gains energy. It is then said to be in a **stationary state.** If that state is also the lowest possible orbit, with the least amount of energy, the electron is said to be in the **ground state.**

These ideas contradict the classical laws of electromagnetism (p. 91). An orbiting electron must experience a centripetal acceleration and accelerating charges are supposed to emit electromagnetic waves and, in so doing, lose energy. The electrons in their stationary state, therefore, should continue to lose energy and gradually

spiral inward toward the nucleus, until the atom collapses. But atoms do not collapse and, unless excited, do not radiate EM waves. Clearly, the classical laws of physics required modification, and Bohr provided it.

Under ordinary conditions, the electrons in an atom position themselves in the lowest available orbits, those with the lowest energy levels. However, the orbit and energy of the electrons can be raised through the process of **excitation.** This occurs when atoms absorb energy by such means as heating, collision with particles, or irradiation. According to Bohr, an atom will only absorb an amount of energy equal to the difference between allowed energy levels. Other amounts of energy cannot be absorbed since doing so would place the electrons in between allowed orbits. The energy values accepted by an atom are referred to as the excitation energies of the atom. Since different atoms have different sets of allowed orbits, they also have different excitation energies.

The only exception are amounts of energy equal to or greater than that needed to remove an electron from an atom. This amount of energy, known as the **ionization potential,** is equal to the difference between the energy of the electron at infinity and its energy in the ground state. Once the electron is removed, it no longer belongs to the atom and restrictions on the energy it may have no longer apply.

An electron that jumps to a higher orbit is said to be in an **excited state.** Soon after becoming excited, such an electron falls to a lower orbit (and lower energy level) by emitting and losing some or all of the energy it gained. As in the case of absorbed energy, the amount of energy emitted must be equal to the difference in energy between allowed orbits.

In summary: *atoms can emit and absorb energy only in quantized amounts.* Since absorption and emission are accomplished by electrons rising and falling between the same fixed energy levels, the quanta of energy that can be absorbed are the same as those that can be emitted. The energy lost by a falling electron is emitted in the form of a photon of EM radiation.

The Hydrogen Atom

The next step for Bohr was to develop a procedure to determine the allowed energy levels of atoms, so that their emission spectra could be explained and predicted. This he succeeded in doing only for the hydrogen atom.

Bohr's successful idea was this: The matter wave associated with an electron in an allowed orbit is a standing wave (Figure 5-4). In other words, the circumference of an allowed orbit is equal to a whole number of wavelengths of the matter wave associated with the electron in that orbit. Since the circumference of an orbit is equal to $2\pi r$, where r is the radius of the orbit, and the wavelength of a matter wave is equal to h/p, the above condition is expressed mathematically as

$$2\pi r = n\left(\frac{h}{p}\right)$$

where n is any positive whole number larger than zero $(1, 2, 3, \ldots)$.

If we replace p with mv and manipulate the variables on both sides of the equation we arrive at

$$mvr = n\left(\frac{h}{2\pi}\right)$$

This restricts the product of an electron's mass, speed, and radius of orbit to one times $h/2\pi$, two times $h/2\pi$, three times $h/2\pi$, and so on. After a few more mathematical manipulations, Bohr arrived at a list of allowed radii and energy levels for the lone electron in a hydrogen atom.

A helpful way to represent the allowed energy levels of an atom is by drawing an energy-level diagram. Figure 5-5 shows the allowed energy levels for hydrogen and mercury atoms.

According to Bohr, luminous gases emit electromagnetic radiation because electrons in their excited atoms descend from higher energy levels to lower energy levels. The energy lost by a descending electron becomes the energy of an emitted photon. Since a photon has energy $E = hf$ or $E = hc/\lambda$ the emitted radiation is of a specific wavelength, frequency, and color.

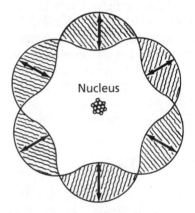

Figure 5-4. The matter wave of an electron in an allowed orbit is a standing wave.

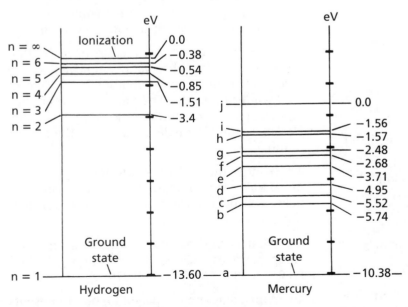

Figure 5-5. Energy levels for the hydrogen atom and some of the energy levels of the mercury atom.

The frequency of an emitted photon is provided by the formula

$$E_{photon} = hf = E_i - E_f$$

where E_i is the energy of the electron in the higher (initial) orbit and E_f is the energy of the electron in the lower (final) orbit.

Bohr demonstrated that each of the wavelengths (colors) in the hydrogen spectrum corresponds to photons emitted by electrons that descend from one of his prescribed energy levels to another. The Balmer series, for example, consists of wavelengths that are emitted by electrons that descend from the third, fourth, fifth, and higher energy levels to the second energy level. Bohr even predicted the existence of series that had not yet been observed, and those series were later found. Every one of their wavelengths matched Bohr's prediction!

The fact that different atoms have different emission spectra implies that they have different sets of allowed energy levels for their electrons. However, Bohr was unable to develop a basis for determining the energy levels of atoms other than hydrogen, nor was he able to explain all aspects of the hydrogen atom, such as why some colors in its spectrum are brighter than others. But much progress has been made in this area since Bohr's time.

Sample Problem

5. What is the wavelength, frequency, and color of the radiation emitted by a hydrogen atom as its excited electron falls from third to the second orbit? (from energy level diagram $E_3 = -1.51$ eV, $E_2 = -3.4$ eV)

Solution:

$$E_{photon} = hf = E_i - E_f$$

$$hf = E_3 - E_2$$

$$(6.6 \times 10^{-34} \, J \cdot s)(f) =$$

$$(-1.51 \, eV)\left(1.6 \times 10^{-19} \frac{J}{eV}\right)$$

$$- (3.4 \, eV)\left(1.6 \times 10^{-19} \frac{J}{eV}\right)$$

(changing eV's to Joules)

$$f = 4.6 \times 10^{14} \, Hz$$

$$\lambda f = c$$

$$(\lambda)(4.6 \times 10^{14} \, Hz) = 3.00 \times 10^8 \, m/s$$

$$\lambda = 6.5 \times 10^{-7} \, m$$

The emitted radiation is red light (from color-frequency table in the Reference Tables).

The Cloud Model

The most recent model of the atom is based on the principles of quantum mechanics and is referred to as the **cloud model.** The cloud model proposes that electrons in atoms do not have precisely described positions and momenta. Instead, only the probability of finding an electron at a specific position with a specific momentum is provided by the laws of nature. The shape of the probability distribution of an electron depends on the number of electrons in the atom and the atom's energy. The region of most probable electron location is known as a **state** and each electron in an atom occupies a state. No more than two electrons can be in the same state at the same time.

The cloud model does not negate the Bohr model; it casts it in a different light. For example, the cloud model's most probable position for the single electron in the ground state of a hydrogen atom coincides with Bohr's lowest allowed orbit. According to the cloud model, the electron is not *prohibited* from being outside that orbit, but the probability of it being inside the orbit is much greater than its being found outside the orbit.

QUESTIONS

41. Rutherford's model showed that most of the volume of the atom is composed of   (1) protons   (2) electrons   (3) neutrons   (4) empty space

42. In alpha particle scattering, the nucleus produces an effect on the scattering angles. This is primarily due to the fact that the nucleus   (1) has a small total charge   (2) has a mass close to that of the alpha particles   (3) exerts coulomb forces   (4) is widely dispersed throughout the atom

43. When alpha particles are scattered by thin metal foils, which observation indicates a very high percentage of space in atoms?   (1) Thicker foils scatter more. (2) The paths are hyperbolic. (3) Most pass through with little or no deflection. (4) The scattering angle is related to the atomic number.

44. In the Rutherford scattering experiment, metal foils were bombarded with   (1) alpha particles   (2) beta particles   (3) protons   (4) neutrons

45. What is the maximum scattering angle for alpha particles incident upon a thin gold foil? (1) 0°   (2) 90°   (3) 180°   (4) 270°

46. Which diagram (on page 145) best represents the path of an alpha particle as it passes near the nucleus of an atom?

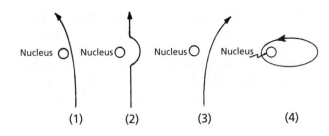

(1)   (2)   (3)   (4)

47. A moving alpha particle enters the space between two oppositely charged plates as indicated in the diagram. Which arrow best represents the path of the alpha particle as it travels between the plates?

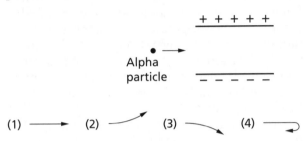

48. Which phenomenon provides evidence that the hydrogen atom has discrete energy levels? (1) emission spectra (2) photoelectric effect (3) alpha particle scattering (4) natural radioactive decay

49. Compared with the total energy of the hydrogen atom in the ground state, the total energy of the atom in an excited state is (1) less (2) greater (3) the same

50. Compared with the amount of energy required to excite an atom, the amount of energy released by the atom when it returns to the ground state is (1) less (2) greater (3) the same

51. If an orbiting electron falls to a lower orbit, the total energy of that atom will (1) decrease (2) increase (3) remain the same

52. An atom changing from an energy state of -0.54 eV to an energy state of -0.85 eV will emit a photon whose energy is (1) 0.31 eV (2) 0.54 eV (3) 0.85 eV (4) 1.39 eV

53. The lowest energy state of an atom is called its (1) ground state (2) ionized state (3) initial energy state (4) final energy state

54. A hydrogen atom emits a photon with an energy of 1.63×10^{-18} J as it changes to the ground state. The radiation emitted by the atom would be classified as (1) infrared (2) ultraviolet (3) blue light (4) red light

55. How much energy is needed to raise a hydrogen atom from the $n = 2$ energy level to the $n = 4$ energy level? (1) 10.2 eV (2) 2.55 eV (3) 1.90 eV (4) 0.65 eV

56. A hydrogen atom is excited to the $n = 3$ state. In returning to the ground state, the atom could *not* emit a photon with an energy of (1) 1.9 eV (2) 10.2 eV (3) 12.1 eV (4) 12.75 eV

57. If a hydrogen atom absorbs 1.9 eV of energy, it could be excited from energy level (1) $n = 1$ to $n = 2$ (2) $n = 1$ to $n = 3$ (3) $n = 2$ to $n = 3$ (4) $n = 2$ to $n = 4$

58. In the Balmer series, during which of the following energy state changes of the hydrogen atom is the photon with the most energy emitted? (1) $n = 5$ directly to $n = 2$ (2) $n = 4$ directly to $n = 2$ (3) $n = 2$ directly to $n = 4$ (4) $n = 2$ directly to $n = 5$

59. What is the minimum energy needed to ionize a hydrogen atom when it is in the $n = 2$ state? (1) 1.9 eV (2) 3.4 eV (3) 12.2 eV (4) 13.6 eV

Thinking and Analyzing

60. Describe the nuclear-shell model of the atom and the experimental evidence that led to its adoption.

61. Describe the two key ideas of the Bohr model that depart from classical physics.

62. Describe the cloud model of the atom. How does it differ from the Rutherford and Bohr models?

63. Explain why Rutherford's model of the atom does not collapse under the influence of the electric attraction between the protons in the nucleus and the electrons in the shells.

64. Sketch the path of an alpha particle as it approaches and then passes by the nucleus of an atom. Then, using the same nucleus, sketch the path of an alpha particle that approaches closer to the nucleus but that is not headed directly into it.

65. Explain why the vast majority of alpha particles aimed at a sheet of gold foil pass through the foil undeflected, while a small fraction of them are deflected and an even smaller fraction reverse course and rebound off the foil.

66. Describe the phenomenon of emission spectra and how the Bohr model attempts to provide a basis for it in the case of the hydrogen atom.

67. Describe the association between the energy levels available to the electron in the Bohr model of the hydrogen atom and the wavelength of the de Broglie matter wave of that electron.

68. Compare and contrast the nuclear, electric, and gravitational forces. Provide two characteristics that any two of them have in common, and two characteristics that differentiate any two of them.

69. What is the wavelength and frequency of the radiation emitted by a hydrogen atom as its excited electron falls from the fourth to the third orbit? ($E_4 = -1.51$ eV, $E_4 = -0.85$ eV)

70. What is the wavelength and frequency of the radiation emitted by a mercury atom as its excited electron falls from the fourth to the third energy level? See Figure 5-5 on page 143.

THE NUCLEUS

Protons and Neutrons

The nucleus of an atom contains most of the mass and all of the positive charge of the atom. The particles in the nucleus, protons, and neutrons, are called **nucleons.** A proton carries one elementary unit of positive charge (1.6×10^{-19} C), equal in amount to the negative charge on an electron. In addition, a proton has approximately 1800 times the mass of an electron. Neutrons carry no net charge and have approximately the same mass as protons.

The number of protons in the nucleus is referred to as the **atomic number** of the atom and is symbolized by the letter Z. The atomic number is also the number of electrons when the atom is electrically neutral. Every element of the *Periodic Table of the Elements* has a unique atomic number.

The number of nucleons, or the total number of protons and neutrons, is known as the **mass number** of the atom, and is symbolized by the letter A. The number of neutrons is thus equal to $A - Z$.

Subatomic Particles Extensive experimentation led to the discovery that, in addition to the proton, neutron, and electron, many other subatomic particles exist. These include the **neutrino** (a particle with no charge and much less mass than the electron), the various types of **mesons** (with masses in between that of the electron and the proton), and the **hyperons** (with masses greater than that of a neutron). Furthermore, each subatomic particle has an **antiparticle**—a particle with the same mass but opposite charge. For example, the **positron** (or anti-electron) has the mass of an electron but is positively charged. The anti-proton has a negative charge.

Recent theories have proposed that the heavier particles (protons, neutrons, and hyperons), called **baryons,** as well as the intermediate mass mesons, are composed of constituent particles called **quarks.** Quarks carry the amount of charge equal to one-third or two-thirds of the elementary unit of charge.

The Nuclear Force

In addition to the forces of gravity and electromagnetism, there exists in nature another force, called the **nuclear force,** or the strong force. Like gravity, this is an attractive force that acts between masses. But, unlike gravity, the nuclear force is effective only across extremely small distances. Particles separated by distances of 10^{-15} meters or less exert very strong, mutually attractive nuclear forces on each other. At distances of about 10^{-14} meters, the nuclear force is much weakened, and at 10^{-13} meters or more, it is practically nonexistent.

This attractive force overcomes the electric repulsion between the protons in a nucleus and prevents them from flying apart. The nuclear force provides the "glue" that binds the nucleons together into a tightly packed and cohesive unit.

Binding Energy

The nuclear force does work on particles it acts on. The presence of a nuclear force therefore implies that nuclear potential energy exists. We refer to this form of potential energy simply as **nuclear energy.**

When a nucleus is formed, the nuclear force acts to bring the nucleons together. This means that the process of forming a nucleus involves a loss of nuclear energy, just as gravitational potential energy is lost when Earth acts to attract an object to itself. If this lost energy were to remain with the nucleons in some other form, such as kinetic energy, a stable nucleus could not be formed. The nucleons, after coming together, would bounce off each other and the energy would be reconverted to nuclear potential energy, just as a falling object's kinetic energy becomes gravitational potential energy again when the object bounces elastically off the ground.

A stable nucleus, therefore, is formed only when the lost nuclear energy is removed from the nucleons as they come together. The energy lost by the coalescing nucleons is emitted as photons and is referred to as the **binding energy** of the nucleus. It is different for different nuclei, since the number of nucleons varies from nucleus to nucleus, as does their size and shape. The binding energy of the nucleus is also the amount of work that needs to be done to pry the nucleons away from one another.

The binding energy of a nucleus divided by the number of nucleons is the **binding energy per nucleon** of that nucleus. It is a measure of how much work went into bringing each nucleon into the nucleus.

The Mass Defect

Experiments have revealed that the mass of every nucleus is less than the sum of its parts. The mass of the C-12 nucleus, for example, is less than the sum of the masses of 6 protons and 6 neutrons. This discrepancy exists for every one of the hundreds of different types of nuclei that exist. The differences between the mass of a nucleus and the sum of the masses of its nucleons is called the **mass defect.** What happened to the missing mass?

This puzzle was solved when Albert Einstein postulated the equivalence of mass and energy in his theory of special relativity. Mass is a form of energy, and energy is associated with mass. As an object's energy increases, its mass increases; as its energy decreases, its mass decreases.

The binding energy of a nucleus is the reason for its mass defect. Since energy is removed from nucleons when they come together to form a nucleus, mass is also removed. Although the mass loss is small, it is significant and detectable when compared with the extremely small masses of nuclei.

Atomic Mass Unit

It is customary to express the masses of nuclei and subatomic particles in terms of atomic mass units, symbolized by the letter u. One atomic mass unit is defined as $\frac{1}{12}$ the mass of the C-12 atom, an amount equal to 1.66×10^{-27} kg. The mass of a single proton or neutron is slightly greater than 1 u.

The Mass-Energy Relationship

The mass associated with a specific amount of energy is provided by the formula

$$E = mc^2$$

where E is the energy, in joules, m is the mass, in kg, and c is the speed of light, 3.00×10^8 meters per second. Thus, the mass defect of a nucleus, in kg, times c^2 (the speed of light squared), is equal to the binding energy of the nucleus in joules.

6. What is the binding energy of $^4_2$He nuclide if its mass is 4.00260 u? (The mass of a single proton is 1.007825 u, and the mass of a single neutron is 1.008665 u.)

Solution:

$$(2)(1.007825\ u) + (2)(1.008665\ u) = 4.03298\ u$$

The mass defect of $^4_2$He is equal to

$$4.03298\ u - 4.00260\ u = .03038\ u$$

The mass defect in kg:

$$(3.0038\ u)\left(1.66 \times 10^{-27}\frac{\text{kg}}{u}\right)$$
$$= 5.04 \times 10^{-29}\ \text{kg}$$

Binding energy = (mass defect)(c²)
$$= (5.04 \times 10^{-29}\ \text{kg})$$
$$(3.00 \times 10^8\ \text{m/s})^2$$
$$= 4.54 \times 10^{-12}\ \text{J}$$

7. What is the energy equivalent of 1 u in electron volts?

Solution:

$$E = mc^2$$
$$= (1.66 \times 10^{-27}\ \text{kg})(3.00 \times 10^8\ \text{m/s})^2$$
$$= 1.49 \times 10^{-10}\ \text{J}$$

Converting to eV's we get

$$\frac{1.49 \times 10^{-10}\ \text{J}}{1.6 \times 10^{-19}\ \text{J/eV}} = 9.3 \times 10^8\ \text{eV or 930 MeV}$$

QUESTIONS

71. Positively charged particles in the nucleus of an atom are called (1) protons (2) photons (3) neutrons (4) electrons

72. What type of particle has a charge of 1.6×10^{-19} C and a rest mass of 1.67×10^{-27} kg? (1) proton (2) electron (3) neutron (4) alpha particle

73. What is the maximum amount of kinetic energy that may be gained by a proton accelerated through a potential difference of 50 volts? (1) 1 eV (2) 10 eV (3) 50 eV (4) 100 eV

74. Which describes the nuclear forces that hold nucleons together? (1) weak and long-range (2) weak and short-range (3) strong and long-range (4) strong and short-range

75. What is the force that holds the nucleons of an atom together? (1) coulomb force (2) magnetic force (3) atomic force (4) nuclear force

76. The energy that must be supplied to a nucleus in order to separate it into its individual protons and neutrons is called (1) ionization energy (2) orbital energy (3) binding energy (4) work function

77. When compared with the total mass of its nucleons, the mass of the nucleus is (1) less (2) greater (3) the same

Base your answer to question 78 on the following information:

Mass of a proton = 1.007277 u

Mass of a neutron = 1.008665 u

Mass of an electron = 0.0005486 u

Mass of a $_2^4$He nucleus = 4.001509 u

78. What is the mass defect of a $_2^4$He nucleus? (1) 1.985567 u (2) 1.985018 u (3) 0.030375 u (4) 0.029278 u

79. How much energy would be produced if 1.0×10^{-3} kilogram of matter was entirely converted to energy? (1) 9.0×10^{13} J (2) 3.0×10^{16} J (3) 9.0×10^{16} J (4) 3.0×10^{19} J

80. Which isotope is used in defining the atomic mass unit? (1) $_1^1$H (2) $_{92}^{238}$U (3) $_8^{16}$O (4) $_6^{12}$C

81. The positron can best be described as a (1) positively charged electron (2) proton (3) positively charged hyperon (4) antiproton

82. The mass of the neutrino is (1) equal to that of an electron (2) less than that of an electron (3) equal to that of a proton (4) between that of an electron and a proton

83. Particles with mass between that of an electron and a proton are called (1) neutrinos (2) hyperons (3) mesons (4) positrons

84. Particles with mass greater than that of a neutron are called (1) neutrinos (2) antiprotons (3) mesons (4) hyperons

85. Which of the following are classified as baryons? (1) mesons and neutrinos (2) positrons and negative protons (3) positrons and electrons (4) protons, neutrons, and hyperons

Thinking and Analyzing

86. How are particles related to their antiparticles?

87. Describe the phenomena known as binding energy and mass defect. How are these phenomena related?

88. Summarize the mass-energy relationship.

89. Explain why the protons in the nucleus of an atom do not move apart in response to the electric force of repulsion they exert on each other.

Reading Comprehension

The Production of Laser Light

Many industries commonly employ lasers for everything from surgical tools to bar code readers. Laser is an acronym for *l*ight *a*mplification by *s*timulated *e*mission of *r*adiation. A laser is a device that can produce a very narrow, intense beam of monochromatic, coherent light. Monochromatic means that the light has one color, and therefore one wavelength. Coherent means that any cross section of the beam has the same phase. In contrast, an ordinary light source emits light in all directions and the emitted light is incoherent.

Our understanding of the action of a laser is based on quantum theory. A photon, a particle of light, can be absorbed by an atom if and only if its energy (hf) corresponds to the energy difference between an occupied energy level of the atom and an available excited state. If an atom is already in the excited state, it may jump spontaneously to the lower state with the emission of a photon. If, however, a photon with this same energy strikes the excited atom, it can stimulate the atom to make the transition to the lower state sooner. This phenomenon is called stimulated emission. When this occurs, the original photon is expelled from the atom along with a second photon of the same frequency. These two photons are exactly in phase and they are moving in the same direction.

Two photons are certainly not enough to produce useful light. However, a laser is designed to produce many identical photons. To accomplish this goal, the lasing material is placed in a narrow tube. A mirror is placed at one end of the tube and a partially transparent mirror is placed at the other end. When the photons strike the mirrors, most are reflected back. As they move in the opposite direction, they strike other excited atoms, causing the release of additional photons. As they bounce back and forth between the mirrors, they continue to stimulate the emission of more photons. A small percentage of photons pass through the partially transparent mirror. These photons make up the laser beam.

QUESTIONS

1. How does laser light differ from ordinary light? How is it the same?
2. Compare spontaneous emission to stimulated emission.
3. Why do lasers contain mirrors on each end? How are the mirrors different from one another?
4. Suggest reasons why laser light is useful for a variety of applications where precision is essential.
5. Some common lasers use a ruby rod consisting of Al_2O_3 with a small percentage of Al atoms replaced by chromium atoms. Other lasers use a mixture of helium and neon gases. How might the lasing material affect the properties of the resulting laser beam?

Enrichment | **Modern Physics**

NUCLEAR SCIENCE

Atoms with identical atomic numbers but different mass numbers are called **isotopes** of the same element, and their chemical behavior is the same.

The nuclei of all carbon atoms, for example, contain six protons. The atomic number, Z, of carbon, therefore, is six. While most carbon atoms also contain six neutrons, some contain as many as 7, 8, 9, or 10. A carbon atom, therefore, can have a mass number, A, of 12, 13, 14, 15, or 16.

We represent elements and their isotopes using the form $^A_Z X$, where X is the chemical symbol of the element, Z the atomic number, and A the mass number. The isotopes of carbon thus appear as follows:

$^{12}_6 C$, $^{13}_6 C$, $^{14}_6 C$, $^{15}_6 C$, $^{16}_6 C$

where C is the symbol for carbon.

Sometimes, the atomic number is omitted, and a nucleus is symbolized in the form of X-A. The isotopes of carbon then appear as follows:

C-12, C-13, C-14, C-15, C-16

Nuclei that possess the same number of protons and neutrons are said to belong to the same nuclear species, called a **nuclide.** Different nuclides with the same atomic number are, therefore, isotopes of the same element.

The de Broglie Wavelength

Earlier you learned that Louis de Broglie described matter waves. Like other waves, matter waves can be described in terms of wavelength. The wavelength of a matter wave, known as the **de Broglie wavelength,** is provided by the formula

$$\lambda = \frac{h}{p}$$

where h is Planck's constant and $\mathbf{p}$ is the momentum of the particle in kg · m/sec. Since the momentum of a particle is equal to $m\mathbf{v}$, this formula can also be written as

$$\lambda = \frac{h}{mv}$$

For subatomic particles with extremely small mass, the wavelength of the matter wave is large enough to be observed and measured. For objects of greater mass, however, the De Broglie wavelength is negligibly small, cannot be detected, and, for all practical purposes, can be ignored.

Sample Problem

8. What is the de Broglie wavelength of an electron moving at 3×10^6 m/s? (The mass of an electron is 9.1×10^{-31} kg.)
Solution:

$$\lambda = \frac{h}{p} = \frac{h}{mv}$$

$$= \frac{6.6 \times 10^{-34} \text{ J} \cdot \text{s}}{(9.1 \times 10^{-31} \text{ kg})(3.0 \times 10^6 \text{ m/s})}$$

$$= 2.4 \times 10^{-10} \text{ m}$$

Observational Tools

Since nuclei are buried deep inside atoms, hidden by clouds of electrons, special tools are needed to investigate their structure and behavior. Much has been learned about nuclei by observing the particles they emit naturally or when bombarded by other particles.

Charged particles are detected by **Geiger counters** that convert the particles' presence into currents of charge and by **scintillation counters** that convert the particles' energy into photons of light. **Photographic plates** are used to record the shapes of the tracks made by charged particles in electric or magnetic fields. The **cloud chamber** is a particularly useful device that reveals the path of a charged particle by creating a trail of condensed vapor in its wake. Knowledge of the deflection experienced by a particle in an electric or magnetic field leads to knowledge of its charge to mass ratio (see pp. 97–98).

Particle accelerators project charged particles at high velocity so that they have enough energy to penetrate, and perhaps smash, nuclei. When these charged particles strike the nucleus of an atom, they upset its stability and new particles may be produced. Positively charged particles, such as protons, are repelled and turned back by the positive nuclei, unless the particles are accelerated, giving them enough kinetic energy to overcome the electric repulsive force. Neutral particles, such as neutrons, need not be accelerated since they are not subject to this repulsion.

Different types of accelerators have been designed, but all use electric and magnetic fields to accelerate the charged particles that are to be aimed at nuclei. The **Van de Graaff generator** accelerates particles by driving them parallel to an intense electric field. In the **cyclotron** and **synchrotron,** charged particles are made to circle in a magnetic field and are accelerated once during every round trip when they pass through an electric field. In the **linear accelerator** the particles are continuously accelerated in an electric field as they travel in a straight line.

NUCLEAR REACTIONS

Natural Radioactivity

All nuclei with atomic numbers greater than 83 are unstable and disintegrate on their own. Many isotopes with atomic numbers less than 84 are also unstable. These nuclei eject parts of themselves and in so doing are changed, or **transmuted,** into new elements with different atomic and mass numbers. This naturally occurring transmutation is called **radioactivity,** and the transmutation of one element into another is called **radioactive decay.** The ejection of particles from radioactive nuclei is always associated with the emission of high energy, short wavelength photons, called **gamma rays.**

Alpha Decay

Different types of particles are ejected by different radioactive nuclei. In a process called **alpha decay,** an alpha particle, consisting of two protons and two neutrons, is emitted from a nucleus. The alpha particle is identical to the nucleus of a helium atom ^4_2He. Thus, the emission of an alpha particle decreases the mass number by four and the atomic number by two. For example, radium-226 nuclei decay into radon-222 nuclei through alpha decay. This is represented by the following nuclear reaction equation:

$$^{226}_{88}\text{Ra} \rightarrow {}^{222}_{86}\text{Rn} + {}^4_2\text{He}$$

Note that the subscripts and superscripts on both sides of the equation are independently balanced ($86 + 2 = 88$, and $222 + 4 = 226$). The subscripts represent elementary units of positive charge (usually protons), and the superscripts represent mass numbers (protons plus neutrons). In all nuclear reactions, the sum of the positive charges and the sum of the mass numbers on both sides of the equation must be so balanced.

Beta Decay (Negative)

In **beta decay (negative),** an electron is ejected from a nucleus. A neutron in the nucleus disintegrates into a proton and an electron; the proton remains in the nucleus, and the electron is ejected. This happens, for example, to thorium-234 nuclei as they decay into protactinium-234 nuclei, as follows:

$$^{234}_{90}\text{Th} \rightarrow {}^{234}_{91}\text{Pa} + {}^{0}_{-1}\text{e}$$

Since the electron carries one elementary unit of negative charge, we assign it a subscript of -1, and since its mass is insignificant compared with that of protons and neutrons, we assign it a superscript of zero. The process of beta (negative) decay increases the atomic number of the nucleus by one, but leaves the mass number intact.

Gamma Radiation

When a nucleus in an excited state returns to a state of lower energy, the energy difference is emitted in the form of gamma ray photons. Since photons have no charge and much less mass than a nucleon, these emissions change neither the atomic number nor the mass number of nuclei and produce no transmutation or decay.

If all the particles and photons involved in a nuclear reaction (those ejected and those remaining) are taken into account, the total mass-energy after the reaction is always equal to the total mass-energy before the reaction. This is referred to as the *law of conservation of mass-energy.*

Half-Life

Each radioactive nuclide decays at a unique rate. The time it takes for half the number of nuclei present in a sample to decay is known as the **half-life** of the radioactive substance. Half-lives range from as little as 10^{-22} seconds for some radioactive substances to as much as 10^{17} years for others. The rate of decay is independent of all environmental factors such as pressure, temperature, and chemical combination with other substances.

At the end of every half-life period, the amount of original material remaining is half the amount that was present at the beginning of that period. This relationship is expressed by the formula

$$m_f = \frac{m_i}{2^n}$$

where m_i is the initial mass of the radioactive material, m_f is the mass remaining, and n is the number of half-lives elapsed.

Sample Problem

9. If 32 grams of a radioactive substance with a half-life of one hour are present at noon, how much of the substance will remain at 4 p.m.?

Solution:

$$m_f = \frac{m_i}{2^n} = \frac{32 \text{ g}}{2^4}$$

$$= \frac{32 \text{ g}}{16} = 2.0 \text{ g}$$

The number of nuclei that decay, and consequently the number of particles ejected, per time decreases as time goes on. In the sample problem, for example, 16 grams decayed in the first hour, 8 grams decayed during the second hour, 4 grams during the third, and so on. But the time it takes for half of the amount present at any time to decay is constant. It is the half-life of the material (1 hour).

Decay Series

Natural radioactivity usually proceeds in a succession of steps, called a **decay series.** After an atom of $^{238}_{92}\text{U}$ decays into $^{234}_{90}\text{Th}$, for example, the thorium atom decays into $^{234}_{91}\text{Pa}$, which then becomes $^{234}_{92}\text{U}$, which then decays into $^{230}_{90}\text{Th}$ and so on. A series comes to an end when the product of a decay step is stable (nonradioactive). The series that starts with $^{238}_{92}\text{U}$ ends, after 14 steps, with $^{206}_{82}\text{Pb}$.

It is customary to illustrate the steps of a decay series with arrows and dots on a mass number versus atomic number graph, as illustrated in Figure 5-6. Every dot represents a nucleus with a particular mass number and atomic number. An arrow that points from one dot to another that is two units to the left and four units

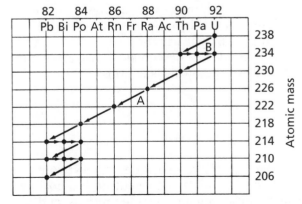

Figure 5-6. The uranium-238 decay series.

down (such as arrow A in the figure) indicates that the decay step decreases the atomic number by two and the mass number by four. Such an arrow, therefore, represents the emission of an alpha particle.

An arrow that points from one dot to another that is one unit to the right (such as arrow B in the figure), indicates that the decay step increased the atomic number by one but left the mass number unchanged. Such an arrow, therefore, represents the emission of a beta particle (electron).

The 14-step series consists of 8 alpha particle emissions and 6 beta particle emissions.

Artificial Transmutation

The first artificial transmutation of one element to another was performed by Rutherford in 1919. Rutherford bombarded nitrogen with energetic alpha particles that were moving fast enough to overcome the electric repulsion between themselves and the target nuclei. The alpha particles collided with, and were absorbed by, the nitrogen nuclei, and protons were ejected. In the process oxygen and hydrogen nuclei were created. This reaction is summarized by the equation

$$\ce{^4_2He} + \ce{^{14}_7N} \rightarrow \ce{^{17}_8O} + \ce{^1_1H}$$

Positron Emission

Since 1919 many other artificially induced transmutations have been performed by the bombardment of nuclei with protons, neutrons, and other particles. Frequently the artificially created elements are themselves radioactive. For example, when energetic alpha particles are aimed at aluminum-27 nuclei, the aluminum nuclei turn into radioactive phosphorus-30 nuclei and emit neutrons. Over time the phosphorus nuclei decay into stable silicon-30 nuclei by emitting positrons. Positrons carry the same amount of mass and charge as electrons, but their charge is positive. They are referred to as **beta positive** (β^+) particles. (When the expression "beta particle" is used without specifying + or −, the reference is to electrons, or β^- particles.)

The reactions described above are represented by the following equations

$$\ce{^4_2He} + \ce{^{27}_{13}Al} \rightarrow \ce{^{30}_{15}P} + \ce{^1_0n}$$

$$\ce{^{30}_{15}P} \rightarrow \ce{^{30}_{14}Si} + \ce{^0_{+1}e}$$

The $\ce{^0_{+1}e}$ particle, or positron, comes from the breakup of a proton into a neutron and positron. The neutron remains in the nucleus and the positron is ejected. By replacing a proton in the nucleus with a neutron, the process of beta-positive decay decreases the atomic number by one and leaves the mass number unchanged.

Another example of an artificially created nucleus that is radioactive and emits positrons is copper-64.

$$\ce{^{64}_{29}Cu} \rightarrow \ce{^{64}_{28}Mg} + \ce{^0_{+1}e}$$

An artificially created nucleus that emits beta-negative particles (electrons) is sodium-24.

$$\ce{^{24}_{11}Na} \rightarrow \ce{^{24}_{12}Mg} + \ce{^0_{+1}e}$$

Electron Capture

A radioactive process that results in the emission of gamma rays is known as **electron capture.** It occurs when a nucleus "captures" and absorbs one of the atom's innermost electrons. The electron then unites with a proton to form a neutron. This decreases the atom's atomic number by one but leaves the mass number unchanged.

An example of such a reaction is the change of potassium-40 into argon-40:

$$\ce{^{40}_{19}K} + \ce{^0_{-1}e} \rightarrow \ce{^{40}_{18}Ar}$$

Sample Problem

10. In the following nuclear reaction equation, what type of particle is X?

$$\ce{^{214}_{82}Pb} \rightarrow \ce{^{214}_{83}Bi} + X$$

Solution: Since the subscripts and superscripts must be independently balanced, X must have a subscript of −1 ($83 - 1 = 82$) and a superscript of zero $214 + 0 = 214$). With a mass number of zero and one elementary unit of negative charge, X must be a negative beta particle (electron).

The Neutron

Neutrons were discovered in 1932 by James Chadwick when he bombarded beryllium with energetic alpha particles. The beryllium nuclei were transmuted to carbon-12 nuclei and neutrons were emitted. This is represented by the equation

$$\ce{^4_2He} + \ce{^9_4Be} \rightarrow \ce{^{12}_6C} + \ce{^1_0n}$$

Neutron emitters are often used to initiate nuclear reactions, because neutrons are very effective as nucleus smashers. Since neutrons carry no charge, they are not repelled electrically by nuclei and, therefore, need not be accelerated in order that they collide with the nuclei. If a neutron merely comes close to a nucleus, the nuclear attractive force acts to bend its path toward the nucleus and a direct hit results. This increases the odds enormously that a collision will occur, since even slow-moving neutrons that are not headed straight into a nucleus can collide with it.

Indeed, slow neutrons are more effective nucleus smashers than fast neutrons. The nuclear attractive force exerted by a nucleus is unable to capture a neutron that moves too fast, unless the neutron is headed straight into the nucleus. But slow neutrons are pulled into nuclei even if their trajectories would not otherwise lead them there.

Moderators

To increase the probability that neutrons will collide with nuclei, power plants that derive their energy from nuclear reactors employ moderators to slow down the neutrons. **Moderators** are materials whose atoms have light nuclei that do not combine with neutrons that collide with them. Typical moderators are hydrogen, deuterium, carbon, water, and paraffin. When fast-moving neutrons pass through these substances, they repeatedly collide with the nuclei and give up part of their energy. Soon the average kinetic energy of the neutrons is approximately equal to that of the atoms of the moderator (about $\frac{1}{25}$ eV). Such slow-moving neutrons are called **thermal neutrons.**

Nuclear Fission

When certain massive nuclei, such as uranium-235 or plutonium-239, are struck by slow thermal neutrons, the nuclei split into two smaller fragments, a number of neutrons are ejected, and energy is released. This process is called **fission.** The binding energy per nucleon of the two new lighter nuclei is greater than that of the original heavier nucleus. Thus, the reaction leads to a loss of more nuclear energy per nucleon—energy that is removed from the nucleons and converted to heat, photons, and other forms. The loss of nuclear energy corresponds to a loss of mass on the part of the nucleons. This mass is converted to the energy released in amounts provided by the relationship $E = mc^2$. A typical equation for this type of fission reaction is

$$\,^{1}_{0}\text{n} + \,^{235}_{92}\text{U} \rightarrow \,^{141}_{56}\text{Ba} + \,^{92}_{36}\text{Kr} + 3\,^{1}_{0}\text{n} + Q \text{ (energy)}$$

The ejected neutrons are available for collisions with other nuclei in the sample of U-235. Those collisions, in turn, liberate more neutrons that collide with still more nuclei. If enough fissionable material is present, a self-sustaining **chain reaction** of collisions leading to more collisions can occur with each collision splitting a nucleus

and releasing energy. In this way a large amount of energy can be released in an uncontrolled manner, as happens when an atomic bomb explodes. The rate at which fission reactions take place, however, can be controlled so that a uniform, continuous, and usable output of energy occurs. Today this process is the basis of the operation of hundreds of nuclear reactors around the world. The minimum amount of fissionable material necessary to initiate a chain reaction is called the **critical mass.**

Reactors

The most common method of preventing a chain reaction from getting out of control is the insertion of **control rods** between small pellets of the fissionable material referred to as the **nuclear fuel.** These rods consist of substances such as boron and cadmium that absorb neutrons. Control rods effectively prevent many of the neutrons that escape from one pellet of fissioning material from reaching a neighboring pellet, thereby slowing down the chain reaction. This controlling mechanism must be carefully adjusted to ensure that the chain reaction is neither shut down nor allowed to accelerate.

Reactors must also have circulating **coolants** to carry the heat generated by the nuclear reaction away from the reactor to the turbines or heat exchangers. Without such coolants, the temperature in the reactor would rise to dangerous levels. Common coolants include water, air, helium, carbon dioxide, molten sodium, and molten lithium. In some reactors, the coolant also serves as the moderator. Heavy water (in which the two hydrogen atoms are H-2, not H-1) is frequently used for both functions.

Reactors must also be **shielded.** An internal shield of steel is used to prevent escaping radiation from damaging the walls of the reactor. An external shield of high density concrete is used to prevent injury to the personnel that operate the plant and to the population in the vicinity of the plant.

A major problem that plagues all reactors is waste disposal. The products of fission are highly radioactive and many remain so for a long time. Therefore, they cannot be discarded without precautions. Underground storage in special containers in isolated areas provides only a temporary solution. More permanent solutions have yet to be found.

The uranium used in nuclear reactors contains more U-238 than U-235, because uranium ore found underground is approximately 97% U-238, and the process of increasing the U-235 content of the uranium pellets is a difficult and expensive one. When a U-238 atom absorbs a neutron, its nucleus does not fission. Instead, it is converted to plutonium-239, a highly radioactive substance that does fission when struck by a neutron. Some reactors treat this plutonium as waste, while others use it as fuel to generate yet more energy. The latter type of reactor is known as a **breeder reactor.**

Nuclear Fusion

Nuclear energy is also released when certain light nuclei are united to become one heavier nucleus. During this process of **nuclear fusion,** the binding energy per nucleon is increased and nuclear energy and mass are lost by the nuclei and released in other forms. It is believed that the sun's enormous energy output derives from the fusion of various hydrogen isotopes into helium nuclei. A typical fusion reaction of this type is

$$^3_1H + ^1_1H \rightarrow ^4_2He + Q$$

Similar fusion reactions are responsible for the uncontrolled release of energy that occurs when a hydrogen bomb explodes.

Fusion reactions release much more energy per nucleon than do fission reactions, but they are more difficult to initiate. Unlike neutrons, nuclei are charged and repel each other. Bringing them together to the point that the short-range nuclear attractive force overcomes the repulsive electric force and fuses the nuclei together requires very high temperatures and pressures.

Since the difficulty of bringing nuclei together increases with the amount of charge on the nuclei, the best materials to use for fusion reactions are nuclei with the smallest possible atomic number. As a result, the isotopes of hydrogen, H-1, H-2 (deuterium), and H-3 (tritium) are used for this purpose.

Controlled Fusion

Scientists continue to be challenged by the task of designing a reactor that would use fusion reactions to liberate energy in a controlled, useable, and efficient manner. Since the oceans of the earth provide an almost limitless supply of hydrogen isotopes (every water molecule contains two hydrogen atoms), and more energy is liberated per nucleon by fusion than by any other process, such a reactor would be a monumental achievement. Thus far, however, the problem of containing the extremely high temperatures needed to initiate a fusion reaction poses an unresolved obstacle to the construction of such a reactor.

QUESTIONS

90. The nucleus of isotope A of an element has a larger mass than the nucleus of isotope B of the same element. Compared with the number of protons in the nucleus of isotope A, the number of protons in the nucleus of isotope B is (1) less (2) greater (3) the same

91. Which is an isotope of $^{44}_{21}Sc$? (1) $^{44}_{20}Ca$ (2) $^{46}_{20}Ca$ (3) $^{46}_{21}Sc$ (4) $^{44}_{22}Ti$

92. An atom consists of 9 protons, 9 electrons, and 10 neutrons. The number of nucleons in this atom is (1) 0 (2) 9 (3) 19 (4) 28

93. The total number of neutrons in the nucleus of any atom is equal to the (1) mass number of the atom (2) atomic number of the atom (3) atomic number minus the mass number (4) mass number minus the atomic number

94. A pair of isotopes is, (1) $^{238}_{92}U$ and $^{239}_{92}U$ (2) $^{239}_{93}Np$ and $^{239}_{92}U$ (3) $^{235}_{92}U$ and $^{239}_{94}Pu$ (4) $^{239}_{93}Np$ and $^{239}_{94}Pu$

95. Which device makes visual observation of the path of a charged particle possible? (1) Geiger counter (2) Van de Graaff generator (3) cyclotron (4) cloud chamber

96. Which device could be used to give a positively charged particle sufficient kinetic energy to penetrate the nucleus of an atom? (1) electroscope (2) Geiger counter (3) cloud chamber (4) Van de Graaff generator

97. Which of the following is used to accelerate a charged particle? (1) a photographic plate (2) an electroscope (3) a cyclotron (4) a cloud chamber

98. Of the following particles the one that can not be accelerated in an atom-smashing machine is the (1) proton (2) neutron (3) alpha particle

99. Which group of particles can *all* be accelerated by a cyclotron? (1) alpha particles, electrons, and neutrons (2) electrons, neutrons, and protons (3) protons, alpha particles, and electrons (4) neutrons, protons, and alpha particles

Base your answers to questions 100 and 101 on the following nuclear equation.

$$^{226}_{88}Ra \rightarrow ^{222}_{86}Rn + ^4_2He$$

100. What is represented by ^4_2He? (1) an alpha particle (2) a beta particle (3) a gamma ray (4) a positron

101. This equation represents the process of (1) alpha decay (2) beta decay (3) fission (4) fusion

102. In which reaction does X represent a beta particle?

(1) $^{234}_{92}U \rightarrow ^{230}_{90}Th + X$

(2) $^{214}_{84}Pa \rightarrow ^{210}_{82}Pb + X$

(3) $^{226}_{88}Ra \rightarrow ^{222}_{86}Rn + X$

(4) $^{214}_{82}Pb \rightarrow ^{214}_{83}Bi + X$

103. In the decay series of U-238, the change from Th-234 to U-234 involves the emission of (1) neutrons (2) positrons (3) alpha particles (4) beta particles

104. How many beta particles are given off when one atom of U-238 completely disintegrates to Pb-206? (1) 6 (2) 8 (3) 10 (4) 14

Base your answers to questions 105 through 107 on the following information.

$^{131}_{53}I$ initially decays by emission of beta particles.

105. Beta particles are (1) protons (2) electrons (3) neutrons (4) electromagnetic waves

106. When $^{131}_{53}I$ decays by beta emission, it becomes (1) $^{130}_{53}I$ (2) $^{129}_{51}Sb$ (3) $^{131}_{54}Xe$ (4) $^{135}_{54}Xe$

107. The half-life of $^{131}_{53}I$ is 8 days. After 24 days, how much of a 100.-gram sample of $^{131}_{53}I$ would remain? (1) 0 g (2) 12.5 g (3) 25.0 g (4) 50.0 g

Base your answers to questions 108 through 112 on the Physics Reference Tables.

108. Which change is the result of the loss of two negative beta particles? (1) U to Th (2) Th to U (3) Pb to Bi (4) Bi to Pb

109. Which of the following pairs of isotopes is found in the Uranium Disintegration Series?

(1) $^{222}_{84}Po$ and $^{218}_{84}Po$

(2) $^{226}_{88}Ra$ and $^{222}_{88}Ra$

(3) $^{214}_{83}Bi$ and $^{210}_{83}Bi$

(4) $^{239}_{92}U$ and $^{238}_{92}U$

110. Which particle is emitted as $^{234}_{90}Th$ changes to $^{234}_{91}Pa$? (1) a neutron (2) an alpha particle (3) a proton (4) a negative beta particle

111. When a nucleus emits an alpha particle, the mass number of the nucleus (1) decreases (2) increases (3) remains the same

112. As a sample of uranium disintegrates, the half-life of the remaining uranium (1) decreases (2) increases (3) remains the same

Base your answers to questions 113 through 117 on the following graph which represents the disintegration of a sample of a radioactive element. At time $t = 0$ the sample has a mass of 4.0 kilograms.

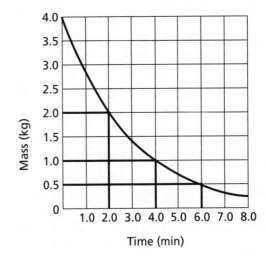

113. What mass of the material remains at 4.0 minutes? (1) 1 kg (2) 2 kg (3) 0 kg (4) 4 kg

114. What is the half-life of the isotope? (1) 1.0 min (2) 2.0 min (3) 3.0 min (4) 4.0 min

115. How many half-lives of the isotope occurred during 8.0 minutes? (1) 1 (2) 2 (3) 8 (4) 4

116. How long did it take for the mass of the sample to reach 0.25 kilogram? (1) 1 min (2) 5 min (3) 3 min (4) 8 min

117. If the mass of this material had been 8.0 kilograms at time $t = 0$, its half-life would have been (1) less (2) greater (3) the same

Base your answers to questions 118 through 122 on the following information.

In the equation $^{231}_{87}Fr \rightarrow X + \gamma + Q$, the letter X represents the nucleus produced by the reaction. γ represents a gamma photon, and Q represents additional energy released in the reaction.

118. Which nucleus is represented by X? (1) $^{217}_{85}X$ (2) $^{221}_{88}X$ (3) $^{220}_{87}X$ (4) $^{221}_{87}X$

119. The rest mass of the gamma ray photon is approximately (1) one atomic mass unit (2) the mass of a proton (3) the mass of a neutron (4) zero

120. If the energy Q equals 9.9×10^{-13} joule, the mass equivalent of this energy is (1) 0 kg (2) 9.1×10^{-31} kg (3) 1.1×10^{-29} kg (4) 3.3×10^{-21} kg

121. The sample of $^{221}_{87}Fr$ (half-life = 4.8 minutes) will decay to one-fourth of its original amount in (1) 4.8 min (2) 9.6 min (3) 14.4 min (4) 19.2 min

122. The gamma photon makes a collision with an electron at rest. During the interaction, the momentum of the photon will (1) decrease (2) increase (3) remain the same

123. A certain radioactive isotope has a half-life of 2 days. If 8 kilograms of the isotope is placed in a sealed container, how much of the isotope will be left after 6 days? (1) 1 kg (2) 2 kg (3) 0.5 kg (4) 4 kg

Base your answers to questions 124 through 128 on the following information and nuclear equations.

When nitrogen is bombarded with protons, the first reaction that occurs is $^{14}_{7}N + ^{1}_{1}H \rightarrow ^{15}_{8}O + X$. The oxygen produced is radioactive with a half-life of 0.10 second, and decays in the following manner: $^{15}_{8}O \rightarrow ^{15}_{7}N + Y$.

124. The first reaction is an example of (1) alpha decay (2) beta decay (3) induced transmutation (4) natural radioactivity

125. In the first reaction, X represents (1) an alpha particle (2) a beta particle (3) a neutron (4) a gamma photon

126. In the second reaction, Y represents (1) an electron (2) a neutron (3) a positron (4) a proton

127. If a 4.0-kilogram sample of $^{15}_{8}O$ decays for 0.40 second, the mass of $^{15}_{8}O$ remaining will be (1) 1.0 kg (2) 2.0 kg (3) 0.50 kg (4) 0.25 kg

128. As the amount of $^{15}_{8}O$ decreases, the half-life (1) decreases (2) increases (3) remains the same

Base your answers to questions 129 through 132 on the following nuclear equations.

$$^{27}_{13}Al + ^{4}_{2}He \rightarrow ^{30}_{15}P + X + energy$$
$$^{30}_{15}P \rightarrow ^{30}_{14}Si + Y + energy$$

129. The first equation indicates that the radioactive phosphorus is produced by bombarding $^{27}_{13}Al$ with (1) neutrons (2) positrons (3) alpha particles (4) protons

130. In the first equation, particle X is (1) a neutron (2) an electron (3) a positron (4) a neutrino

131. In the second equation, particle Y is (1) an alpha particle (2) a neutron (3) an electron (4) a positron

132. The number of neutrons in the nucleus of $^{27}_{13}Al$ is (1) 13 (2) 14 (3) 27 (4) 40

Base your answers to questions 133 through 136 on the following nuclear equation.

$$^{30}_{15}P \rightarrow ^{A}_{Z}Si + ^{0}_{+1}X$$

133. In the equation, X represents (1) a positron (2) an electron (3) a proton (4) a gamma photon

134. What is the value of A in the equation? (1) 28 (2) 29 (3) 30 (4) 31

135. What is the value of Z in the equation? (1) 14 (2) 15 (3) 16 (4) 17

136. The nucleus of $^{30}_{15}P$ has (1) 30 protons (2) 30 neutrons (3) 15 nucleons (4) 15 neutrons

137. The function of the moderator in a nuclear reactor is to (1) absorb neutrons (2) slow down neutrons (3) speed up neutrons (4) produce extra neutrons

138. An atom of U-235 splits into two nearly equal parts. This is an example of (1) alpha decay (2) beta decay (3) fusion (4) fission

139. When a nucleus captures an electron, the atomic number of the nucleus (1) decreases (2) increases (3) remains the same

140. In a nuclear reactor, control rods are used to (1) slow down neutrons (2) speed up neutrons (3) absorb neutrons (4) produce neutrons

141. During nuclear fusion, energy is released as a result of the (1) splitting of heavy nuclei (2) combining of heavy nuclei (3) combining of light nuclei (4) splitting of light nuclei

142. When a neutron is emitted from a nucleus (1) the atomic number decreases (2) the atomic mass decreases (3) the atomic number does not change (4) both (2) and (3)

143. When a beta particle is emitted from a nucleus (1) the atomic number decreases (2) the atomic number increases (3) the atomic mass decreases (4) the atomic mass increases

144. In the nuclear reaction $^{9}_{4}Be + ^{4}_{2}He \rightarrow ^{12}_{6}C + W$ the symbol W represents (1) an electron (2) a proton (3) a neutron (4) an alpha particle

145. In the nuclear reaction $^{239}_{92}U \rightarrow ^{239}_{93}Np + X$, the symbol X represents (1) a deuteron (2) an electron (3) a gamma ray (4) a proton

146. In the nuclear reaction $^{4}_{2}He + ^{14}_{7}N \rightarrow ^{17}_{8}O + Z$, the symbol Z represents (1) a proton (2) a neutron (3) an alpha particle (4) an electron

147. When fission occurs   (1) energy is liberated   (2) the products weigh less than the original material   (3) mass is converted into energy   (4) all of these

148. Fusion is produced by   (1) a chain reaction   (2) neutron bombardment   (3) intense heat   (4) none of these

149. The process of fusion is accompanied by   (1) no change in mass   (2) a loss in mass   (3) a gain in mass   (4) the transmutation of helium to hydrogen

150. The nuclear reaction believed to be taking place in the sun and to be responsible for its release of energy is known as   (1) condensation   (2) fission   (3) fusion   (4) radiation

151. An element suitable for fusion is   (1) uranium   (2) plutonium   (3) hydrogen   (4) all of these

152. The nuclear raw materials for a fusion reaction have a total mass of 3.0067 g. The products of this reaction may have a mass of approximately   (1) 3.0065 g   (2) 3.0067 g   (3) 3.0069 g   (4) 6.0134 g

Base your answers to questions 153 through 155 on the following information.

In the nuclear reaction

$$_1^2H + _1^3H \rightarrow _2^4He + _0^1n + Q$$

Q represents energy released.
The masses of the nuclei are:

$_1^2H = 2.01472$ u

$_1^3H = 3.01697$ u

$_2^4He = 4.00391$ u

$_0^1n = 1.00897$ u

153. The reaction shown is primarily an example of   (1) alpha decay   (2) ionization   (3) fission   (4) fusion

154. The value of Q is nearest to: (1) 5.01288 u   (2) 5.03169 u   (3) 0.01881 u   (4) 2.01472 u

155. In the equation given, the mass-energy of the reactants, as compared with the mass-energy of the product is   (1) twice as great   (2) the same   (3) half as great   (4) one-fourth as great

156. An atom that undergoes electron capture emits   (1) a positron   (2) an electron   (3) a gamma photon   (4) a positron and a neutrino

157. Air can be used in a nuclear reactor as a   (1) coolant   (2) control on the chain reaction   (3) moderator   (4) shield

158. In some reactors the coolant also serves as the   (1) moderator   (2) shield   (3) control   (4) all of the above

159. Steel and concrete can be used in nuclear reactors as   (1) moderators   (2) control rods   (3) shields   (4) coolants

160. Which of the following does not undergo fission?   (1) U-235   (2) U-238   (3) plutonium-239   (4) all of the above

161. Some reactors breed plutonium by bombarding which of the following with neutrons?   (1) U-235   (2) U-238   (3) plutonium-239   (4) barium-141

162. Fusion requires a high temperature to initiate because   (1) atomic nuclei repel each other   (2) neutrons are not charged   (3) gravity must be overcome   (4) mass must be converted to energy

163. Which of the following nuclei would be most difficult to get to "fuse" together?   (1) hydrogen-2 ($_1^2H$)   (2) carbon-12 ($_6^{12}C$)   (3) helium-4 ($_2^4He$)   (4) lithium-7 ($_3^7Li$)

Thinking and Analyzing

164. Complete the following table:

Atom	Number of neutrons	Number of protons	Mass number
1	5	5	
2	8		17
3		118	197

165. How are two atoms related if they are isotopes?

166. How does the mass of a subatomic particle determine whether or not its wavelength can be detected?

167. What is the purpose of a particle accelerator?

168. What happens to an atom when it is transmuted?

169. How do alpha and beta decay affect the atomic number, mass number, and binding energy of an atom?

170. What happens to a radioactive sample after two half-lives?

171. What is a decay series and when does such a series come to an end?

172. What are beta-positive particles and where do they come from in the radioactive process?

173. Describe the process of electron capture.

174. Why is it that neutrons do not need to be accelerated before colliding with target nuclei for research purposes?

175. How does nuclear fusion differ from nuclear fission?

176. Relate the terms *chain reaction* and *critical mass.*

SOLID STATE PHYSICS

Energy Bands

In a previous section (p. 136), we concluded that, within an isolated atom, such as those in gases under low pressure, electrons can have only certain discrete amounts of energy. Atoms that are crowded together, on the other hand, such as those in the **solid state,** interact with one another and alter one another's energy level structure. Every energy level is transformed into a multiplicity of closely spaced sublevels. Instead of sharply defined energy levels, the atoms develop **energy bands,** each of which consists of a range of allowed energy values. In between the energy bands are forbidden zones—an electron cannot have an amount of energy between allowed bands.

The contrast between energy levels and energy bands is diagrammed in Figure 5-7. The highest energy band that contains electrons is called the **valence band.** Above the valence band is the **conduction band.** This is the lowest energy band that provides electrons sufficient energy to migrate away from their atoms. The positive ion left behind by such a migrating electron is referred to as an **atom kernel.**

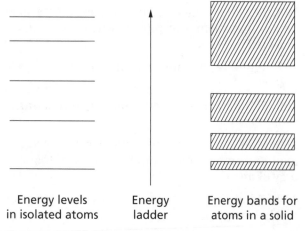

Figure 5-7. Energy levels and energy bands.

Insulators

A solid in which the conduction band and valence band are separated by a large energy gap is a poor conductor of electric current (Figure 5-8). Even an increase in temperature and the presence of a large potential difference cannot provide the valence electrons with sufficient energy to jump over the large gap and reach the empty conduction band. The electrons remain locked in the valence band where they do not have sufficient energy to drift away from their atoms.

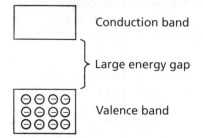

Figure 5-8. Insulator.

Such solids are called **insulators.** Examples of insulators are diamond, phosphorus, iodine, glass, and rubber. Insulators are typically nonmetallic substances.

Conductors

A solid in which the conduction band overlaps the valence band is a good conductor of electric current (Figure 5-9). Electrons in the highest sublevels of the valence band need gain only a small increment of energy to be promoted to the conduction band. The necessary energy may be obtained from the thermal motion of the atoms, even at room temperature. When a potential difference is applied to the solid, these electrons move through the solid in one direction and constitute an electric current. Most metals, particularly aluminum, copper, and silver, behave this way and are called **conductors.**

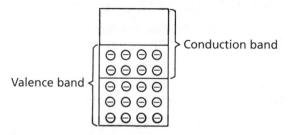

Figure 5-9. Conductor.

The **resistivity** of a solid is the resistance in ohms of a uniform rod of unit length and with unit cross-section area. The **conductivity** of a solid is the reciprocal of its resistivity. Increasing the temperature of a conductor decreases its conductivity because the electron migration through the solid is interrupted more effectively and more frequently by collision with the more energetic atom kernels of the solid. These collisions result in the conversion of electron kinetic energy to heat.

Semiconductors

Metalloids such as silicon and germanium have small forbidden gaps between their valence and conduction bands and are called **semiconductors** (Figure 5-10). At low temperatures semiconductors behave as insulators, because only the most energetic electrons can jump over to the conduction band. The presence of a potential difference, therefore, leads only to a small electric current. As the temperature rises, however, more and more electrons make the transition from the valence band to the conduction band, and an applied potential difference then leads to more current. The conductivity of semiconductors, therefore, increases with increasing temperature.

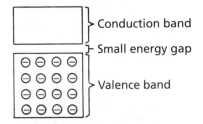

Figure 5.10. Semiconductor.

The Electron-sea Model

A major accomplishment of the modern **Band Model** is that it explains why increasing the temperature improves the conductivity of some solids (semiconductors) but weakens the conductivity of others (conductors). The classical **Electron-sea Model** did not recognize the existence of energy bands. Instead, it postulated that conductivity and resistivity is decided by the number of electrons that can be dislodged from their atoms and made to join the current. The dichotomy of the opposite effects of increasing temperature could not be explained with that model in mind.

QUESTIONS

177. Energy bands exist in atoms that are in (1) the gaseous state   (2) the solid state   (3) the plasma state   (4) any state

178. The highest energy band that contains electrons is the   (1) valence band   (2) energy gap band   (3) conduction band   (4) forbidden zone band

179. The largest separation between the valence and conduction bands exists in   (1) conductors   (2) insulators   (3) semiconductors   (4) superconductors

180. Increasing the temperature of a conductor (1) increases its conductivity   (2) increases its resistivity   (3) has no effect on its conductivity or resistivity

181. Overlapping valence and conduction bands exist in   (1) conductors   (2) semiconductors   (3) insulators   (4) none of the above

Thinking and Analyzing

182. How are energy bands different from energy levels?

183. What is the conduction band of a solid material?

184. Compare and contrast materials that are electrical conductors, insulators, and semiconductors. How do they behave differently from each other? What is the physical basis for this difference?

185. What is resistivity and conductivity and how are these quantities related?

186. What was a major shortcoming of the classical Electron-sea model?

TYPES OF SEMICONDUCTORS

Earlier you learned about the general properties of semiconductors. Now you are ready to learn about the different types of semiconductors and how each one can be used in electronic devices.

N-Type Semiconductors

Inserting small amounts of certain impurities into a semiconducting material dramatically increases the conductivity of the semiconductor. This process is called **doping.** For example, if a small amount of arsenic is added to a molten sample of silicon, the arsenic atoms become distributed uniformly throughout the mixture as the sample solidifies. The silicon atoms have four valence electrons each, and, in the solid state, each of the four forms a covalent bond with a valence electron of a neighboring atom. But arsenic atoms have five valence electrons each. Four of these electrons form covalent bonds with neighboring silicon atoms, while the fifth remains unbound or "free."

The presence of these free electrons introduces new allowed energy levels between the original valence and conduction bands of the silicon. The new energy levels lie just below the conduction band and are occupied by the "free" electrons. Since these electrons are closer to the conduction band, they require less additional energy to be promoted into it. The thermal energy of the solid, therefore, suffices to promote more electrons into the conduction band and, under the influence of a potential difference, the electrons migrate through the sample. Thus, the conductivity of the semiconductor is improved by the introduction of the "impurity" atoms.

A silicon crystal under these conditions is said to be **doped** with arsenic. Doping agents such as arsenic or antimony that introduce free electrons into the semiconductor are called **donor** materials. Since the majority charge carriers are negative (free electrons), the doped silicon crystal is referred to as an **N-type semiconductor.**

P-Type Semiconductors

If small amounts of gallium, indium, or aluminum, whose atoms have only three valence electrons, are introduced into silicon or germanium crystals, only three covalent bonds are formed between the impurity atoms and the neighboring atoms of the semiconductor. One of the four valence electrons of every silicon atom that is in contact with an impurity atom lacks an electron with which to form a bond. The absence of the fourth electron is described as a **hole.** Once again, new allowed energy levels are introduced between the valence and conduction bands of the semiconductor. In this case the new levels lie just above the valence band.

At room temperature there is sufficient thermal energy to promote valence electrons from nearby covalent bonds to the new levels, since the gap between the valence band and the new levels is small. These promoted electrons have enough energy to break away from their own bonds, migrate toward a hole, and fill it by forming the missing bond. In the process of doing so, however, the migrating electron creates a hole at its original location. The hole, therefore, is transferred, rather than eliminated.

In the presence of an applied potential difference, the promoted electrons will fill holes by moving in one direction—toward the positive end of the semiconductor. This movement of electrons results in the migration of the holes toward the negative, and lower potential, end of the semiconductor. An analogous process is the bubble of air that rises in a liquid as it is successively filled with liquid material.

Since the holes migrate to the negative end of the semiconductor, they behave like free positive charges. Semiconductors doped in this way are therefore called **P-type semiconductors.** Since these doping agents introduce holes that accept electrons, they are referred to as **acceptor** materials. The majority charge carriers in a P-type semiconductor are the holes. Some electrons may also migrate across the semiconductor under the influence of the potential difference, but they are the minority charge carriers.

SEMICONDUCTOR DEVICES

Diodes (—▶■—)
The simplest and most fundamental semiconductor device used in electronics is the **diode.** It consists of a P-type semiconductor joined to an N-type semiconductor. The interface region between the two types of semiconductors is referred to as a **P-N junction.** The arrow in the symbol for the diode always points from the P-type to the N-type semiconductor.

In the vicinity of the P-N junction, free electrons in the N-type come near holes in the P-type. This leads to a certain amount of migration of electrons and holes across the junction. Free electrons from the N-types that encounter holes in the P-type "fall" into the holes, form the missing covalent bond, and remain locked there. Soon the N-type develops a net positive charge and the P-type develops a net negative charge (Figure 5-11). The resulting electric field then acts to prevent any further diffusion of electrons and holes across the junction and is known as the **electric field barrier.**

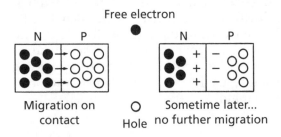

Figure 5-11. A P-N junction.

Biasing
When a potential difference is applied across a diode, the electric field barrier may be enhanced or opposed, depending upon the polarity of the potential difference. This phenomenon is known as **biasing.**

Reverse Biasing If the N-type (or cathode) is connected to the positive terminal of a battery, and the P-type (or anode) to the negative terminal, (Figure 5-12), the electric field barrier is reinforced. The free electrons in the N-type and the holes in the P-type migrate away from the junction, toward opposite ends of the diode. The diode is emptied of both free electrons and holes. The N-type acquires an even greater net positive charge and the P-type acquires an even greater net negative charge. The battery does not replenish the stock of free electrons and holes since the negative end of the diode is connected to the negative terminal of the battery, and the positive end of the diode is connected to the positive terminal. In the absence of free electrons and holes, the diode behaves more like an insulator, and only a very small current flows through it. Under these conditions the diode is said to be **reverse biased.** Only when the potential difference is truly large (200–300 volts) does this process break down, and an "avalanche" of electric current occurs.

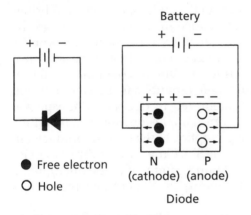

Figure 5-12. Reverse biasing.

Forward Biasing If, on the other hand, the N-type semiconductor of the diode is connected to the negative terminal of a battery and the P-type is connected to the positive terminal, the results are very different (Figure 5-13). In this case, the electric field barrier is negated, and free electrons in the N-type and the holes in the P-type migrate toward the N-P junction and each other. The free electrons "fall" into the holes, and both are annihilated. Electrons are then drawn from the negative terminal of the battery into the now positively charged N-type, replenishing the stock of free electrons in that half of the diode. Similarly, electrons are drawn from the now negatively charged P-type into the positive terminal of the battery, thereby re-creating the holes in that half of the diode. The newly arrived free electrons and holes migrate to the junction and the entire process is

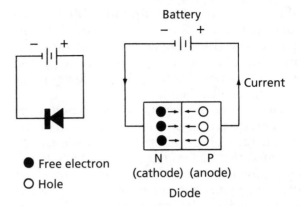

Figure 5-13. Forward biasing.

repeated over and over again. As a result, a large current flows through the diode and the circuit. For this process to occur, the applied potential difference (the "bias") must, of course, be greater than the potential set up by the barrier.

A diode connected to a potential difference in this manner is said to be **forward biased.** The current through the diode does not obey Ohm's Law. Instead, the current-potential difference relationship is typically as shown in Figure 5-14.

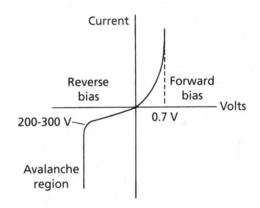

Figure 5-14. Current versus potential difference for forward and reverse bias of diode.

Applications of the Diode

If a diode is connected to a source of alternating current, it will allow current through in one direction (when forward biased), but not in the opposite direction (when reversed biased). The diode then serves as a **rectifier,** converting alternating current to direct current.

When a diode is forward biased, the free electrons of the N-type that "fall" into the holes of the P-type at the junction lose energy. The lost energy is emitted as photons of light in a manner analogous to the photons emitted by electrons that descend from higher to lower energy levels in an atom (p. 143). The junction area of the diode, as a result, glows and serves as a **semiconductor light**

bulb. Such **LED's** (**Light Emitting Diodes**) are widely used as digital displays in electronic calculators, digital clocks, traffic lights, and other instruments. LED's require much less energy and have much longer lifetimes than ordinary tungsten-filament light bulbs.

The reverse process occurs in **photodiodes.** When protons strike the function area of a diode, their energy is absorbed by electrons. The excited electrons are raised from the valence band to the conduction band. This creates free electrons and holes that migrate through the diode. A current is thereby produced in the external circuit and is sustained so long as light shines on the diode. The current produced can operate instruments connected to the circuit. Burglar alarms, automatic door openers, and many other devices function on the basis of this principle.

Transistors

Another semiconducting device is the **transistor** (a combination of the words transfer and resistor). A transistor consists of one type of semiconductor sandwiched between two semiconductors of the opposite type. In an NPN transistor, two N-types share a P-type; in the PNP transistor, two P-types share an N-type. The middle semiconductor, called the **base,** is made very narrow, usually about one-hundredth of a centimeter thick, and is much less heavily doped than the other two semiconductors.

Suppose an NPN transistor is connected to two batteries as in Figure 5-15. The N-type connected to the negative terminal of battery *A* becomes the primary source of free electrons in the transistor; it is labeled the **emitter.** The other N-type is then called the **collector.** The emitter-

base junction is forward biased by battery *A*, while the collector-base junction is reverse biased by battery *B*. The negative terminal of battery *A* pushes the free electrons in the emitter toward the junction with the base. Since the P-type base is very narrow and lightly doped, the migrating electrons encounter few holes. About 98% of them make it through the base without becoming trapped in a hole. These electrons enter the collector where they are attracted to the positive terminal of the battery. As a result, a large current flows through the emitter-collector path of the circuit.

The 2% of migrating electrons that are absorbed by holes lead to the creation of a much smaller current through the emitter-base path of the circuit, since the emitter-base junction is forward biased. Thus a small emitter-base current is associated with a much larger emitter-collector current. The two currents are directly proportional to each other.

Transistorized Circuits

A small change in the emitter-base current brings about a large change in the current through the collector. This enables a transistor to **amplify** variations in a small current, such as that produced by sound in a circuit containing a microphone, into larger variations in a greater current, such as that required to operate a loudspeaker system. The current in the loudspeaker, therefore, is an amplified replica of the current produced in the microphone. Since the current varies in magnitude as the sound coming into the microphone changes, the loudspeaker faithfully reproduces the sound.

The operation of a PNP transistor is similar to that of the NPN type. The only differences are that the polarities of the connections are reversed and holes, rather than free electrons, do the moving (Figure 5-16).

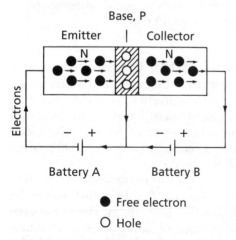

Figure 5-15. An NPN transistor connected to two batteries.

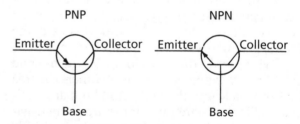

Figure 5-16. Symbols for transistors.

Integrated Circuits (I.C.'s)

By placing minute amounts of donor and acceptor impurities at particular locations within a single silicon crystal (called a **chip**), it is possible to create complicated networks of diodes, transistors, and resistors (undoped silicon) within a small area. Such miniaturized circuits are referred to as **integrated circuits.** Some chips have been designed to contain more than one thousand circuit components within the area of a thumbnail. These chips have made possible a massive reduction in the size of electronic instruments, and have revolutionized our way of life—from home computers to digital circuits to a host of other applications. More and greater advances are sure to come.

QUESTIONS

187. A doping material with three valence electrons is classified as   (1) an acceptor   (2) a resistor   (3) a donor   (4) a thermistor

188. N-type semiconductors are doped with   (1) gallium   (2) arsenic   (3) aluminum   (4) silicon

189. A semiconductor with *holes* is known as   (1) an N-type semiconductor   (2) a P-type semiconductor   (3) an H-type semiconductor   (4) an undoped semiconductor

190. A *donor* material donates   (1) free holes   (2) free protons   (3) free electrons   (4) free atoms

191. A doping material containing five valence electrons is classified as   (1) an acceptor   (2) a thermistor   (3) an intensifier   (4) a donor

192. What does the following circuit diagram represent?   (1) forward-biased diode   (2) reverse-biased diode   (3) forward-biased transistor   (4) reverse-biased transistor

193. As the temperature of a semiconductor increases, its conductivity   (1) decreases   (2) increases   (3) remains the same

194. Which would occur if the connections to the source of potential difference in the following diagram were reversed?   (1) The current in the circuit would decrease. (2) The current in the circuit would increase. (3) The current in the circuit would remain the same.

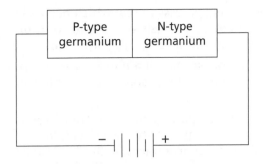

195. An example of a semiconductor is   (1) germanium   (2) diamond   (3) copper   (4) phosphorus

196. A *hole* is created by   (1) a missing atom   (2) an electric drill   (3) an unbound valence electron

197. When a free electron and a hole meet, they   (1) are mutually annihilated   (2) repel each other   (3) pass through each other

198. The N-type semiconductor of a junction diode   (1) develops a net negative charge   (2) develops a net positive charge   (3) remains neutral   (4) develops alternating charge types

199. To establish a reverse biased diode, you   (1) connect the P-type to the positive terminal of a battery   (2) connect the N-type to the positive terminal of a battery   (3) connect opposite ends of the diode to the same battery terminal

200. A reverse biased diode allows   (1) almost no current through   (2) a current of holes from the P-type to the N-type   (3) a current of electrons from the N-type to the P-type

201. To establish a forward biased diode, you   (1) connect the N-type to the negative terminal of a battery   (2) connect the N-type to the positive terminal of a battery   (3) connect opposite ends of the diode to the same battery terminal

202. For current to flow through a diode, it must be   (1) connected to a small potential difference   (2) reverse biased   (3) forward biased   (4) at a high temperature

203. A diode connected to a source of alternating current   (1) rectifies the A.C. to D.C. (2) allows the current through it to alternate in direction   (3) allows no current through   (4) amplifies the current

204. An LED consists of a diode that   (1) is reverse biased   (2) is forward biased   (3) contains an incandescent filament   (4) is neither forward nor reverse biased

205. The reverse process of that which occurs in LED's occurs in   (1) transistors   (2) forward biased diodes   (3) rectifiers   (4) photodiodes

206. The middle section of a transistor is known as the   (1) emitter   (2) collector   (3) divider   (4) base

207. The emitter part of an NPN transistor is   (1) either of the two N-type semiconductors   (2) the P-type semiconductor   (3) the N-type connected to the positive terminal of a battery   (4) the N-type connected to the negative terminal of a battery

208. The emitter-collector current in a transistor is   (1) greater than the emitter-base current   (2) equal to the emitter-base current   (3) smaller than the emitter-base current

209. Small variations in one current can be amplified into larger variations in another current by   (1) a forward biased diode   (2) a transistor   (3) a rectifier   (4) an acceptor

210. In which of the following is the energy of photons converted to electrical energy?   (1) photodiodes   (2) transistors   (3) LED's   (4) rectifiers

Thinking and Analyzing

211. What occurs during the process of doping?

212. How does the electron configuration of the impurity atoms relate to that of the semiconductor atoms in an N-type semiconductor?

213. How does the electron configuration of the impurity atoms relate to that of the semiconductor atoms in a P-type semiconductor?

214. What is a diode? What happens when a diode is reverse biased? Forward biased?

215. How does a transistor use semiconductor materials?

216. What is the significance of integrated circuits?

Laboratory Skills

Students are expected to master a number of skills as part of the Physical Setting: Physics course. Some of these are general skills, applicable to any scientific investigation, while others are specific laboratory procedures.

GENERAL SKILLS

1. Apply basic mathematics to data in order to arrive at an appropriate solution to a problem.

2. Formulate a question or define a problem for investigation; and develop a hypothesis to be tested.

3. Collect, organize, and graph data.

4. Make predictions based on experimental data.

5. Formulate generalizations or conclusions based on an investigation.

6. Demonstrate safety skills in handling equipment, using chemicals, heating materials, setting up electric circuits, and working with radioactive substances.

EXAMPLES OF SPECIFIC LABORATORY PROCEDURES

1. Determine the change in length of a spring as a function of force. Graph the experimental data.

2. Determine the period of a pendulum for a given mass and a given length.

3. Set up series and parallel circuits, each consisting of a power supply and two resistors. Determine the current through and the potential difference across each resistor and the circuit as a whole.

4. Map a magnetic field using a compass and a permanent magnet or electromagnet.

5. Determine the path of a light ray passing from air through another medium and back into air. Draw the ray diagram.

6. Formulate inferences about the contents of a black box (a sealed system into which one cannot see) by making external observations.

General Skills

1. **Apply basic mathematics to data in order to arrive at an appropriate solution to a problem.** You should be able to determine the precision of instruments used in an investigation. You should also be able to record data to the correct number of significant digits based on the precision of the instrument used. (See Mathematical Skills section, pp. 1–2.)

You should be able to organize collected data into appropriate categories, graph the data when applicable, and arrive at valid relationships based on the data. In general, the four basic operations—addition, subtraction, multiplication, and division—are all that are necessary to solve a problem. Occasionally, squaring and finding the square root are part of the solution. Examples of these skills are presented later in this section (see spring experiment).

Frequently, graphed data results in a straight line with a y-intercept of zero. You should be able to calculate the slope of such a line by using the formula slope $= \Delta y/\Delta x$. The value of the slope is often an important physical constant.

2. **Formulate a question, or define a problem for investigation, and develop a hypothesis to be tested.** Before proceeding with an experiment, you should define the problem under investigation and formulate a hypothesis. This helps to structure the experiment and to clarify its purpose. For example, one hypothesis that might be formulated when investigating a swinging pendulum might be as follows: *If the length of a pendulum is increased while its angle of swing and mass are kept constant, then the period will also increase.*

Note some key characteristics of the above hypothesis:

a) It has an If . . . , then . . . format.
b) It describes the experiment to be done.

c) It specifies what measurements will be made.
d) It proposes what will occur, which may or may not be found to be true.

These are features of an ideal hypothesis.

Note also that the above hypothesis requires that the length of the pendulum will be changed while its angle of swing and mass will be kept constant. During an experiment, you should change only one variable at a time when possible and hold all others constant. This helps to regulate the experiment. This is also called the definition of a **controlled experiment.**

3. **Collect, organize, and graph data.** During an experiment, raw data are collected. These data may be recorded in a log, chart, or data table. It is important to organize the chart or data table before beginning the experiment. For example, suppose you are measuring the voltage across a circuit every 10 seconds. You will only have time to enter your voltage reading before the next reading must be taken. If you had to enter the elapsed time, too, you might not be able to record the data quickly enough. Therefore, prepare as much of the table as possible.

Graphed data often displays a relationship between variables that cannot be easily ascertained from raw data alone. Choose the size of the intervals on both axes appropriately so that your graph is neither too small nor too large. Once chosen, keep the intervals uniform. Axes should be labelled with their variable name and unit. The entire graph should be given a title.

In many cases in physics, it is unnecessary for the line to run through every data point on the graph. A reasonable best-fit line suffices to establish the relationship between the variables being plotted. A best-fit line is one that follows the trend of the data but might leave some data points off the line on either side.

4. **Make predictions based on experimental data.** Graphing is an excellent method of presenting data clearly. Graphs also help to predict values that are not data points through *interpolation* and *extrapolation.*

For example, consider the graph of experimental data in Figure LS-1 that shows change of length of a spring plotted as a function of the force on the spring. From the graph you can predict that a force of 27 newtons will stretch the spring approximately 0.13 m (prediction A in Figure 6-1). If the spring were to be stretched to 0.225 m, you can predict that a force of 45 N will be needed (prediction B in the figure). These are examples of **interpolation.** These predicted values are *within* the range of the original data, namely 0–50 N and 0–0.25 m.

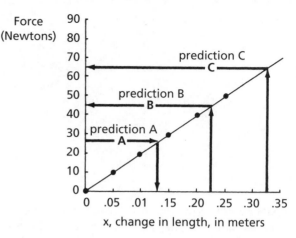

Figure LS-1. Force vs. change in length of a spring.

You could also predict how much force will be needed to stretch the spring to 0.33—approximately 65 N (prediction C in the figure). This is an example of **extrapolation.** The predicted values are *outside* the range of the original data. Extrapolation must be done cautiously. It is reasonable to predict values that lie slightly beyond the ends of the range of original data, but not too far beyond them. It would not be reasonable to extend the graph to predict a force needed to stretch the spring 0.70 m. That amount of stretch might cause the spring to be deformed or snap.

5. **Formulate generalizations or conclusions based on an investigation.** The results of an experiment are collected and analyzed. For a conclusion to be meaningful, the experiment must be repeated many times, and all the data obtained must be included in the analysis. The scope of the conclusion must be limited by the experimental data.

It is important to have confidence in data obtained. The best way to do this is to make several trials of each measurement and, if the results are close, determine an average value. Below are four measurements of the period of a pendulum whose length is 10.0 cm:

Trial 1 — 0.636 s/swing
Trial 2 — 0.632 s/swing
Trial 3 — 0.855 s/swing
Trial 4 — 0.635 s/swing

Trial 3 seems out of line with the other measurements and may indicate a procedural error. All the data should be rechecked and the measurements redone.

6. **Safety in the Laboratory.** You should practice the following safety precautions in the laboratory.

- Do not handle equipment or chemicals until you have been given specific instructions by your teacher.

- Report at once any equipment in the laboratory that appears to be unusual (broken, cracked, frayed), or any activity that appears to be proceeding in an abnormal fashion.
- Lab work space must be kept clean and uncluttered. Clothing and hair must not restrict your movement, interfere with equipment, or present potential hazards. When using chemicals, wear safety glasses and aprons. Do not play or run in the laboratory.
- Familiarize yourself with the location and use of the fire extinguisher, fire blanket, and eye baths.
- Some physics experiments may involve the firing of projectiles. Make sure the area where the projectile will be 'shot' is clear. Take care in loading, cocking, and firing the spring mechanism. Give a warning signal before firing.
- When using chemicals, never taste, touch, or inhale them. Never work with a combustible chemical if there is an open flame nearby.
- When heating material, use proper equipment such as gloves or tongs to handle hot objects. If you are heating material in a test tube, be sure the open end is not pointed toward anyone.
- Electrical wiring should be checked for fraying, bare metal exposure, and loose connections. Always have a circuit checked out by your instructor. Whenever possible use low voltage and low current arrangements. Never work with electricity if you or the working area are wet. Do not touch "live" wires. Turn the electricity off first.
- Always use tongs when handling radioactive material. Keep radioactive sources at arm's distance.
- Be aware of the symbols often used to indicate hazards (Figure LS-2).

Use safety goggles and aprons.

Noxious or poisonous vapors.

Danger of breakage, as with glass.

Open flame.

Poisonous.

Material is caustic or corrosive.

Electric shock caution.

Potentially explosive.

Radioactive.

Figure LS-2. Hazard symbols.

Specific Laboratory Procedures

1. **Determine the change in length of a spring as a function of force. Graph the experimental data.** The procedure for performing this laboratory investigation is as follows:
   a. Mark the position of the bottom of the unstretched spring as shown by position A in Figure LS-3.
   b. Suspend a known weight (in newtons) from the spring. (If only the mass of the suspended object is provided, convert mass to weight by using the formula

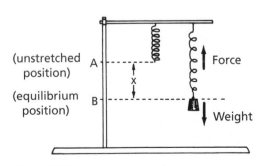
Figure LS-3.

$W = mg$.) Wait for equilibrium to be established. At equilibrium the weight (acting downward) is equal to the force exerted by the spring (acting upward).

c. Mark the new position of the bottom of the stretched spring, as shown by position B in Figure LS-3.

d. Measure the distance (in meters) between points A and B with a ruler. This distance is the change in the length of the spring.

e. Repeat steps a through d with at least five different weights. In each case record the force, F, (which is equivalent to the weight) in one column and the corresponding change in length (x) in another column. Make sure the columns are properly labelled, as in the sample in Table LS-1.

Table LS-1

Force (F) in newtons	Change in length (x) in meters
0.30	.0201
0.60	.0402
1.15	.0701
1.50	.1003
2.20	.1500

f. The relationship between force and change in length is best visualized by plotting the data points on a graph. Axes should be labelled properly and an appropriate scale chosen for each. Choose scales so that all data points appear on the graph but are as far apart as possible (see Figure LS-4).

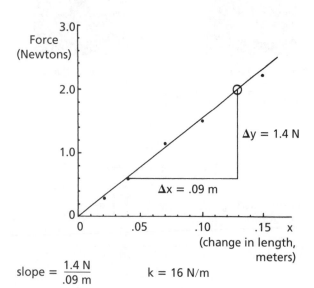

slope $= \dfrac{1.4\ N}{.09\ m}$ $k = 16\ N/m$

Figure LS-4.

g. A straight line graph with a y-intercept of zero indicates that $F = kx$, where k is a constant equal to the slope of the line. The force, F, exerted by the spring is directly proportional to the change in its length, x (Hooke's Law). The value of k as determined from the graph in Figure LS-4 is 16. N/m. (Note that the line does not run precisely through every data point. It is the best-fit line for the data obtained.)

2. **Determine the period of a pendulum for a given mass and a given length.**

The procedure for performing this laboratory investigation is as follows:

a. Record the length of the pendulum, measured from the top of the string to the center of the bob.

b. Pull the bob to one side and, while holding the string taut, measure the angle formed between the vertical and the string with a protractor (angle A in Figure LS-5).

c. Release the bob of the pendulum and start the stopwatch at the same time.

d. Allow the pendulum to swing through twenty complete round trips (see Figure LS-5).

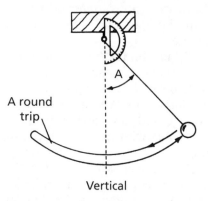

Figure LS-5. Determining the period of a pendulum.

e. At the instant the twentieth round trip is completed (when the bob returns to its starting point) stop the watch. Record the time to the correct precision.

f. The period, T, is the time it takes for the pendulum to complete one round trip. Divide the total time measured in step e by 20.0 to find the period of the pendulum for the given mass and length.

g. To verify that each of the 20 swings took the same amount of time, repeat the experiment by holding the bob at different angles. The period, T, turns out to be independent of the amplitude, angle A.

3. **Set up series and parallel circuits, each consisting of a power supply and two resistors. Determine the current through and the potential difference across each resistor and the circuit as a whole.**

a. Set up a series circuit as shown in Figure LS-6.

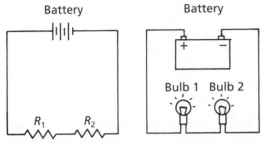

Figure LS-6. A series circuit.

b. Current, in amperes, is measured by inserting an ammeter in series with the branch of the circuit whose current is to be measured. In the case of a series circuit there is only one branch. To find the current through either resistor or through the circuit as a whole, insert the ammeter in series anywhere in the circuit. (See Figure LS-7.) Care must be taken to connect the terminals of the ammeter correctly. If those terminals are labeled plus and minus, the plus terminal of the ammeter should be connected to the wire coming from the plus terminal of the power supply. Likewise, the minus terminal of the ammeter should be connected to the wire coming from the minus terminal of the power supply. If the ammeter is hooked up incorrectly the needle on the scale will move in the wrong direction, below the zero mark.

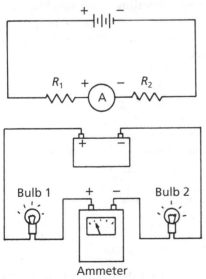

Figure LS-7. An ammeter in a series circuit.

c. Read the current on the scale and record the value to the correct number of significant digits. The reading on the ammeter scale in Figure LS-8, for example, should be recorded as 0.66 amperes. (The smallest marked intervals on the scale represent 0.1 amperes each, so the precision of the ammeter is 0.01 amperes. See Mathematical Skills section.)

Figure LS-8. Reading an ammeter scale.

d. Potential difference, in volts, is measured by connecting a voltmeter in parallel with the circuit element whose potential difference is to be measured. To find, for example, the potential difference across bulb 1 in Figure LS-6, connect the voltmeter in parallel with that bulb, as in Figure LS-9. To measure the potential difference of the circuit as a whole, connect the voltmeter in parallel with the power supply (see Figure LS-10). Again, care must be taken to connect the terminals of the voltmeter properly (follow the same procedure as in step b). Record the potential difference to the correct number of significant figures.

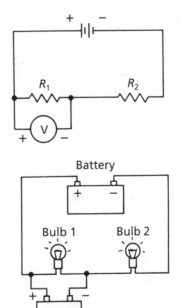

Figure LS-9. Finding the potential difference across bulb 1.

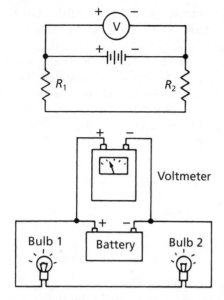

Figure LS-10. Finding the potential difference of the series circuit as a whole.

e. Set up a parallel circuit as shown in Figure LS-11.

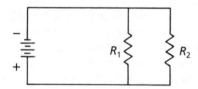

Figure LS-11. A parallel circuit.

f. To measure the current through each resistor (bulb) connect the ammeter in series with each branch. (See Figure LS-12.) To measure the current in the circuit as a

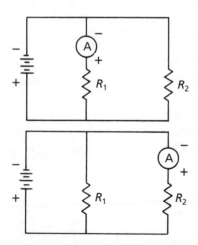

Figure LS-12. *a.* Ammeter measures current through resistor 1. *b.* Ammeter measures current through resistor 2.

whole, connect the ammeter in series with the main line of the circuit. (See Figure LS-13.)

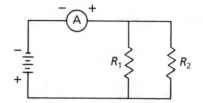

Figure LS-13. Ammeter measures current in the circuit as a whole.

g. To measure the potential difference across either resistor or the circuit as a whole, connect the voltmeter in parallel with all three, as shown in Figure LS-14.

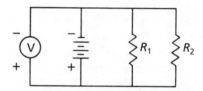

Figure LS-14. Measuring potential difference in a parallel circuit.

4. **Map a magnetic field using a compass and a permanent magnet or electromagnet.**

   a. Use the compass as a "test magnet." Place it in various locations in the vicinity of the permanent magnet or electromagnet and observe the direction in which the N-pole of the compass points. At each location draw a small arrow near the compass indicating the direction assumed by the N-pole of the compass. (See Figure LS-15.) This is the direction of the magnetic field at each location.

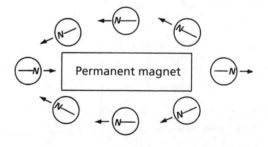

Figure LS-15.

   b. After a sufficient number of arrows have been drawn, the magnetic field can be "mapped." Draw field lines so that they pass through or near the arrows in a parallel manner. Deduce the north and south end of the magnet from the direction of the field lines. (See Figure LS-16.)

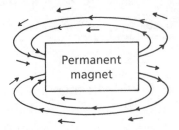

Figure LS-16.

5. **Determine the path of a light ray passing from air through another medium and back into air.** Draw the ray diagram.

   a. Place a rectangular block of glass or lucite on a piece of paper. The paper should rest on top of a piece of cardboard or styrofoam.

   b. Trace the shape of the block on the paper with a sharp-pointed pencil. Remove the block; then draw and label point P_1, as shown in Figure LS-17.

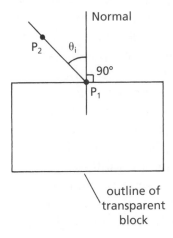

Figure LS-17.

   c. Using a ruler and protractor, draw a line through point P_1, perpendicular to the top line of the traced block outline. (See Figure LS-17.) Label this line the "normal."

   d. Using a ruler, draw a second line through point P_1 at some angle, θ, from the normal. Label this angle θ_i, the angle of incidence.

   e. Draw and label point P_2 on the second line, as shown in Figure LS-17, at a distance of approximately 5 cm from point P_1.

   f. Insert a pin through each of the points P_1 and P_2. Make sure each pin stands vertically. Place the block back on the paper so that its edges match the original tracing.

   g. Lower your head until the plane of the paper is at eye level. With only one eye open, look through the transparent block at the two pins. Move your head until the pins appear to be lined up one behind the other. Place a ruler on the paper so that it is aimed from your eye to the image of the lined-up pins. Trace a line in this direction on the paper all the way to the block. (See Figure LS-18.)

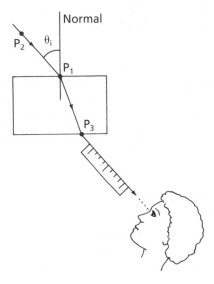

Figure LS-18.

   h. Remove the block; then draw and label point P_3 (see Figure LS-18) where the traced line meets the block.

   i. Draw a straight line connecting points P_1 and P_3. The light ray coming from P_2 in the direction of P_1 passed through the transparent block in the direction of line $\overline{P_1P_3}$ and emerged at point P_3 to enter your eye. The path from P_2 to P_1 to P_3 to your eye constitutes the ray diagram in this case. It should appear bent, or refracted, twice, when entering and exiting the block.

6. **Formulate inferences about the contents of a black box (a sealed system into which one cannot see) by making external observations.**

   Use any available tool to determine the nature or characteristics of the contents of the box (other than opening it and looking inside). A compass should reveal whether the contents are magnetic. A charged pith ball can be helpful in determining whether the contents are charged or electrically neutral. Shaking the box and listening to the sounds made, weighing it, smelling it, measuring its temperature, and a host of other techniques all provide clues to help solve the mystery of what is in the box.

The Robots Are Coming, But They're too Small to See

Look around you. You are surrounded by a variety of manufactured products from the home you live in to the clothes you wear to the vehicle you ride in to get to school. Every one of these products is put together from raw materials. Lumber, glass, and concrete, for example, are some of the raw materials used to construct a building. Steel, rubber, and vinyl are some of the raw materials used to assemble an automobile.

There is a technology on the horizon that plans to utilize raw materials on a much smaller scale—so small that you can't even see them without high-powered instruments. The technology is generally termed nanotechnology. The prefix *nano-* means one billionth, so one nanometer is one billionth of a meter (1×10^{-9} m). This is roughly about the size of 3 or 4 atoms put together. Atoms, and the molecules they combine to form, are the building blocks of matter. The combination of atoms and molecules determines the characteristics of matter. A drop of water, for example, contains trillions of water molecules that are made up of hydrogen and oxygen atoms.

Nanotechnology is manufacturing on a molecular level, building products using atoms and molecules as raw materials. The raw materials for buildings and automobiles might then become atoms and molecules from dirt, sand, and air. Through nanotechnology, researchers expect to be able to use a few elements to make anything from consumer products to food to medicine. Nanotechnology would revolutionize manufacturing as digital technologies have revolutionized information storage.

To manipulate the trillions of atoms required to make useful products, researchers will have to develop tiny robots, or nanorobots. These robots would arrange atoms according to the directions provided by nanocomputers. In addition, they would make copies of themselves. One nanorobot would copy itself, and then those copies would make copies of themselves. In a short time, trillions of nanorobots working together would be able to assemble new products quickly and efficiently.

In some ways, manufacturing would be similar to placing a sheet of paper on a copy machine. Just as the copy machine will make copies without any further human effort, nanorobots will copy themselves and their products without further human effort. Rather than focusing on manufacturing, the human effort will instead lie in the design and planning of new products.

The potential benefits of nanotechnology are astounding. For one thing, arranging atoms into exact positions will eliminate defects in products. As a result, the quality and reliability of manufactured products will improve dramatically. In addition, nanorobots could arrange atoms so that they behave in a certain way. For example, a street might repair itself when a crack appears. As a result, products won't wear out, break down, or fall apart over time.

Another advantage is that the cost of products will drop as a result of nanotechnology because the raw materials, atoms and molecules, will come from readily available resources that may be as simple as water, soil, or grass. And, because nanorobots will be able to copy themselves, the cost of manufacturing will be low.

As you may have concluded by now, nanotechnology will also benefit the environment. Raw materials, such as trees and coal, will no longer need to be removed from the earth. In addition, waste will be minimal since every atom will be accounted for in product design. Thus pollution won't be released into the environment.

Nanotechnology is still several years off. The concept of nanotechnology was first introduced in 1959 by Richard Feynmen, a scientist who won the 1965 Nobel prize in physics. However, it wasn't until new types of microscopes and powerful computer programs were developed that his ideas are finally turning into reality. Some estimate that it will take another decade to truly utilize nanotechnology, but others expect the visible result to take much longer.

Don't look at the length of time as an unfortunate delay, however. Society will definitely need the time to adjust to the changes brought about by nanotechnology. After all, this technology has the potential to completely change the structure of society. For one thing, nanorobots will take over much of the work people currently do. Thus the nature of work and employment will change. In addition, products of nanotechnology will be so readily available and inexpensive that money and wealth will no longer have meaning.

Nanotechnology will introduce another issue by developing products that do not wear out or can repair themselves. For one thing, these materials may not break down easily in the natural environment. Businesses are currently based on the fact that people buy new products as old ones wear out. The nature and goals of business will have to change as a result of nanotechnology. In addition, researchers will have to find ways to recycle products that don't break down over time.

Nanotechnology also has some associated dangers. Some researchers have warned that humans may lose control of nanorobots programmed to copy themselves. Even more dangerous is the possibility that nanotechnology will be deliberately misused for military aggression and germ warfare. Dealing with these issues before the technology becomes a reality is crucial to the positive development of nanotechnology. Government and other organizations have already begun studying these issues in an attempt to propose guidelines for the development of the technology.

The first results of nanotechnology will be small compared with the possibilities it holds. Nanotechnology won't truly happen until the first self-replicating nanorobot is developed. Until then, researchers around the world are joining in this technological revolution.

Questions

1. What is meant by the term nanotechnology?
2. What are some of the benefits of products manufactured through nanotechnology?
3. How will nanotechnology affect the environment, both positively and negatively?
4. In what ways might nanotechnology affect people living in poor countries who presently do not have access to food and education?
5. How will nanotechnology change the meaning of wealth in society?

A Laboratory in Space

Circling Earth every 90 minutes is a state-of-the-art research facility known as the International Space Station. The Space Station resembles a small city in space that orbits at a distance of 400 kilometers. The space station is a place where people from around the world can live and work for long periods of time.

The first piece of the space station was Zarya, the Russian control module that was launched into orbit November 20, 1998. A few weeks later, on December 4, 1998, the U.S. module Unity was launched into space. On December 7, 1998, the two modules were connected. Onto this base, more than 100 other pieces will be connected before the station is complete. The final components are scheduled for 2006, but the final date may be later than that due to technical and financial delays.

When complete, the Space Station will be about the size of two football fields. It is composed of many modules, most of which are being constructed and attached in space. Sixteen countries, including the United States, Japan, Russia, Canada, Belgium, Denmark, France, Germany, Italy, Netherlands, Norway, Spain, Sweden, Switzerland, United Kingdom, and Brazil are collaborating to produce the space station. Assembling the Space Station will require 45 launches—36 from the United States and 9 from Russia. In addition, construction will involve more than 1,700 hours of space walks, which is about double the number of hours U.S. astronauts have walked in space throughout the entire space program.

The first full-time crew moved into the International Space Station on November 2, 2000. The three-person crew and its succes-

sors will be living aboard a relatively small module known as the Zvezda module. A larger component for living quarters, the U.S. habitation module, is scheduled for development in 2005. Once this larger module is connected to the station, a crew of up to seven people will be able to live and work aboard the station at one time.

The idea of living in space isn't all that new. Russian cosmonauts have been living in space for more than 30 years, beginning with the Salyut space station and then in the Mir space station. Prior to the International Space Station, Mir was the largest space station every built. *Mir*, which is Russian for peace, became a base for international cooperation in exploring space, including dockings by United States space shuttles.

The main purpose of the International Space Station is research and exploration. In fact, astronauts aboard the Space Station will spend more time working on experiments than anything else. The main areas of research are in the life sciences, Earth sciences, space science, engineering research, space product development, and microgravity science.

The reason for all the research is that the Space Station provides a unique environment in several ways. First, the Space Station environment has practically no gravity. Under these conditions, called microgravity, chemical reactions and human processes behave differently than they do on Earth. For example, molecules can be blended and substances created that would be impossible on Earth. The microgravity conditions will also allow scientists to study physics, combustion science, fluid flow, and crystal growth in a completely new way. Scientists hope that these experiments will lead to new industrial products and materials that can be used on Earth. In addition, watching the long-term effects of gravity in space will teach us about biological processes back on Earth, such as aging and osteoporosis.

The Space Station environment is also unique in that it allows researchers to observe Earth from different angles over long periods of time. The Space Station will help scientists identify changes in Earth's environment. They will use these observations to guide research projects conducted within the Space Station in order to improve our understanding of Earth's environment and the universe.

Finally, the Space Station is unique in that it serves as a stepping stone to future and more distant space exploration. In order to travel to other planets, such as Mars, scientists must understand the effects of long journeys on the human body. During past space travel scientists learned that living in microgravity leads to the weakening of bones and muscles. The Space Station will not only allow scientists to understand these effects, but also to study solutions that may make long-term space travel possible.

This research is no doubt exciting, but it does not come without a price. The Space Station is the most expensive single object ever built. The United States' participation has been estimated at $96 billion—a figure that nearly equals the combined cost of all of the Apollo missions to the moon. Some question whether the research is worth the cost, especially to the United States.

In addition to the monetary price, numerous astronauts and cosmonauts are risking their lives to complete the assembly in space. After new modules are docked with the space station, crew members must perform dangerous space walks on the exterior of the station to connect wires, deploy antennas, and complete other maintenance tasks. In the hostile environment of space, a mistake could be deadly. Equipment breakdowns and human errors have led to several accidents.

The countries spending billions of dollars, taking the risks, and waiting many years believe the benefits of the station will ultimately outweigh the enormous costs. Do you?

Questions

1. What is the International Space Station? Who is responsible for its development?
2. Is the International Space Station the first of its kind? Explain.
3. What type of research will be conducted from the Space Station?
4. What are some developments that may result from research conducted aboard the Space Station?
5. Provide an argument for and against the use of tax money to be spent on the Space Station.

Using and Conserving Earth's Natural Resources

Whenever you turn on an appliance, you are using electricity that was produced by a generator at your local power company. A generator is a device that converts mechanical into electrical energy. The mechanical energy is usually applied to a turbine, a device made up of many blades, each much like a propeller. The turbine must spin to turn the generator.

The source of the mechanical energy used to turn a turbine can vary. The most common sources are fossil fuels: coal, oil, and natural gas. When fossil fuels are burned, they release heat that is used to convert water into steam. The steam pushes against the blades of a turbine, spinning it. As a result, the generator produces electricity.

Fossil fuels are the most cost-effective sources of energy because they are relatively inexpensive to obtain and, for now, their supplies are readily available. However, obtaining and using fossil fuels damages the environment. Mining them damages land and water. Accidents, such as oil spills, damage ecosystems. Burning fossil fuels releases pollution into the atmosphere. In addition, supplies of fossil fuels are limited.

Fossil fuels are nonrenewable natural resources. A nonrenewable natural resource exists in a limited supply on Earth. This type of resource is used at a rate faster than the rate at which it is produced.

A renewable resource is one that is replaced in nature at a rate close to the rate at which it is used. Several renewable resources are being utilized as alternatives to fossil fuels. These energy sources are used in much smaller percentages than fossil fuels are.

Energy related to moving water is known as hydroelectric energy. One way to harness this energy is by placing a dam across a river and then using the flowing water to spin turbines, producing electricity. Because this process does not rely on the burning of fossil fuels, it does not pollute the atmosphere. However, damming a river changes the environment by flooding large areas of land behind the dam. This may displace people, destroy valuable farmland, and destroy the natural habitats of animals. In addition, hydroelectric power plants are limited to locations where large volumes of water flow and that are not too far from the people who will use the electricity.

The motion of ocean tides can also produce electricity. To utilize tidal power, a dam is built along a coastline. When the tide comes in, water is allowed to move upstream but not back down. This creates a pool of water at a higher elevation behind the dam. When the tide goes out, the water above the dam is allowed to flow back through the dam spinning the turbines, which in turn run electric generators.

Few tidal power plants have been constructed because there are few areas where the motion of the tide is great enough. In addition, tidal power plants must be designed to protect local marine species. Special care must be taken to ensure that fish do not become entangled in the devices.

Another source of electricity is the wind. A windmill is basically a turbine. The wind turns the blades of the turbine, which turn the generator. Wind power is good for the environment because it does not change the structure of the land and it does not release toxic gases. However, to produce useful amounts of electricity, a large number of wind turbines must be used, which requires large areas of land.

So many wind turbines can be quite expensive and can also generate a great deal of noise. In addition, locations suitable for wind power are limited. Further, wind turbines must be combined with either an energy storage system or a different energy source to use when the wind does not blow.

The sun's energy can be utilized in two ways. One way is to convert the sun's energy into heat, producing steam, which is used to turn a turbine. Another way is to use devices that convert the sun's energy directly into electricity.

Solar energy is an important source because it is continuously produced by the sun and because it does not pollute the environment. In fact, Earth receives solar energy equal to about 200,000 times the total world electrical-generating capacity. However, the intensity of solar radiation is low at Earth's surface. As a result, solar collectors must cover large areas in order to produce practical amounts of electricity. Because darkness and bad weather limit production, solar power plants must be able to store energy or use alternate sources as necessary. So although solar energy itself is free, the cost of collecting it, converting it to electricity, and storing it is high and therefore limits its use.

Nuclear power is produced when energy stored in the nucleus of an atom is released by splitting the nucleus. This process, known as nuclear fission, results in huge amounts of energy from small amounts of fuel. The energy produced during controlled fission reactions can power submarines and other ships, and generate electricity. In nuclear power plants, the energy is used to form the steam, which is used to turn turbines.

Nuclear fission is associated with serious problems. Fission plants produce hot wastewater that damages the environment. In addition, nuclear power plants generate radioactive wastes that remain dangerous for long periods. These wastes must be isolated to protect the environment from radioactivity. An accident at a nuclear power plant or during the transport of wastes can release harmful radioactivity into the air. The construction of safe nuclear power plants is very expensive.

Geothermal energy comes from underground water that is heated by molten rock until it becomes steam. Power companies can drill wells and pump the hot water or steam to the surface, where it can be used to generate energy. Geothermal energy is limited to areas where hot rocks lie near Earth's surface.

Although there are several sources of energy, each source has advantages and disadvantages. As fossil fuels continue to be depleted, society must seek alternates. The many issues must be weighed as each source is considered, and as new ways to utilize these sources are developed.

Questions

1. What is a generator? How are turbines related to generators?
2. What are fossil fuels? What are some of the advantages and disadvantages of using fossil fuels as a source of electrical energy?
3. In what ways can moving water be used as a source of electrical energy? Describe some of the issues related to these sources of energy.
4. Prepare a chart listing solar, nuclear, and geothermal energy in one column. In the next two columns list some of the advantages and disadvantages of each source of energy.

Sending Information Through the Air

Years ago, people were limited to making telephone calls from their homes, offices, and other sources of land-based telephone lines (landlines). Today, telephone calls can be made from just about anywhere thanks to the development of cellular telephone technology. A cellular telephone is a device that can send and receive signals in the form of radio waves. Rather than traveling through wires as in the case of landline telephone signals, radio waves are electromagnetic waves.

Cellular telephones are not the only devices that use radio waves. For example, two-way radios, as might be used by taxi companies or police departments, also use radio waves. These systems use a single antenna located near the center of the covered area. The antenna emits a very strong signal so as to cover the entire area. A conversation in this system occurs on a specific channel. If there are 100 channels in the system, there can be no more than 100 simultaneous conversations.

A cellular system is different in that it operates by dividing a large geographical service area into many small sections, called cells. Each cell has its own transmitter and receiver mounted on a cellular tower. A cell is assigned a set of voice channels and a control channel. When a user places a cellular telephone call, the phone first scans the control channels to find the strongest signal. The strongest signal will generally come from the closest cell site.

The phone will then transmit a short message containing several pieces of information. One piece of information is the mobile identification number. This is a number that identifies the phone to the cellular system. It is a ten-digit number, similar to a landline telephone number, which is assigned by the cellular service provider. This number can be changed if the cellular service provider is changed. The next piece of information is the electronic serial number. Every cellular telephone has an electronic serial number, which is a 32-digit number assigned by the manufacturer. This number can never be changed and can be used to track a particular telephone. The last piece of information is the telephone number dialed.

Once the cellular service provider receives the information and verifies that the telephone is valid, the cell site will send a channel assignment message to the phone. This message tells the phone which channel it can use. The phone then tunes into the assigned channel and begins the call. The signal is sent by the cellular telephone to the receiver on the cellular tower. The signal is then passed on to the transmitter, which in turn sends the signal on to a receiver in the next cell. This process continues until the signal reaches its intended receiver. If the cellular phone user moves during the call, the signal is transferred (handed off) from one cell site to the next with little interruption.

Many different users in the same area can use their cellular phones with little interruption because cells that are next to each other are assigned different voice channels. Cellular telephone signals are strong enough to reach only a few nearby cells. They are designed not to travel long distances. In this way, the same group of channels can be reused elsewhere in the same service region.

All the cells in a cellular system are connected to a mobile telephone switching office (MTSO) by landline or microwave links. The MTSO controls the switching of calls between the public telephone network and the cell site whenever calls are placed from landline to cell phones or from cell phones to landlines. The MTSO is also responsible for switching calls to other cells.

The process just described applies to analog telephone systems. Cellular telephone systems can be analog or digital. Older systems are generally analog whereas newer systems are usually digital. An analog signal varies continuously over time whereas a digital signal consists of short pulses of information. With analog transmissions, interference is translated directly into the signal received. The same interference is eliminated from the digital signal when it is received.

Cellular telephones and the related technologies have revolutionized communication and business by linking computers and people without the inconvenience of costly, hard-to-maintain copper wires. However, there are some concerns that the technology is racing out of control. For one thing, cellular towers are popping up everywhere. They can be found along highways, near neighborhoods as well as on apartment buildings, water towers, churches, schools, billboards, highway signs, lamp posts, and traffic lights. Some fear that no locations will be off limits, including such places as national parks and other revered natural wonders. While there are towers that resemble trees, such towers have not been used commonly because they are significantly more expensive than ordinary towers.

Other people are concerned that a portion of the electromagnetic spectrum has been put up for sale by the Federal Commu-nications Commission (FCC). The FCC auctions off blocks of the electromagnetic spectrum for cellular telephone use. These people question the right to own large parts of the electromagnetic spectrum.

Another issue being raised at this time involves the effects of cellular technology on human health. There is some question as to whether the energy from a cellular phone is imparted to the brain while a person is speaking on the telephone. Further, there is some question about the safety of being constantly bombarded by radio waves on a daily basis. Presently, studies are being conducted on cellular telephones and towers and their energy emissions. At present, the studies remain contradictory and inconclusive.

Questions

1. How is a cellular telephone system different from a two-way radio system?
2. How is a call transmitted in a cellular telephone system?
3. Why are cellular telephones relatively protected from usage if they are stolen?
4. Think of a business or profession that has been changed by the development of cellular technology. Write a paragraph describing the benefits of the technology.
5. Do you think people will stop using cellular telephones if found hazardous to human health? How might product development play a role in continuing the use of cellular technology in this case?

Using Lasers to Improve Vision

If you wear glasses or contact lenses, you have probably imagined what it would be like to have perfect vision. Since 1998, millions of people who have wondered this same thing have undergone a procedure to rid themselves of glasses. The procedure, known as LASIK, involves applying a laser to change the structure of the eye.

To understand how LASIK works, you must first understand that the images you see are a result of the light that enters the eye. Light entering the eye first passes through the cornea, a transparent tissue at the front of the eye. Light then passes through the pupil, a hole in the middle of the iris, or colored part of your eye. The light then passes through the lens, which lies directly behind the iris. The lens changes shape to help focus the image onto the retina. The retina is a tissue at the back of the eye that converts the light into electrical signals, which are then sent to the brain.

The lens provides only a portion of the eye's focusing power. The rest of the focusing power comes from the cornea. If the eye is nearsighted, it produces clear images of nearby objects but light from distant sources is focused at a point somewhere in front of your retina. This can happen if the curve of the cornea is too steep relative to the length of the eye or if the eye is too long relative to the corneal curve. If the eye is farsighted, the lens produces clear images of distant objects, but light from nearby objects is focused behind the retina. This can happen if the cornea is too flat relative to the length of the eye, or vice versa.

For many years, doctors have hoped to correct vision by changing the way the cornea focuses light rather than by adding corrective lenses in front of the eye. At-tempts began as early as the 1950s and by the 1970s, Soviet doctors used scalpels to reshape the corneas of nearsighted patients in an operation called radial keratotomy. The surgeon made a spokelike ring of incisions on the eye. This surgery never really caught on in the United States because the results were so difficult to predict and the healing process was often slow and painful.

The problem was not the theory, but the tools. The tool that revolutionized eye surgery was the excimer laser, originally developed in the 1970s to etch computer chips. LASIK is short for laser-assisted in situ keratomileusis. The 15-minute procedure involves a few basic steps. It begins when a liquid anesthetic is dropped into the patient's eye in order to numb it for surgery. The physician then gently props the eyelids open and applies a suction ring designed to hold the eye steady.

The next step is for the surgeon to raise a thin layer of the cornea, or corneal flap, with the microkeratome. The surgeon carefully lifts the corneal flap out of the way, exposing the underlying layers. Guided by a computer program, the excimer laser reshapes the internal cornea (the stroma) with accuracy up to 0.25 microns, or 1/4000 of a millimeter. To correct nearsightedness, the laser trims the cornea's center, making it flatter. For farsightedness, a doughnut-shaped ring of tissue is removed. The flap is then put back in place. After a few minutes of drying, it rebonds with the rest of the cornea. Because tissue destruction is minimal, there's little healing and pain. Patients see clearly almost immediately after the operation.

LASIK is a surgical procedure and therefore has associated risks. For one thing, there is always a risk of infection. And there is the risk of surgical errors. Aside from errors on the surgeon's part, the patient might suddenly shift his eyes during the procedure. The surgeon can turn the laser off very quickly to accommodate large movements, but the surgeon cannot compensate for the small, involuntary eye movements. These motions generally aren't a problem, but they can lead to variability in results of the surgery.

For about 7 out of 10 patients, LASIK corrects their vision to 20/20. Most of the remaining patients see well enough to stop using glasses. By 2010, some surgeons predict that LASIK will have advanced to the point that 90 percent of patients will see better than 20/20 after the procedure.

Another consideration is that LASIK will not eliminate the need for glasses ever again. For one thing, LASIK cannot correct presbyopia, which usually develops with age. Although researchers hope to be able to correct for this in the future, patients over 35 will probably need glasses to read and for close work even after LASIK. Many patients are also likely to need glasses at night or in dark places such as in movie theaters.

Nearly everyone who undergoes LASIK experiences at least some glare and halos. This occurs because the pupil widens in dim light, allowing incoming light to pass through both the corrected and uncorrected sections of the cornea, creating either a blinding or a hazy image. The problems usually diminish within six months but a small portion of patients continue to be substantially bothered by glare and halos. Some patients report serious vision problems after LASIK that can no longer be corrected with their glasses. These patients must undergo a second LASIK procedure to complete their correction.

To minimize the risks, doctors must select candidates best suited to the procedure. These are generally adults whose sight is only moderately distorted, whose vision is stable, and who have no other eye problems. Since there are no official guidelines for LASIK, it is up to each surgeon to decide who is the best candidate. The requirements might vary from one surgeon to the next.

Each person must decide whether the benefits are worth the small, but very real, risk of irreversible damage to eyesight. In addition, prospective patients must consider the financial cost. On average, LASIK costs upwards of $2,500 an eye and isn't covered by most insurance companies. Only the future will show the success of LASIK and the technological improvements that will develop in the years to come.

Questions

1. How does the eye see?
2. What might cause an eye to be nearsighted? Farsighted?
3. In what way were early attempts to correct vision through surgery similar to LASIK? In what way were they different?
4. Why might it be important to have government regulation and restrictions procedures such as LASIK?

Nuclear Wastes: What Will Become of Them?

Nearly 85 percent of the energy sources used on Earth come from fossil fuels. Given that Earth contains only a limited amount of fossil fuels, the amount will eventually run out. This fact becomes more significant as the rate at which fossil fuel is used continues to increase. In fact, the amount of fossil fuel used to produce energy has nearly doubled every 20 years since 1900.

This is one reason that alternate sources of energy are being pursued. One such source is nuclear energy. Nuclear energy is the energy stored in the nuclei, or centers, of atoms. In many ways, nuclear power plants are similar to fossil-fuel power plants. However, instead of using such fuels as coal or oil, almost all reactors use uranium. And instead of burning the fuel, nuclear power plants control fission reactions in which nuclei split in two. As a nucleus splits, it releases energy. The fission of 1 kilogram of uranium releases more energy than the burning of 3 million kilograms of coal. That energy is converted largely into heat, which can be used to make steam much like in a fossil-fuel plant. The steam is then used to generate electric energy.

Nuclear power plants have two main advantages over fossil-fuel plants. One, a nuclear plant can be less expensive to operate than a fossil-fuel plant because a nuclear plant uses a much smaller volume of fuel. Two, unlike fossil fuels, uranium does not release chemical or solid pollutants into the air during use.

Unfortunately, nuclear power has serious disadvantages as well. First, nuclear plants are more expensive to construct than fossil-fuel plants. Second, nuclear power plants must meet rigid guidelines so that they are prepared to deal with any kind of emergency related to the use of hazardous amounts of radioactive materials. Third, nuclear power plants generate waste that remains dangerous for many years.

While the first two issues can be addressed by spending additional money for construction and preparation, the third issue has no clear solution at this point. The reason is that the fissioning of U-235, for example, produces many radioactive isotopes. Wastes that contain strontium 90, cesium 137, and barium 140 can remain dangerously radioactive for about 600 years because of the strontium and cesium isotopes. After that time, enough of the strontium and cesium will have decayed into stable isotopes so that they no longer present a severe problem. However, plutonium and other artificially created elements in the wastes remain radioactive for thousands of years.

The method of disposing of nuclear waste currently planned by all countries with nuclear power plants is called geologic disposal. This means that all conditioned nuclear wastes are to be buried deep underground. The plan is to sink shafts into solid rock with corridors extending from the central shaft. Areas, or rooms, would be located off these corridors. The waste will be placed in holes drilled into the floors of these rooms. Then the holes will be sealed and the rooms and corridors filled. Eventually, the main shafts will be filled and sealed as well.

Where should the waste be buried? Selecting an appropriate site may be the greatest problem with this plan, both politically and technically. Several conditions must be met for a site to be acceptable. For example, the location must not be near a populated area. The rock must be at least 300 meters deep. The site must be naturally sealed from aquifers so that water supplies cannot be contaminated. The site must be dry so that the waste containers do not corrode. The storage site must lie in a highly stable area that is free of earthquakes, faulting, and other geologic activity. Lastly, the site must be planned so that future generations do not dig into it accidentally or otherwise.

At the present time, commercial nuclear power plants in the United States store used fuel and other wastes in pools of water. However, a law passed by the United States Congress in 1982 required the federal government to build two sites for nuclear wastes. This law, the Nuclear Waste Policy Act of 1982, established the Office of Civilian Radioactive Waste Management (OCRWM) within the U.S. Department of Energy (DOE) to develop and manage a Federal system for disposing of all spent nuclear fuel from commercial nuclear reactors and high-level radioactive waste resulting from atomic energy defense activities. In 1987, the law was changed to require a single site. The Nuclear Waste Policy Amendments Act of 1987 directed the DOE to study only Yucca Mountain, Nevada, to determine its suitability. As of the writing of this article, this location is still being debated.

What's wrong with this solution? Opponents pose several arguments. For one thing, they argue that transporting the waste is unsafe. Moving dangerous waste spreads risk along transportation routes where hospitals, police, and rescue personnel may not be equipped to respond effectively to a radiological emergency. The current proposal to transport 70,000 metric tons of high-level radioactive waste from weapons facilities and commercial nuclear reactors to Yucca Mountain, for example, would carry the waste through 734 counties that have a total population of 138 million people. Opponents propose that the waste shipments would expose workers and residents along transportation routes to unnatural amounts of radiation.

Aside from the transportation, some research shows that the proposed site lies in an active earthquake zone and shows evidence that water seeps through the rock. If this is true, a freshwater aquifer beneath Yucca Mountain could become radioactively contaminated, poisoning the only source of drinking water for area residents. Further, the water could cause the waste canisters to corrode, releasing dangerous wastes. The waste canisters have been tested through computer simulations only so no one knows for sure how they will hold up under real conditions.

The plan to bury nuclear waste is not perfect, but it is the best plan at the present time. Supporters continue to argue its merits while opponents voice their concerns. What do you think should happen?

Questions

1. How are nuclear power plants similar to fossil-fuel plants? How are they different?
2. What are two advantages that nuclear power plants have over fossil-fuel plants?
3. What are three disadvantages of nuclear power plants?
4. Why is it important to pursue the development and research of nuclear power plants despite their problems?

Joining Atoms to Produce Electricity

Nuclear energy is energy released as the nucleus of an atom is changed in certain ways. Existing nuclear power plants release this energy by splitting heavy nuclei in a process known as nuclear fission. To initiate fission, a particle, such as a neutron, is used to bombard a target material, such as U-235. Nuclear fission occurs when the bombarding particle splits a nucleus in the target material into two parts. Each part consists of a nucleus with about half the neutrons and protons of the original nucleus. During this process, energy is released in many forms, most of which eventually takes the form of heat.

In a different type of nuclear reaction, nuclear fusion, two lightweight nuclei join together to form a nucleus of a heavier element. The products of the fusion have less mass than the original nuclei had. The lost mass is converted into energy. Fusion reactions that produce large amounts of energy can be created by means of extremely intense heat. Such reactions are called thermonuclear reactions. Thermonuclear reactions result in the energy of both the sun and the hydrogen bomb.

A thermonuclear reaction can occur only in a form of matter called plasma. Plasma is made up of free electrons and free nuclei, which are nuclei without electrons. Normally, nuclei repel one another because of the positive charges of their protons. However, if a plasma containing lightweight atomic nuclei is heated to many millions of degrees, the nuclei begin moving so fast that they overcome the force of repulsion and fuse.

Fusion has some advantages over fission. First, the "fuel" for fusion could be a mixture of deuterium and tritium, which are isotopes of hydrogen. Ordinary seawater would provide a tremendous supply of deuterium and tritium. One barrel of seawater contains enough of these substances to produce as much energy as the burning of about one-fifth of a barrel of oil. In addition, fusion devices are safer than fission devices. And fusion would not create a waste disposal problem because most products of fusion reactions are not radioactive.

So why don't nuclear power plants use fusion instead of fission? The reason is that scientists have not yet succeeded in harnessing the energy of fusion to produce electricity. The first problem scientists have is developing a container that can hold plasma because of its high temperature. Most experimental fusion reactors are designed to hold the hot plasma in "bottles" made of magnetic fields. The actual walls of the bottles are made of copper or some other metal and are surrounded by electromagnets. When an electric current is passed through the electromagnets, a magnetic field is created on the inside of the walls. The magnetic field pushes the plasma away from the walls.

Another kind of fusion reactor uses a process called inertial confinement. In this case, there is no container to hold the fuel. Instead, the fuel's inertia holds it long enough for fusion to occur. In one kind of inertial confinement fusion (ICF) reactor, scientists use extremely powerful laser beams to strike a cylindrical case made of metal. A pea-sized sphere containing deuterium and tritium gas is placed inside the case. The laser beams heat the case, causing it to turn to plasma. The plasma then bombards the sphere with X rays, rapidly heating the shell of the sphere. As a result, the shell both expands and pushes inward. The inward push compresses the fuel, which causes fusion.

All the fusion devices developed so far use much more energy than they create. One goal of fusion research is to produce enough energy to create and heat the plasma. This is known as the break-even level. The most successful type of fusion reactor is called a tokamak. Tokamak comes from Russian words meaning toroidal (doughnut-shaped) chamber and magnetic coil. A tokamak uses magnetic confinement. To reach the break-even level, a tokamak of the design presently under development must heat the plasma to at least 100,000,000°C. In addition, each cubic centimeter of the plasma must contain about 100 trillion nuclei, and the magnetic field must confine the plasma for about 1 second. These conditions have not yet been met at the same time.

In 1989, two chemists announced that they had achieved fusion at room temperature. They reported that this so-called cold fusion had occurred in a laboratory experiment with a simple electrolytic cell. How-ever, many scientists tried to repeat the experiment but detected no sign of fusion. Most scientists agree that there is no evidence that cold fusion can take place, but it would have been nice.

Fusion holds great potential to solve society's energy problems without introducing hazardous waste if only researchers can unlock the secrets that would make it possible!

Questions

1. How does nuclear fusion differ from nuclear fission?
2. What is plasma and why is it necessary for nuclear fusion?
3. In what ways are scientists attempting to contain nuclear fusion reactions?
4. How is the scientific method important to scientists conducting nuclear fusion experiments?
5. How would society benefit from a successful nuclear fusion reactor?

Glossary

absolute error: the absolute value of the difference between the measured value and the accepted value; absolute errors are always expressed as positive numbers.

absolute index of refraction: the ratio of the speed of light in a vacuum to the speed of light in a given medium.

absolute temperature: temperature measured on the Kelvin scale.

absolute zero: the lowest possible temperature (0 K or $-273°C$).

acceleration: the time-rate of change of velocity.

accuracy: the agreement of a measured value with the true or accepted value.

alpha decay: the emission of an alpha particle from a nucleus.

alternating current: electric current that varies in magnitude and alternates in direction.

ammeter: a modified galvanometer used to measure larger amounts of current.

ampere: the fundamental unit of electric current, equal to 1 coulomb/second.

amplitude: the maximum disturbance in a wave cycle.

angle of incidence: the angle formed between the incident ray and a line normal (perpendicular) to the surface.

angle of reflection: the angle formed between the normal and reflected ray.

angle of refraction: the angle formed between the normal and the refracted ray.

antinodes: points of constructive interference.

antiparticle: a particle with the same mass but opposite charge of its counterpart subatomic particle.

atom kernel: the positive ion left behind by a migrating electron.

atomic number: the number of protons in a nucleus.

average speed: the distance traveled per unit time.

back EMF: the electromotive force that develops in a circuit from the magnetic effects of the induced current and that opposes the electromotive force producing the current.

baryons: heavier nuclear particles such as protons, neutrons, and hyperons.

base: the middle semiconductor in a transistor.

beta decay: the disintegration of a neutron into a proton and an electron; the electron is emitted from the nucleus.

biasing: the enhancement or opposition of the electric field barrier when a potential difference is applied across a diode.

binding energy: the energy lost as nucleons coalesce to form a stable nucleus; it is equivalent to the work needed to pry the nucleons away from one another.

breeder reactor: a reactor that uses its own nuclear waste as fuel.

cathode ray tube: an evacuated tube that contains a source of electrons at one end and a fluorescent screen at the other end.

Celsius scale: a temperature scale such that 0 degrees is the freezing point of water, 100 degrees is the boiling point of water, and each degree equals one one-hundredth of the interval between these points.

center of curvature: the point that corresponds to the center of a sphere, with a segment being a concave mirror.

centripetal acceleration: the acceleration experienced by an object in uniform circular motion.

centripetal force: the force that causes centripetal acceleration; the net force on a circling object that acts to change the object's direction.

chain reaction: a self-sustaining series of collisions between neutrons and radioactive nuclei.

chip: a single silicon crystal that has been doped to produce complex networks of diodes, transistors, and resistors.

circuit: a closed loop formed by a source of electrons and a conductor, with no gaps across which electrons cannot travel.

cloud chamber: a device that reveals the path of a charged particle by creating a trail of condensed vapor in its wake.

coefficient of friction: a value derived by dividing the force of friction by the normal force; it represents the nature of the surfaces rubbing together.

coherent light waves: waves of the same frequency produced by sources in phase.

compass: a magnet used to determine direction on Earth.

concave: thinner in the middle than at the edges.

concave mirror: a small segment of a sphere with a reflecting surface on the inside of the sphere.

concurrent forces: two or more forces acting on an object at the same time and at the same point.

conduction band: the lowest energy band above the valence band that provides electrons sufficient energy to migrate away from their atoms.

conductivity: the reciprocal of a solid's resistivity.

conductor: a substance that allows electrons to flow through it.

conservative force: any force such that the work done by the force is independent of the path taken.

constructive interference: the production of a larger disturbance at the point where waves meet.

contact: a method of charging a neutral object by making contact with a charged object.

controlled experiment: an experiment in which one variable is changed while the others are held constant.

conventional current: theoretical flow of positive charges from the positive to the negative terminal of a battery.

converging lens: a lens that acts to bring light rays together at a point on the other side of the lens.

converging mirror: a mirror that acts on incoming light rays parallel to the principal axis and converges them to a point.

convex: thicker in the middle than at the edges.

convex mirror: a small segment of a sphere with a reflecting surface on the outside.

coulomb: the unit of charge, symbolized by C, equal to the charge carried by 6.25×10^{18} electrons.

critical angle: an angle of incidence for which the corresponding angle of refraction is 90°.

critical mass: the minimum amount of fissionable material necessary to initiate a chain reaction.

cycle: one complete repetition of the pattern in a periodic wave.

cyclotron: a device that accelerates particles by making them circle in a magnetic field and accelerating them once during every round trip when they pass through an electric field; similar to a synchrotron.

de Broglie wavelength: the wavelength of a matter wave.

derived unit: a unit that consists of a combination of fundamental units; the newton (N) is a derived unit equivalent to 1 kilogram meter per second squared $(kg \cdot m/s^2)$.

destructive interference: the production of a smaller disturbance, or none at all, at the point where waves meet.

diode: a P-type semiconductor joined to an N-type semiconductor.

dispersive media: materials that allow waves of different frequencies to pass through them at different speeds.

displacement: a change of position in a particular direction.

diverging lens: a lens that acts to separate light rays as they pass through the lens.

diverging mirror: a mirror that acts on incoming light rays parallel to the principal axis and separates them.

donor: doping material that introduces free electrons into a semiconductor.

doping: inserting small amounts of certain impurities into a semiconductor.

dynamic equilibrium: a condition that exists when no net force acts on an object in motion; the object maintains a constant velocity.

dynamics: the study of the relationship between forces and motion.

elastic potential energy: the energy stored in a spring when it is compressed or stretched.

electric current: a flow of charged particles, usually negative.

electric field: the entity around a charged object that affects other charges.

electric field barrier: an electric field that prevents further diffusion of electrons and holes across the P-N junction in a diode.

electric field direction: the direction of force exerted by an electric field on a positive test charge.

electric field intensity: the force that an electric field exerts on one coulomb of positive charge at a given point; also referred to as the field's magnitude.

electric motor: a device that makes use of the force exerted by magnets on currents to convert electrical energy into rotational kinetic energy.

electric potential: the total amount of work an electric field can do on one coulomb of positive charge by moving the charge from a given point in the field to infinity.

electric potential energy: the ability of a charged object to do work, due to its position in an electric field.

electromagnet: a solenoid whose magnetic field is intensified by the insertion of certain materials.

electromagnetic induction: the process by which a magnetic field generates an electric current and a potential difference.

electromagnetic radiation: the propagation of electric and magnetic fields away from the vicinity of an accelerating charge.

electromagnetic spectrum: a representation of all types of electromagnetic waves in order of decreasing wavelengths and increasing frequency.

electromagnetic waves: a periodic wave of electric and magnetic fields that is radiated outward from the vicinity of an oscillating charge.

electron: a negatively charged subatomic particle.

electron capture: a radioactive process in which a nucleus absorbs one of the atom's innermost electrons; the electron units with a proton to form a neutron, decreasing the atomic number by one but leaving the mass number unchanged.

electron volt: unit of energy and work equal to the work done on one elementary charge between two points separated by a potential difference of 1 volt.

electroscope: a device that consists of a metal knob attached to two light metallic leaves; used to detect the presence of excess charge on an object.

elementary unit of charge: an amount equal to the positive charge on one proton or the negative charge on one electron; equal to 1.6×10^{-19} coulombs.

ellipse: a closed curve such that the sum of the distances from any point on the curve to two fixed points, called the foci, is constant.

emission spectrum: electromagnetic radiation of only certain wavelengths and frequencies that is unique to each element.

energy: the ability to do work.

energy band: a range of allowed energy values for an electron in an atom in the solid state.

entropy: the amount of disorder in a system.

equilibrant: the balancing force that creates equilibrium.

equivalent resistance: the single resistance that can replace all the resistances of branches in parallel; also known as the combined resistance.

escape velocity: the minimum speed an object must have to escape the influence of a body's gravitational pull.

excitation: an increase in the orbital distance, or energy, of an electron.

excited state: the condition of an electron that jumps to a higher orbit.

extrapolation: predicting values outside the range of experimental data.

ferromagnetic: a material whose insertion causes the magnetic field of a solenoid to become stronger.

field lines: lines used to diagram the direction and intensity of an electric or magnetic field.

fission: the process of splitting a nucleus into smaller fragments.

fluid friction: the force that resists the motion of an object through a fluid such as water or air.

flux density: the number of magnetic field lines per unit area.

flux lines: magnetic field lines.

focal length: the distance between the center of a lens or mirror and the focal point.

focal point: the point where incoming parallel light rays meet; also called the principal focus.

force: a push or a pull.

free fall: motion due solely to the attraction of Earth's gravitational pull.

frequency: the number of cycles produced per second by a vibrating source.

friction: the force that opposes the motion of one surface over another.

fusion: the process of uniting light nuclei to become one heavier nucleus.

galvanometer: a device consisting of a coil-shaped wire placed between the opposite poles of a permanent magnet that is used to measure small amounts of current.

gamma rays: high energy, short wavelength photons.

geiger counter: a device that detects nuclear particles emitted from atoms.

generator: a device that creates electric current by moving a conducting wire across magnetic field lines.

geosynchronous orbit: an orbital period of a satellite equal to the period of Earth's rotation.

gravitational field: the entity around a mass that acts on other masses.

gravitational force: the universal attraction of one piece of matter for another.

gravitational potential energy: the energy an object has due to its position.

grounded: connected to an object so large that it can either accept or give up a significant number of electrons without becoming noticeably charged.

ground state: an electron in the lowest possible orbit with the least amount of energy.

half-life: the time it takes for half the number of nuclei present in a radioactive sample to decay.

heat energy: energy that is transferred from warm objects to cooler ones due to the temperature difference between them.

heat of fusion: the amount of heat needed to change one kilogram of a solid into a liquid at its melting point, with no change in temperature.

heat of vaporization: the amount of heat needed to change one kilogram of a liquid into a gas at its boiling point, with no change in temperature.

hertz: a derived unit for frequency that stands for cycles per second.

hyperons: subatomic particles with masses greater than neutrons.

ideal gas: a low density gas with an average distance between molecules that is much larger than the diameter of each molecule; the forces between molecules are negligible except during collisions.

impulse: the product of the net force acting on an object and the time during which the force acts.

induced current: a current created either by moving a conducting wire across magnetic field lines or by changing the intensity of the magnetic field.

induced EMF: a potential difference created either by moving a conducting wire across magnetic field lines or by changing the intensity of the magnetic field.

induction: a method of charging a neutral object by attaching it to a ground and then bringing a charged object near it.

induction coil: a device, similar in purpose to a transformer, that induces a time-varying voltage and potential difference in the secondary coil by successively turning the current on and off in the primary coil.

inertia: the property of matter that resists change in motion.

instantaneous velocity: the slope of a line tangent to a displacement-time graph at any given point.

insulator: a material that strongly resists the flow of electrons through it.

integrated circuit: a miniaturized circuit created within a chip.

interference pattern: alternating lines of constructive and destructive interference.

internal energy: the total kinetic and potential energy associated with the molecules of an object, apart from any kinetic or potential energy the object as a whole may possess.

interpolation: predicting values within the range of experimental data.

ionization potential: the amount of energy needed to remove an electron from an atom.

isotopes: atoms with the identical atomic numbers but different mass numbers.

joule: the work done on an object when a one-newton force displaces the object one meter.

Kelvin scale: a temperature scale measuring absolute temperature whose lower fixed point is absolute zero.

kinematics: the study of motion.

kinetic energy: the energy an object has due to its motion.

kinetic friction: the force opposing the motion of an object sliding over a surface.

laser: an acronym for Light Amplification by Stimulated Emission of Radiation; a device that emits coherent, monochromatic, very intense light.

linear accelerator: a device that accelerates particles continuously in an electric field as they travel in a straight line.

longitudinal waves: waves in which the disturbances are parallel to the direction of wave motion.

magnet: a long, slender piece of ore that aligns itself, when free to do so, with one end pointing north and the other pointing south.

magnetic field: the entity around a moving charge or magnet that exerts a force on other moving charges or magnets.

magnetic field direction: the direction in which the N-pole of a test magnet is made to point by a magnetic field.

magnetic field intensity: the force that a magnetic field exerts on a one-meter-long wire in the field carrying one ampere of current.

magnetic force: the force that moving charges exert on other moving charges.

magnification: the ratio of image size to object size.

mass defect: the difference between the mass of a nucleus and the sum of the masses of its nucleons.

mass number: the number of nucleons in a nucleus.

mass spectrometer: a device that separates atoms of the same element with different masses.

matter waves: the waves associated with moving particles.

medium: a body of matter through which a disturbance travels.

mesons: subatomic particles with masses in between that of an electron and a proton.

moderators: materials used in nuclear reactors to slow down neutrons.

momentum: the product of a moving object's mass and velocity.

net force: the resultant of concurrent forces acting on an object.

newton: the force applied to a one-kilogram mass to accelerate it one meter per second per second.

neutrino: a subatomic particle with no charge and much less mass than an electron.

nodes: points of destructive interference.

nonconservative force: any force such that the work done by the force depends on the path taken.

normal force: the force that presses two surfaces together.

nuclear energy: the potential energy that exists in a nucleus because of the work done on particles by the nuclear force.

nuclear force: an attractive force that acts between masses but is only effective across extremely small distances; it binds nucleons together into a tightly packed and cohesive unit.

nuclear fuel: small pellets of fissionable material.

nucleon: a particle in the nucleus of an atom.

nucleus: the tiny, heavy core where most of an atom's mass and all of its positive charge are located.

nuclides: nuclei with the same number of protons and neutrons.

observed frequency: the number of wave cycles passing by a given point per second.

ohm: the unit of electrical resistance; defined as the resistance of a material that allows one ampere of current when a potential difference of one volt exists between the ends of the material.

parallel circuit: an electrical circuit in which the current flows through more than one branch.

particle accelerator: a device used to accelerate charged particles to speeds approaching that of light.

period: the time for a complete wave cycle to be produced or to pass a given point.

periodic wave: a regularly repeating series of pulses, also called a wave train.

phase: a form in which matter can exist, including liquid, solid, gas, and plasma.

photoelectric effect: a phenomenon in which electrons are ejected from certain materials and escape into space when electromagnetic radiation strikes the materials.

photoelectrons: electrons emitted as a result of the photoelectric effect.

photoemissive: applied to materials that demonstrate the photoelectric effect.

photon: the fundamental particle of all forms of electromagnetic radiation.

P-N junction: the interface region in a diode between the P-type semiconductor and the N-type semiconductor.

point charges: two or more charged objects that are much smaller than the distance between them.

polaroid: a filter that allows only light waves vibrating in one particular plane to pass through it.

polychromatic: consisting of light waves of different colors and frequencies.

positron: an antiparticle that has the same mass as an electron but a positive charge; also called an anti-electron.

potential difference: the work required to move a test charge of one coulomb from one point to another in an electric field.

potential energy: the energy an object has due to its position or condition.

power: the amount of work done per unit time.

precision: the degree of refinement with which a measurement is made.

pressure: the result of gas molecules colliding with the walls of the container; the force per unit surface area.

primary coil: the coil of a transformer that is connected to an ac source.

principal axis (lens): a line drawn perpendicularly to the plane of a lens and through its center.

principal axis (mirror): a line that connects the center of curvature to the geometric center of the mirror.

projectile: any object that is launched by some force and continues to move by its own inertia.

pulse: a single vibratory disturbance.

quanta: discrete amounts of energy.

quarks: the proposed constituent particles of baryons and intermediate mass mesons; quarks carry a charge of either one-third or two-thirds of an elementary unit of charge.

radioactive decay: the transmutation of one element into another.

radioactivity: naturally occurring transmutations.

radius of curvature: the distance between the center of curvature and a concave mirror.

random error: an error in measurement due to fluctuations in the environment.

rarefaction: a pocket of expanded air.

real image: an image created by the actual convergence of rays of light; such images are always inverted.

rectifier: a diode that converts alternating current to direct current.

resistance: the opposition of material to the flow of electrons through it.

resistivity: the resistance, in ohms, of a uniform rod of unit-length and unit cross-sectional area.

resistor: any conductor with a measurable resistance.

resonance: a phenomenon produced when an object is disturbed by a wave whose frequency is the same as the object's natural vibration frequency; the amplitude of vibration of the object continues to increase.

resultant: a vector that represents the sum of two or more other vectors.

rolling friction: the force opposing the motion of one object rolling over another; it is usually weaker than sliding friction.

satellite: any body that revolves around a larger body.

scalar quantity: a measurement that has magnitude but no direction.

scientific notation: the expression of a number in the form $A \times 10^n$, where A is any number equal to or greater than 1 but less than 10, and the exponent n is an integer.

scintillation counter: a device that detects nuclear particles emitted from atoms by converting their energy into photons of light.

secondary coil: the coil of a transformer that is not connected to any source of current.

semiconductor: a metalloid that behaves as an insulator at low temperatures but whose conductivity increases with increasing temperature.

series circuit: an electrical circuit in which only one path exists for the current.

shunt: a device in an ammeter whose resistance is much smaller than that of the galvanometer coil; it is connected in parallel with the coil.

significant figures: those digits in a measurement that are obtained properly and directly from an instrument, including the final estimated digit.

solenoid: a coil-shaped, current-carrying wire.

sources in phase: wave sources that vibrate at the same frequency and produce waves of equal amplitude.

specific heat: the amount of heat energy that one kilogram of a substance must absorb or liberate in order for its temperature to increase or decrease by 1°C.

speed: a scalar quantity equal to the magnitude of the velocity vector.

split-ring commutator: a device in which each end of a wire loop is connected to a conducting material in the shape of a half-ring; used in motors and generators.

standing waves: created by two interfering waves that repeatedly pass through each other in such a way that certain points always show constructive interference while other points always show destructive interference.

static equilibrium: a condition that exists when no net force acts on an object at rest; the object remains at rest.

static friction: the frictional force that must be overcome to start an object moving over a surface; sometimes called starting friction.

statics: the study of forces on stationary objects.

stationary state: an electron that is circling the nucleus in an allowed orbit and is neither losing nor gaining energy.

step-down transformer: a transformer in which the voltage in the secondary coil is less than that in the primary coil.

step-up transformer: a transformer in which the voltage in the secondary coil is greater than that in the primary coil.

superconductor: a material that offers virtually no resistance to the passage of electrons through it; no energy is lost to heat when current flows through such a material.

systematic error: an error in measurement due to flaws in the instruments used.

temperature: how hot or cold an object is with respect to a chosen standard.

thermal equilibrium: the point at which materials in contact reach the same temperature and heat exchange ceases.

thermionic emission: the emission of electrons from metallic substances when they are heated to incandescence.

thermodynamics: the study of heat and its relationship to other forms of energy and to work.

threshold frequency: a frequency below which no photoelectrons will be emitted no matter how intense the radiation.

transformer: a device inserted into a circuit carrying alternating current to change the voltage to some higher or lower value.

transistor: a semiconducting device in which one type of semiconductor is sandwiched between two semiconductors of the opposite type.

transmitted frequency: the number of cycles produced by a source per second.

transmutation: the change of an unstable nucleus of one element into another as nuclear particles are emitted.

transverse waves: waves in which the disturbances are perpendicular to the direction of the wave motion.

uniform acceleration: a change in the velocity of a moving object by a fixed amount per second.

uniform circular motion: movement of an object along a circular path at a constant speed.

uniform velocity: movement of an object at a constant speed and direction.

valence band: the highest energy band that contains electrons.

van de Graaff generator: a device that accelerates particles by driving them parallel to an intense electric field.

vector: a geometric representation of a vector quantity as an arrow whose length represents the magnitude and whose direction is the same as that of the vector quantity.

vector quantity: a measurement that has magnitude and direction.

velocity: the change in displacement per unit time.

virtual focal point: the point where incident rays parallel to the principal axis appear to be coming from after they are refracted by a diverging lens or reflected by a diverging mirror.

virtual image: an image not produced by waves of light actually coming to a point, but merely appearing to be coming from a point; such images are always upright.

volt: the unit of potential difference, equal to one joule/coulomb.

voltage: another term for the potential difference between two points in an electric field.

voltage drop: the potential difference between the entry and exit points of a particular resistor in a circuit.

voltmeter: a modified galvanometer used to measure potential difference.

watt: the derived unit of power, equal to one joule/second.

wavelength: the length of one complete wave cycle.

wave speed: the distance traveled per unit time for any part of a wave.

weight: the amount of gravitational force an object experiences.

work: the product of the force on an object and the resultant displacement.

Index

Mechanics *(continued)*
   scalar quantities in, 5
   statics in, 5, 14–16
   two-dimensional motion and
     trajectories in, 29
   uniform circular motion in, 29–30
   units of measurement in, 5
   vector addition in, 5–6
   vector quantities in, 5
Medium, 104
Mesons, 146
Metals, as conductors, 64
Meter (m), 5
Metric system, 5
Microgravity, 174–175
Mir, 174
Mirrors
   concave, 129-130
   converging, 130
   convex, 131
   defects in, 132
   diverging, 131
Mobile telephone switching office,
   178–179
Models
   of atom, 140–146
   Band, 159
   electron-sea, 159
Moderators, 153
Momentum, 25–27
   conservation of, 26–27
   impulse in, 26
   Newton's third law of motion and,
     27
   photon, 138
Monochromatic, coherent light, 148
Motion
   first law of, 18
   free fall and, 20, 32
   graph of accelerated, 11–12
   projectile, 32–34
   satellite, 35–36
   second law of, 18, 20, 30
   third law of, 18–19, 20, 61
     and momentum, 27
   two-dimensional, 29
   uniform circular, 29–30
Motors, 78, 94–95
Multiplication, 165
   of numbers in scientific notation, 4
   rounding off answer in, 3

N
Nanorobots, 172–173
Nanotechnology, 172–173
Natural magnets, 73
Natural radioactivity, 150
Natural resources, using and
   conserving, 176–177
Negative charge, 60–61
Net force, 14
Neutrino, 146
Neutrons, 60, 146, 152–153
Newton, Sir Isaac, 18–19, 27, 35
Newton's Laws, 18–19
Newton/coulomb, 84
Newton (n), 5, 14, 18, 20, 30, 61, 84
Nodal lines, 110
Nodes, 110
Nonconservative forces, 43–44
Nondispersive media, 120
Nonmetallic solids, as insulators, 64
Nonrenewable natural resources, 176
Normal force, 24
North pole, 73
N-type semiconductors, 159–160, 162

Nuclear energy, 146
Nuclear fission, 153, 177, 184
Nuclear force, 146
Nuclear fuel, 153
Nuclear fusion, 154
Nuclear power, 177
Nuclear power plants, 182
Nuclear reactions, 150–154
Nuclear science, 149–150
Nuclear shell model, 141–142
Nuclear Waste Policy Act (1982), 183
Nuclear Waste Policy Amendments
   Act (1987), 183
Nuclear wastes, disposal of, 182–183
Nucleons, 146
   binding energy, 147
Nucleus, 60, 146–147
Nuclide, 149
Numerator, 4

O
Object distance, 126
Observed frequency, 107
Office of Civilian Radioactive Waste
   Management, 183
Ohm (Ω), 65
Ohm's law, 65, 68, 69, 98
Orbit
   geosynchronous, 36
   of planet, 34–35
Oscilloscope, 97
Out of phase, 106

P
Parallel circuits, 68–69
Parallelogram method of vector
   addition, 5–6
Particle accelerators, 97, 150
Particles
   alpha, 141
   charged, in magnetic fields, 96
   subatomic, 146
Pascal (Pa), 55
Pendulum, determining period of,
   168
Percent error, 2
Periodic Table of the Elements, 146
Periodic waves, 104–105
Period of wave, 105
Phased circuits, 169–170
Phases, 51
   change in, 51
   of wave, 106
Photodiodes, 162
Photoelectric effect, 136–137
Photoelectrons, 136
Photoemissive materials, 136
Photographic plates, 150
Photon momentum, 138
Photons, 137, 148–149
Physics, solid state, 158–159
Planck's constant, 136, 137, 150
Plane surfaces, 126
Plasma, 184
Plum pudding model of atom, 140
P-N junction, 160
Point charges, 61
Polarization, 136
   of light, 115
Polaroids, 115
Polychromatic light, 120
Positive charge, 60–61
Positron, 146
Positron emission, 152
Potential differences, 63

Potential energy, 39, 44, 49
   elastic, 40
   electric, 62–63
   gravitational, 39
Power, 37–38
Precision in measurement, 1
Predictions, making, based on
   experimental data, 166
Pressure, 55–56
   as constant, 56
Pressure cooker, 53
Primary coil, 102
Primary seismic waves, 123–124
Principal axis, 126, 129
Principal focus, 126, 130
Principle of superposition, 109
Projectiles, 29
   angular launch of, 29
   horizontal launch of, 29
   maximum range of, 29
   motion of, 29, 32–34
Protons, 60, 146
P-type semiconductors, 160, 162
Pulses, 104
Pythagorean theorem, 6

Q
Quanta, 137
Quantities
   scalar, 5, 7
   vector, 5, 74
Quantum theory, 137–138, 148
Quarks, 146

R
Radiation
   electromagnetic, 91
   gamma, 151
Radioactive decay, 150
Radioactive wastes, 177
Radioactivity, 150
   natural, 150
Radio waves, 178–179
Radius of curvature, 129
Random errors, 1
Range, 29
   maximum, 29
Rarefactions, 105
Reactors, 153–154
Real images, 127
Rectifier, 161
Reflection
   angle of, 117
   diffuse, 118
   law of, 117, 129–130
   regular, 117–118
   total internal, 119–120
Refraction
   absolute index of, 118
   angle of, 118
   law of, 118
   of light, 118–120
   relative index of, 119
Refrigerator, 47–48
Regular reflection, 117–118
Relative index of refraction, 119
Renewable resources, 176
Resistance, 65–66
   combined, 69
   equivalent, 69
Resistivity, 66, 158
Resistor, 67
Resolution
   of forces, 15–16
   of vectors, 6–7
Resonance, 111

2002 Edition ❖ Reference Tables for Physical Setting/Physics

List of Physical Constants

Name	Symbol	Value
Universal gravitational constant	G	6.67×10^{-11} N•m^2/kg^2
Acceleration due to gravity	g	9.81 m/s^2
Speed of light in a vacuum	c	3.00×10^8 m/s
Speed of sound in air at STP		3.31×10^2 m/s
Mass of Earth		5.98×10^{24} kg
Mass of the Moon		7.35×10^{22} kg
Mean radius of Earth		6.37×10^6 m
Mean radius of the Moon		1.74×10^6 m
Mean distance—Earth to the Moon		3.84×10^8 m
Mean distance—Earth to the Sun		1.50×10^{11} m
Electrostatic constant	k	8.99×10^9 N•m^2/C^2
1 elementary charge	e	1.60×10^{-19} C
1 coulomb (C)		6.25×10^{18} elementary charges
1 electronvolt (eV)		1.60×10^{-19} J
Planck's constant	h	6.63×10^{-34} J•s
1 universal mass unit (u)		9.31×10^2 MeV
Rest mass of the electron	m_e	9.11×10^{-31} kg
Rest mass of the proton	m_p	1.67×10^{-27} kg
Rest mass of the neutron	m_n	1.67×10^{-27} kg

Prefixes for Powers of 10

Prefix	Symbol	Notation
tera	T	10^{12}
giga	G	10^9
mega	M	10^6
kilo	k	10^3
deci	d	10^{-1}
centi	c	10^{-2}
milli	m	10^{-3}
micro	μ	10^{-6}
nano	n	10^{-9}
pico	p	10^{-12}

Approximate Coefficients of Friction

	Kinetic	Static
Rubber on concrete (dry)	0.68	0.90
Rubber on concrete (wet)	0.58	
Rubber on asphalt (dry)	0.67	0.85
Rubber on asphalt (wet)	0.53	
Rubber on ice	0.15	
Waxed ski on snow	0.05	0.14
Wood on wood	0.30	0.42
Steel on steel	0.57	0.74
Copper on steel	0.36	0.53
Teflon on Teflon	0.04	

The Electromagnetic Spectrum

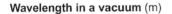

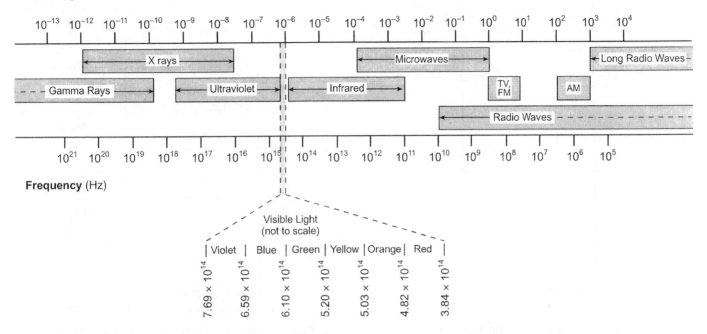

Frequency (Hz)

Visible Light
(not to scale)

| Violet | Blue | Green | Yellow | Orange | Red |

7.69×10^{14} 6.59×10^{14} 6.10×10^{14} 5.20×10^{14} 5.03×10^{14} 4.82×10^{14} 3.84×10^{14}

Absolute Indices of Refraction	
$(f = 5.09 \times 10^{14}$ Hz$)$	
Air	1.00
Corn oil	1.47
Diamond	2.42
Ethyl alcohol	1.36
Glass, crown	1.52
Glass, flint	1.66
Glycerol	1.47
Lucite	1.50
Quartz, fused	1.46
Sodium chloride	1.54
Water	1.33
Zircon	1.92

Energy Level Diagrams

Hydrogen

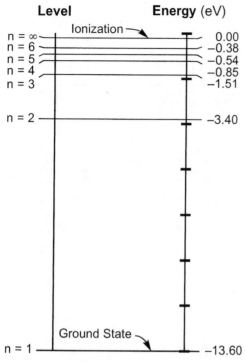

Energy Levels for the Hydrogen Atom

Mercury

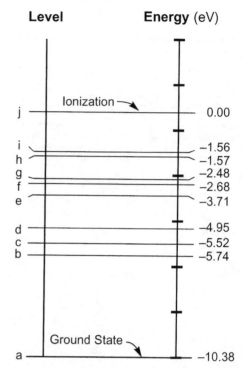

A Few Energy Levels for the Mercury Atom

Classification of Matter

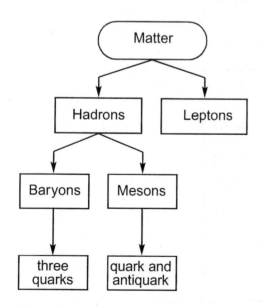

Particles of the Standard Model

Quarks

Name	up	charm	top
Symbol	u	c	t
Charge	$+\frac{2}{3}e$	$+\frac{2}{3}e$	$+\frac{2}{3}e$

	down	strange	bottom
	d	s	b
	$-\frac{1}{3}e$	$-\frac{1}{3}e$	$-\frac{1}{3}e$

Leptons

electron	muon	tau
e	μ	τ
$-1e$	$-1e$	$-1e$

electron neutrino	muon neutrino	tau neutrino
ν_e	ν_μ	ν_τ
0	0	0

Note: For each particle there is a corresponding antiparticle with a charge opposite that of its associated particle.

Electricity

$$F_e = \frac{kq_1q_2}{r^2}$$

$$E = \frac{F_e}{q}$$

$$V = \frac{W}{q}$$

$$I = \frac{\Delta q}{t}$$

$$R = \frac{V}{I}$$

$$R = \frac{\rho L}{A}$$

$$P = VI = I^2R = \frac{V^2}{R}$$

$$W = Pt = VIt = I^2Rt = \frac{V^2t}{R}$$

A = cross-sectional area
E = electric field strength
F_e = electrostatic force
I = current
k = electrostatic constant
L = length of conductor
P = electrical power
q = charge
R = resistance
R_{eq} = equivalent resistance
r = distance between centers
t = time
V = potential difference
W = work (electrical energy)
Δ = change
ρ = resistivity

Series Circuits

$$I = I_1 = I_2 = I_3 = \ldots$$

$$V = V_1 + V_2 + V_3 + \ldots$$

$$R_{eq} = R_1 + R_2 + R_3 + \ldots$$

Parallel Circuits

$$I = I_1 + I_2 + I_3 + \ldots$$

$$V = V_1 = V_2 = V_3 = \ldots$$

$$\frac{1}{R_{eq}} = \frac{1}{R_1} + \frac{1}{R_2} + \frac{1}{R_3} + \ldots$$

Circuit Symbols

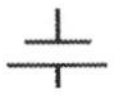

cell

battery

switch

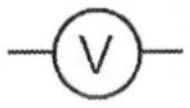

voltmeter

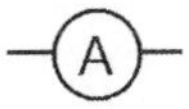

ammeter

resistor

variable resistor

lamp

Resistivities at 20°C	
Material	**Resistivity ($\Omega \bullet m$)**
Aluminum	2.82×10^{-8}
Copper	1.72×10^{-8}
Gold	2.44×10^{-8}
Nichrome	$150. \times 10^{-8}$
Silver	1.59×10^{-8}
Tungsten	5.60×10^{-8}

Waves and Optics

$v = f\lambda$

$T = \dfrac{1}{f}$

$\theta_i = \theta_r$

$n = \dfrac{c}{v}$

$n_1 \sin \theta_1 = n_2 \sin \theta_2$

$\dfrac{n_2}{n_1} = \dfrac{v_1}{v_2} = \dfrac{\lambda_1}{\lambda_2}$

c = speed of light in a vacuum

f = frequency

n = absolute index of refraction

T = period

v = velocity

λ = wavelength

θ = angle

θ_i = incident angle

θ_r = reflected angle

Modern Physics

$E_{photon} = hf = \dfrac{hc}{\lambda}$

$E_{photon} = E_i - E_f$

$E = mc^2$

c = speed of light in a vacuum

E = energy

f = frequency

h = Planck's constant

m = mass

λ = wavelength

Geometry and Trigonometry

Rectangle

$A = bh$

Triangle

$A = \frac{1}{2}bh$

Circle

$A = \pi r^2$

$C = 2\pi r$

Right Triangle

$c^2 = a^2 + b^2$

$\sin \theta = \dfrac{a}{c}$

$\cos \theta = \dfrac{b}{c}$

$\tan \theta = \dfrac{a}{b}$

A = area

b = base

C = circumference

h = height

r = radius

Mechanics

$$\bar{v} = \frac{d}{t}$$

$$a = \frac{\Delta v}{t}$$

$$v_f = v_i + at$$

$$d = v_i t + \frac{1}{2}at^2$$

$$v_f^2 = v_i^2 + 2ad$$

$$A_y = A \sin \theta$$

$$A_x = A \cos \theta$$

$$a = \frac{F_{net}}{m}$$

$$F_f = \mu F_N$$

$$F_g = \frac{Gm_1m_2}{r^2}$$

$$g = \frac{F_g}{m}$$

$$p = mv$$

$$p_{before} = p_{after}$$

$$J = Ft = \Delta p$$

$$F_s = kx$$

$$PE_s = \frac{1}{2}kx^2$$

$$F_c = ma_c$$

$$a_c = \frac{v^2}{r}$$

$$\Delta PE = mg\Delta h$$

$$KE = \frac{1}{2}mv^2$$

$$W = Fd = \Delta E_T$$

$$E_T = PE + KE + Q$$

$$P = \frac{W}{t} = \frac{Fd}{t} = F\bar{v}$$

a = acceleration

a_c = centripetal acceleration

A = any vector quantity

d = displacement/distance

E_T = total energy

F = force

F_c = centripetal force

F_f = force of friction

F_g = weight/force due to gravity

F_N = normal force

F_{net} = net force

F_s = force on a spring

g = acceleration due to gravity or gravitational field strength

G = universal gravitational constant

h = height

J = impulse

k = spring constant

KE = kinetic energy

m = mass

p = momentum

P = power

PE = potential energy

PE_s = potential energy stored in a spring

Q = internal energy

r = radius/distance between centers

t = time interval

v = velocity/speed

$\bar{v}$ = average velocity/average speed

W = work

x = change in spring length from the equilibrium position

Δ = change

θ = angle

μ = coefficient of friction

Sample
Examinations

PHYSICS
JUNE 2001

Part I

Answer all 55 questions in this part. [65]

Directions (1–55): For *each* statement or question, select the word or expression that, of those given, best completes the statement or answers the question. Record your answer on the separate answer paper in accordance with the directions on the front page of this booklet.

1 Which terms both represent scalar quantities?

(1) displacement and velocity
(2) distance and speed
(3) displacement and speed
(4) distance and velocity

2 A mass of one kilogram of nickels has a monetary value in United States dollars of approximately

(1) $1.00
(2) $0.10
(3) $10.00
(4) $1000.00

3 Which graph best represents the motion of an object whose speed is increasing?

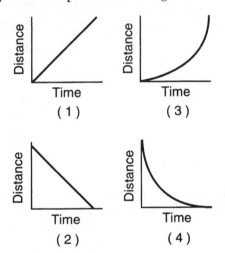

4 An astronaut weighs 500 newtons on Earth and 25 newtons on asteroid *X*. The acceleration due to gravity on asteroid *X* is approximately

(1) 1 m/s^2
(2) 2 m/s^2
(3) 0.2 m/s^2
(4) 0.5 m/s^2

5 A car having an initial velocity of 12 meters per second east slows uniformly to 2 meters per second east in 4.0 seconds. The acceleration of the car during this 4.0-second interval is

(1) 2.5 m/s^2 west
(2) 2.5 m/s^2 east
(3) 6.0 m/s^2 west
(4) 6.0 m/s^2 east

6 Two students push on a sled. One pushes with a force of 30. newtons east and the other exerts a force of 40. newtons south, as shown in the top-view diagram below.

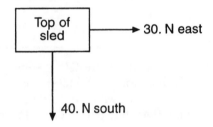

Which vector best represents the resultant of these two forces?

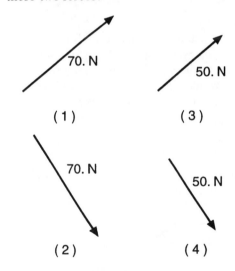

7 In an automobile collision, a 44-kilogram passenger moving at 15 meters per second is brought to rest by an air bag during a 0.10-second time interval. What is the magnitude of the average force exerted on the passenger during this time?

(1) 440 N
(2) 660 N
(3) 4400 N
(4) 6600 N

8 A series of unbalanced forces was applied to each of two blocks, A and B. The graphs below show the relationship between unbalanced force and acceleration for each block.

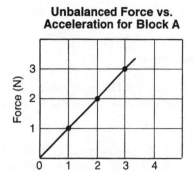
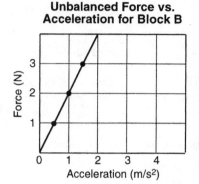

Compared to the mass of block A, the mass of block B is

(1) the same
(2) twice as great

(3) half as great
(4) four times as great

9 Two cars, A and B, are 400. meters apart. Car A travels due east at 30. meters per second on a collision course with car B, which travels due west at 20. meters per second. How much time elapses before the two cars collide?

(1) 8.0 s
(2) 13 s

(3) 20. s
(4) 40. s

10 A 50.-newton horizontal force is needed to keep an object weighing 500. newtons moving at a constant velocity of 2.0 meters per second across a horizontal surface. The magnitude of the frictional force acting on the object is

(1) 500. N
(2) 450. N

(3) 50. N
(4) 0 N

11 The diagram below represents a block sliding down an incline.

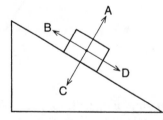

Which vector best represents the frictional force acting on the block?

(1) A
(2) B

(3) C
(4) D

12 A different force is applied to each of four 1-kilogram blocks to slide them across a uniform steel surface at constant speed as shown below. In which diagram is the coefficient of friction between the block and steel *smallest*?

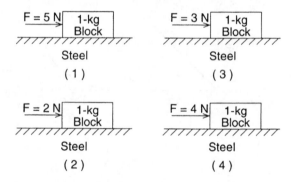

13 The magnitude of the momentum of an object is 64.0 kilogram•meter per second. If the velocity of the object is doubled, the magnitude of the momentum of the object will be

(1) 32.0 kg•m/s
(2) 64.0 kg•m/s

(3) 128 kg•m/s
(4) 256 kg•m/s

14 An airplane originally at rest on a runway accelerates uniformly at 6.0 meters per second^2 for 12 seconds. During this 12-second interval, the airplane travels a distance of approximately

(1) 72 m
(2) 220 m

(3) 430 m
(4) 860 m

15 Satellite A has a mass of 1.5×10^3 kilograms and is traveling east at 8.0×10^3 meters per second. Satellite B is traveling west at 6.0×10^3 meters per second. The satellites collide head-on and come to rest. What is the mass of satellite B?

(1) 2.7×10^3 kg   (3) 1.5×10^3 kg

(2) 2.0×10^3 kg   (4) 1.1×10^3 kg

16 Which combination of units can be used to express work?

(1) $\dfrac{\text{newton} \cdot \text{second}}{\text{meter}}$ (3) newton/meter

(2) $\dfrac{\text{newton} \cdot \text{meter}}{\text{second}}$ (4) newton•meter

17 A 2000-watt motor working at full capacity can vertically lift a 400-newton weight at a constant speed of

(1) 2×10^3 m/s   (3) 5 m/s

(2) 50 m/s   (4) 0.2 m/s

18 Which graph best represents the relationship between gravitational potential energy (PE) and height (h) above the ground for an object near the surface of Earth?

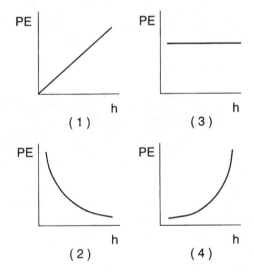

19 An alpha particle consists of two protons and two neutrons. The alpha particle's charge of +2 elementary charges is equivalent to

(1) 8.0×10^{-20} C   (3) 1.2×10^{19} C

(2) 3.2×10^{-19} C   (4) 3.2×10^{19} C

20 A 3.0-kilogram mass is attached to a spring having a spring constant of 30. newtons per meter. The mass is pulled 0.20 meter from the spring's equilibrium position and released. What is the maximum kinetic energy achieved by the mass-spring system?

(1) 2.4 J   (3) 1.2 J

(2) 1.5 J   (4) 0.60 J

21 The diagram below shows block A, having mass $2m$ and speed v, and block B having mass m and speed $2v$.

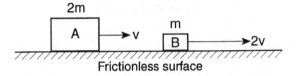

Compared to the kinetic energy of block A, the kinetic energy of block B is

(1) the same   (3) one-half as great

(2) twice as great   (4) four times as great

22 Two similar metal spheres possessing +1.0 coulomb of charge and –1.0 coulomb of charge, respectively, are brought toward each other. Which graph best represents the relationship between the magnitude of the electric force between the spheres and the distance between them?

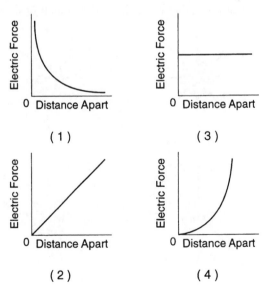

23 The diagram below shows two metal spheres charged to $+1.0 \times 10^{-6}$ coulomb and $+3.0 \times 10^{-6}$ coulomb, respectively, on insulating stands separated by a distance of 0.10 meter.

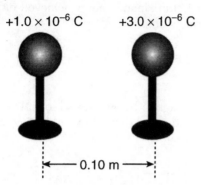

$+1.0 \times 10^{-6}$ C $+3.0 \times 10^{-6}$ C

|← 0.10 m →|

The spheres are touched together and then returned to their original positions. As a result, the magnitude of the electrostatic force between the spheres changes from 2.7 N to

(1) 1.4 N   (3) 3.6 N
(2) 1.8 N   (4) 14 N

24 An electrostatic force of 20. newtons is exerted on a charge of 8.0×10^{-2} coulomb at point P in an electric field. The magnitude of the electric field intensity at P is

(1) 4.0×10^{-3} N/C   (3) 20. N/C
(2) 1.6 N/C   (4) 2.5×10^2 N/C

25 Which diagram best represents the electric field around a negatively charged conducting sphere?

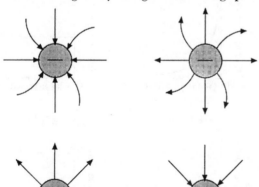

26 A 12-volt automobile battery has 8.4×10^3 coulombs of electric charge. The amount of electrical energy stored in the battery is approximately

(1) 1.0×10^5 J   (3) 7.0×10^2 J
(2) 8.4×10^3 J   (4) 1.4×10^{-3} J

27 Which graph best represents the relationship between potential difference across a metallic conductor and the resulting current through the conductor at a constant temperature?

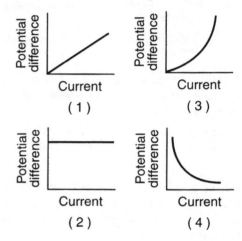

28 Plastic insulation surrounds a wire having diameter d and length ℓ as shown below.

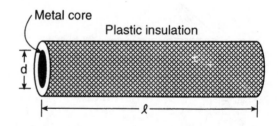

A decrease in the resistance of the wire would be produced by an increase in the

(1) thickness of the plastic insulation
(2) length ℓ of the wire
(3) diameter d of the wire
(4) temperature of the wire

29 Which diagram below correctly shows currents traveling near junction P in an electric circuit?

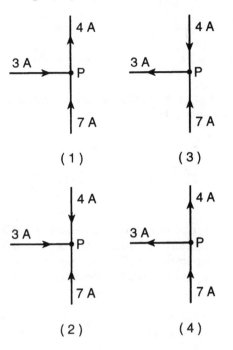

(1)   (3)

(2)   (4)

30 The diagram below shows three resistors, R_1, R_2, and R_3, connected to a 12-volt battery.

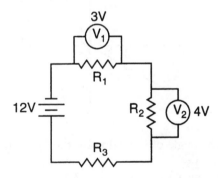

If voltmeter V_1 reads 3 volts and voltmeter V_2 reads 4 volts, what is the potential drop across resistor R_3?

(1) 12 V   (3) 0 V
(2) 5 V   (4) 4 V

31 A current of 3.0 amperes is flowing in a circuit. How much charge passes a given point in the circuit in 30. seconds?

(1) 0.10 C   (3) 33 C
(2) 10. C   (4) 90. C

Base your answers to questions 32 and 33 on the diagram below, which shows two resistors connected in parallel across a 6.0-volt source.

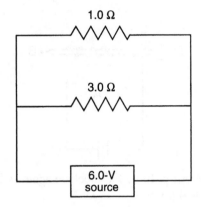

32 The equivalent resistance of the two resistors is

(1) 0.75 Ω   (3) 1.3 Ω
(2) 2.0 Ω   (4) 4.0 Ω

Note that question 33 has only three choices.

33 Compared to the power dissipated in the 1.0-ohm resistor, the power dissipated in the 3.0-ohm resistor is

(1) less
(2) greater
(3) the same

34 The diagram below represents the magnetic lines of force around a bar magnet.

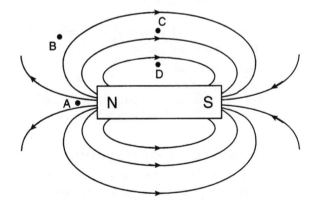

At which point is the magnitude of the magnetic field strength of the bar magnet the greatest?

(1) A   (3) C
(2) B   (4) D

35 The diagram below shows an electromagnet made from a nail, a coil of insulated wire, and a battery.

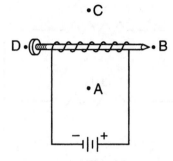

The south pole of the electromagnet is located closest to point

(1) A
(2) B
(3) C
(4) D

36 The diagram below shows light rays in air about to strike a glass window.

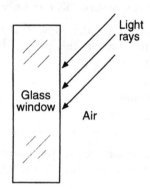

When the rays reach the boundary between the air and the glass, the light is

(1) totally refracted
(2) totally reflected
(3) partially reflected and partially diffracted
(4) partially reflected and partially refracted

37 Which phrase best describes a periodic wave?

(1) a single pulse traveling at constant speed
(2) a series of pulses at irregular intervals
(3) a series of pulses at regular intervals
(4) a single pulse traveling at different speeds in the same medium

38 Which equation correctly relates the speed v, wavelength λ, and period T of a periodic wave?

(1) $v = \dfrac{T}{\lambda}$
(2) $v = T\lambda$
(3) $v = \dfrac{\lambda}{T}$
(4) $v = \dfrac{\lambda^2}{T}$

39 What are the amplitude and wavelength of the wave shown below?

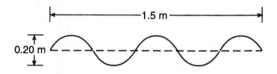

(1) amplitude = 0.10 m, wavelength = 0.30 m
(2) amplitude = 0.10 m, wavelength = 0.60 m
(3) amplitude = 0.20 m, wavelength = 0.30 m
(4) amplitude = 0.20 m, wavelength = 0.60 m

40 A ray of monochromatic light traveling in air is incident on a plane mirror at an angle of 30.°, as shown in the diagram below.

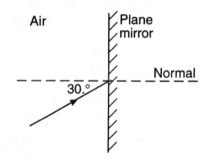

The angle of reflection for the light ray is

(1) 15°
(2) 30.°
(3) 60.°
(4) 90.°

41 What type of wave is sound traveling in water?

(1) torsional
(2) transverse
(3) elliptical
(4) longitudinal

42 The diagram below shows two waves, A and B.

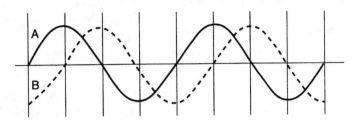

The phase difference between A and B is
(1) 0°
(2) 45°
(3) 90°
(4) 180°

43 The diagram below represents monochromatic light incident on a pair of slits, S_1 and S_2, that are separated by a distance of 2.0×10^{-6} meter. A, B, and C are adjacent antinodal areas that appear on a screen 1.0 meter from the slits. The distance from A to B is 0.34 meter.

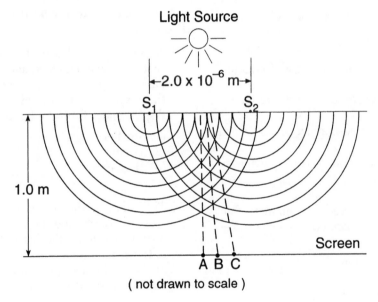

(not drawn to scale)

What is the wavelength of the incident light?
(1) 6.8×10^{-7} m
(2) 5.9×10^{-6} m
(3) 1.7×10^{5} m
(4) 6.8×10^{7} m

44 The hertz is a unit that describes the number of
(1) seconds it takes to complete one cycle of a wave
(2) cycles of a wave completed in one second
(3) points that are in phase along one meter of a wave
(4) points that are out of phase along one meter of a wave

45 As a wave travels between two points in a medium, the wave transfers
(1) energy, only
(2) mass, only
(3) both energy and mass
(4) neither energy nor mass

46 The diagram below shows a ray of light ($\lambda = 5.9 \times 10^{-7}$ meter) traveling from air into medium X.

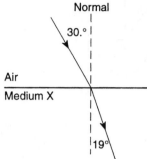

Normal

30.°

Air

Medium X

19°

If the angle of incidence is 30.° and the angle of refraction is 19°, medium X could be

(1) air
(2) alcohol
(3) Canada balsam
(4) glycerol

47 As a monochromatic beam of light passes obliquely from flint glass into water, how do the characteristics of the beam of light change?

(1) Its wavelength decreases and its frequency decreases.
(2) Its wavelength decreases and its frequency increases.
(3) Its wavelength increases and it bends toward the normal.
(4) Its wavelength increases and it bends away from the normal.

48 Alpha particles were directed at a thin metal foil. Some particles were deflected into hyperbolic paths due to

(1) gravitational attraction
(2) electrostatic repulsion
(3) electrostatic attraction
(4) magnetic repulsion

49 The threshold frequency in a photoelectric experiment is most closely related to the

(1) brightness of the incident light
(2) thickness of the photoemissive metal
(3) area of the photoemissive metal
(4) work function of the photoemissive metal

50 The momentum of a photon is inversely proportional to the photon's

(1) frequency
(2) mass
(3) weight
(4) wavelength

51 The electron in a hydrogen atom drops from energy level $n = 2$ to energy level $n = 1$ by emitting a photon having an energy of approximately

(1) 5.4×10^{-19} J
(2) 1.6×10^{-18} J
(3) 2.2×10^{-18} J
(4) 7.4×10^{-18} J

52 In the currently accepted model of the atom, a fuzzy cloud around a hydrogen nucleus is used to represent the

(1) electron's actual path, which is not a circular orbit
(2) general region where the atom's proton is most probably located
(3) general region where the atom's electron is most probably located
(4) presence of water vapor in the atom

Note that questions 53 through 55 have only three choices.

53 A softball player leaves the batter's box, overruns first base by 3.0 meters, and then returns to first base. Compared to the total distance traveled by the player, the magnitude of the player's total displacement from the batter's box is

(1) smaller
(2) larger
(3) the same

54 The radius of Mars is approximately one-half the radius of Earth, and the mass of Mars is approximately one-tenth the mass of Earth. Compared to the acceleration due to gravity on the surface of Earth, the acceleration due to gravity on the surface of Mars is

(1) smaller
(2) larger
(3) the same

55 A mosquito flying over a highway strikes the windshield of a moving truck. Compared to the magnitude of the force of the truck on the mosquito during the collision, the magnitude of the force of the mosquito on the truck is

(1) smaller
(2) larger
(3) the same

Part II

This part consists of six groups, each containing ten questions. Each group tests an optional area of the course. Choose two of these six groups. Be sure that you answer all ten questions in each group chosen. Record the answers to the questions in accordance with the directions on the front page of this booklet.   [20]

Group 1 — Motion in a Plane

If you choose this group, be sure to answer questions 56–65.

56 A football player kicks a ball with an initial velocity of 25 meters per second at an angle of 53° above the horizontal. The vertical component of the initial velocity of the ball is

(1) 25 m/s   (3) 15 m/s
(2) 20. m/s   (4) 10. m/s

57 A student throws a stone upward at an angle of 45°. Which statement best describes the stone at the highest point that it reaches?

(1) Its acceleration is zero.
(2) Its acceleration is at a maximum.
(3) Its potential energy is at a minimum.
(4) Its kinetic energy is at a minimum.

58 A red ball and a green ball are simultaneously thrown horizontally from the same height. The red ball has an initial speed of 40. meters per second and the green ball has an initial speed of 20. meters per second. Compared to the time it takes the red ball to reach the ground, the time it takes the green ball to reach the ground will be

(1) the same   (3) half as much
(2) twice as much   (4) four times as much

59 A baseball player throws a ball horizontally. Which statement best describes the ball's motion after it is thrown? [Neglect the effect of friction.]

(1) Its vertical speed remains the same, and its horizontal speed increases.
(2) Its vertical speed remains the same, and its horizontal speed remains the same.
(3) Its vertical speed increases, and its horizontal speed increases.
(4) Its vertical speed increases, and its horizontal speed remains the same.

Base your answers to questions 60 and 61 on the information and diagram below.

A 1200-kilogram car traveling at a constant speed of 9.0 meters per second turns at an intersection. The car follows a horizontal circular path with a radius of 25 meters to point P.

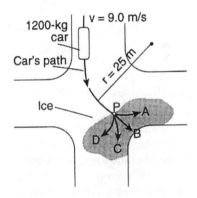

60 The magnitude of the centripetal force acting on the car as it travels around the circular path is approximately

(1) 1.1×10^4 N   (3) 3.9×10^3 N
(2) 1.2×10^4 N   (4) 4.3×10^2 N

61 At point P, the car hits an area of ice and loses all frictional force on its tires. Which path does the car follow on the ice?

(1) A (3) C
(2) B (4) D

_____

62 An amusement park ride moves a rider at a constant speed of 14 meters per second in a horizontal circular path of radius 10. meters. What is the rider's centripetal acceleration in terms of g, the acceleration due to gravity?

(1) 1g (3) 3g
(2) 2g (4) 0g

63 The diagram below shows the elliptical orbit of a comet around the Sun. The comet's closest approach to the Sun is at point A.

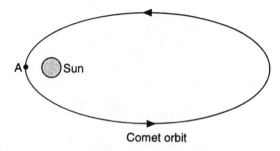

Comet orbit

Which statement best describes the comet's energy as it passes through point A?

(1) Its kinetic energy is at a minimum and its potential energy is at a minimum.
(2) Its kinetic energy is at a minimum and its potential energy is at a maximum.
(3) Its kinetic energy is at a maximum and its potential energy is at a minimum.
(4) Its kinetic energy is at a maximum and its potential energy is at a maximum.

64 The chart below gives the mass and orbital period of each of four satellites, A, B, C, and D, orbiting Earth in circular paths.

Satellite	Mass (kilograms)	Orbital Period (hours)
A	500	4
B	500	2
C	100	6
D	100	3

Which satellite is closest to Earth?

(1) A (3) C
(2) B (4) D

65 The Moon's orbit is *not* classified as geosynchronous because

(1) the Moon's position over Earth's surface varies with time
(2) the Moon's mass is very large compared to the mass of all other Earth satellites
(3) the Moon is a natural satellite, rather than an artificial one
(4) the Moon always has the same half of its surface facing Earth

Group 2 — Internal Energy

If you choose this group, be sure to answer questions 66–75.

Base your answers to questions 66 and 67 on the graph and information below.

The graph below represents a cooling curve for 10. kilograms of a substance as it cools from a vapor at 160.°C to a solid at 20.°C. Energy is removed from the sample at a constant rate.

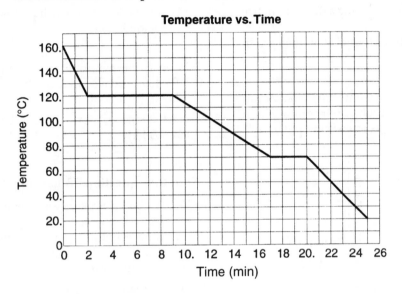

Temperature vs. Time

Note that question 66 has only three choices.

66 While the substance is cooling during the liquid phase, the average kinetic energy of the molecules of the substance

(1) decreases
(2) increases
(3) remains the same

67 The melting point of the substance is

(1) 0°C   (3) 100.°C
(2) 70.°C   (4) 120.°C

68 What is the change in temperature of a sample of water as it is heated from its freezing point to its boiling point at standard pressure?

(1) 373 K   (3) 212 K
(2) 273 K   (4) 100. K

69 Equal amounts of heat are applied to equal masses of four different substances initially at –10°C. Which substance has the largest change in temperature?

(1) aluminum   (3) iron
(2) ice   (4) alcohol

70 Why do some transportation agencies spread a mixture of sand and salt on icy roads in winter?

(1) Sand decreases the frictional force between vehicle tires and the road, and salt lowers the melting point of ice.
(2) Sand decreases the frictional force between vehicle tires and the road, and salt raises the melting point of ice.
(3) Sand increases the frictional force between vehicle tires and the road, and salt lowers the melting point of ice.
(4) Sand increases the frictional force between vehicle tires and the road, and salt raises the melting point of ice.

71 The air pressure inside an automobile tire is lower during cold weather than during warm weather. The lower air pressure is most likely due to

(1) an increase in molecular potential energy of the air molecules in the tire

(2) a decrease in the speed of the air molecules in the tire

(3) salt on the roads producing a decrease in tire volume

(4) cold air in the tire producing an increase in tire volume

72 Which graph best represents the relationship between volume and absolute temperature for a fixed mass of an ideal gas at constant pressure?

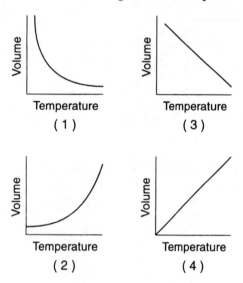

(1)   (3)

(2)   (4)

73 Heat will flow from a region of low temperature to a region of higher temperature if

(1) the specific heat of the cooler region is greater than the specific heat of the warmer region

(2) the temperature of the cooler region is near absolute zero

(3) work is done to produce the flow

(4) the cooler region is liquid and the warmer region is solid

74 What is the minimum heat required to change 5.0 kilograms of copper at 1083°C from a solid to a liquid?

(1) 0.20 kJ   (3) 41 kJ
(2) 0.39 kJ   (4) 1.0×10^3 kJ

Note that question 75 has only three choices.

75 When a box of beakers was dropped, the beakers broke into many pieces. Dropping the box a second time could *not* cause the pieces to reform into the original beakers because this would require entropy to

(1) decrease
(2) increase
(3) remain the same

Group 3 — Electromagnetic Applications

If you choose this group, be sure to answer questions 76–85.

Base your answers to questions 76 and 77 on the information and diagram below.

An electromagnet with an air core is located within the magnetic field between two permanent magnets.

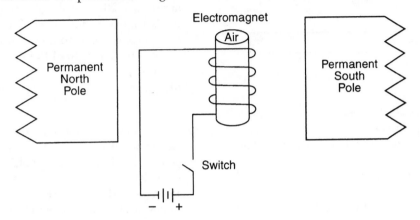

76 At the instant the switch is closed and a current begins to flow through the coil of the electromagnet, the coil will experience

(1) no electromagnetic force
(2) a force directed out of the page
(3) a counterclockwise torque
(4) a clockwise torque

Note that question 77 has only three choices.

77 The air core of the electromagnet is replaced with an iron core. Compared to the strength of the magnetic field in the air core, the strength of the magnetic field in the iron core is

(1) less
(2) greater
(3) the same

78 The two ends of a wire are connected to a galvanometer, forming a complete electric circuit. The wire is then moved through a magnetic field, as shown in the diagram below.

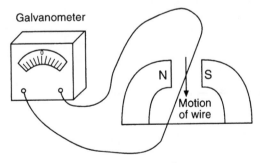

The galvanometer is being used to measure

(1) current
(2) potential difference
(3) temperature change
(4) resistance

79 Which device converts electrical energy into mechanical energy?

(1) motor
(2) generator
(3) source of emf
(4) thermocouple

80 The diagram below shows a point, *P*, located midway between two oppositely charged parallel plates.

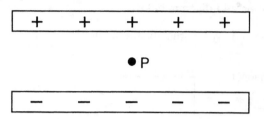

If an electron is introduced at point *P*, the electron will

(1) travel at constant speed toward the positively charged plate
(2) travel at constant speed toward the negatively charged plate
(3) accelerate toward the positively charged plate
(4) accelerate toward the negatively charged plate

81 The diagram below shows a proton moving with velocity *v* about to enter a uniform magnetic field directed into the page. As the proton moves in the magnetic field, the magnitude of the magnetic force on the proton is *F*.

```
        X   X   X   X
        X   X   X   X   Magnetic Field
 (+) v→                 Directed into
        X   X   X   X      the Page
        X   X   X   X
```

If the proton were replaced by an alpha particle under the same conditions, the magnitude of the magnetic force on the alpha particle would be

(1) *F*   (3) $\frac{F}{2}$

(2) 2*F*   (4) 4*F*

82 The isotopes of an element can be separated using a

(1) cathode ray tube   (3) Geiger counter
(2) diffraction grating (4) mass spectrometer

83 A potential difference of 12 volts is induced across a 0.20-meter-long straight wire as it is moved at a constant speed of 3.0 meters per second perpendicular to a uniform magnetic field. What is the strength of the magnetic field?

(1) 180 T   (3) 13 T
(2) 20. T   (4) 7.2 T

84 A step-down transformer used to run a toy train has an input of 120 volts to its primary coil. A potential difference of 12 volts is induced in the secondary coil, which carries a current of 12 amperes. If the transformer operates at 75% efficiency, what is the current in the primary coil?

(1) 0.90 A   (3) 90. A
(2) 1.6 A   (4) 160 A

85 What is the origin of the light emitted by a laser?

(1) thermionic emission from an incandescent filament
(2) emission of mechanical waves from vibrating matter
(3) emission of photoelectrons from a photosensitive surface
(4) emission of photons from excited atoms

Group 4 — Geometric Optics

If you choose this group, be sure to answer questions 86–95.

86 Which diagram best represents image *I*, which is formed by placing object *O* in front of a plane mirror?

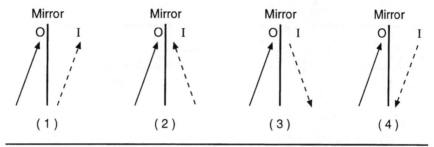

(1)   (2)   (3)   (4)

---

87 The diagram below shows an arrow placed in front of a converging lens.

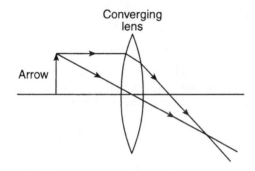

The lens forms an image of the arrow that is

(1) real and inverted
(2) real and erect
(3) virtual and inverted
(4) virtual and erect

88 Light rays from a candle flame are incident on a convex mirror. After reflecting from the mirror, these light rays

(1) converge and form a virtual image
(2) converge and form a real image
(3) diverge and form a virtual image
(4) diverge and form a real image

89 The diagram below shows an object located at point *P*, 0.25 meter from a concave spherical mirror with principal focus *F*. The focal length of the mirror is 0.10 meter.

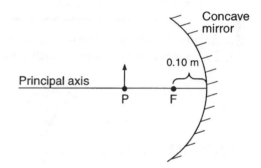

How does the image change as the object is moved from point *P* toward point *F*?

(1) It's distance from the mirror decreases and the size of the image decreases.
(2) It's distance from the mirror decreases and the size of the image increases.
(3) It's distance from the mirror increases and the size of the image decreases.
(4) It's distance from the mirror increases and the size of the image increases.

90 The diagram below shows light ray R incident on a glass lens in air.

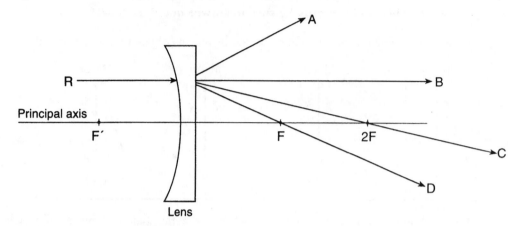

Which ray best represents the path of light ray R after it passes through the lens?

(1) A (3) C
(2) B (4) D

---

91 The diagram below shows two parallel light rays, X and Y, approaching a concave spherical mirror.

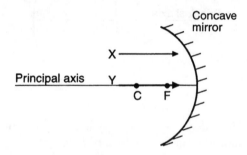

Which light will reflect through the mirror's center of curvature, C?

(1) ray X, only
(2) ray Y, only
(3) both ray X and ray Y
(4) neither ray X nor ray Y

92 Which optical devices in air can both form real images?

(1) concave mirror and convex lens
(2) concave mirror and concave lens
(3) plane mirror and convex lens
(4) plane mirror and concave lens

---

93 An object is located 0.15 meter from a converging lens with focal length 0.10 meter. How far from the lens is the image formed?

(1) 0.060 m   (3) 0.15 m
(2) 0.10 m   (4) 0.30 m

94 When a student 1.5 meters tall stands 5.0 meters in front of a lens, his image forms on a screen located 0.50 meter behind the lens. What is the height of the student's image?

(1) 0.015 m   (3) 1.5 m
(2) 0.15 m   (4) 15 m

95 Which phenomena cause chromatic aberration to occur when polychromatic light passes through a lens?

(1) diffraction and refraction
(2) diffraction and reflection
(3) dispersion and refraction
(4) dispersion and reflection

Group 5 — Solid State

If you choose this group, be sure to answer questions 96–105.

96 A material having extremely low conductivity would be classified as

(1) a conductor   (3) an insulator
(2) a semiconductor   (4) a metalloid

97 The diagram below represents the band model of a substance.

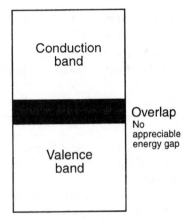

The substance is best classified as

(1) an insulator   (3) a conductor
(2) a semiconductor   (4) a nonmetal

98 Magnetic-card door locks utilize many electronic components on one small piece of semiconductor material. This combination of components on a single chip is called

(1) a transistor
(2) an integrated circuit
(3) a printed circuit board
(4) a diode

99 The Band Model has replaced the Electron-sea Model of conduction because the Electron-sea Model

(1) only works for gases
(2) only works for liquids
(3) does not account for the conduction properties of metals
(4) does not account for the conduction properties of semiconductors

100 The diagram below shows a portion of the Periodic Table of the Elements.

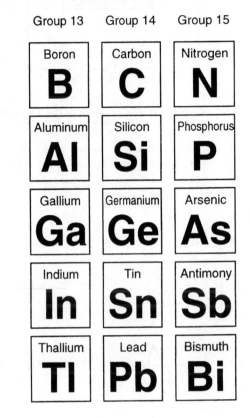

Based on the information in this diagram, which three elements could all be used as doping agents to produce the holes of a *P*-type semiconductor?

(1) boron, aluminum, and gallium
(2) boron, carbon, and nitrogen
(3) thallium, germanium, and phosphorus
(4) nitrogen, phosphorus, and arsenic

101 The diagram below shows a circuit with a battery applying a potential difference across a *P*-type semiconductor.

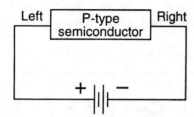

The majority charge carriers in the semiconductor are

(1) negative electrons moving to the right
(2) negative electrons moving to the left
(3) positive holes moving to the right
(4) positive holes moving to the left

102 Which diagram best represents a diode?

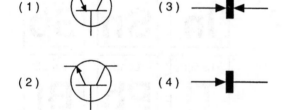

(1)   (3)

(2)   (4)

103 In the *P-N* junction region of an operating diode, an electric field barrier is produced by free electrons in the

(1) *N*-type material crossing into the *P*-type material
(2) *N*-type material going away from the *P*-type material
(3) *P*-type material crossing into the *N*-type material
(4) *P*-type material going away from the *N*-type material

104 In a *P-N-P* transistor, what is the function of the two types of material?

(1) The *N*-type material functions as the base, and the *P*-type material is both emitter and collector.
(2) The *N*-type material functions as both base and emitter, and the *P*-type material is the collector.
(3) The *N*-type material functions as the emitter, and the *P*-type material is both base and collector.
(4) The *N*-type material functions as the collector, and the *P*-type material is both emitter and base.

Note that question 105 has only three choices.

105 As the temperature of a semiconductor increases, the number of holes in the valence band will

(1) decrease
(2) increase
(3) remain the same

Group 6 — Nuclear Energy

If you choose this group, be sure to answer questions 106–115.

106 Which nuclide has a mass number of 8?

(1) $^{6}_{2}\text{He}$

(3) $^{15}_{7}\text{N}$

(2) $^{8}_{4}\text{Be}$

(4) $^{16}_{8}\text{O}$

107 The binding energy of a uranium-235 nucleus is the energy equivalent of its

(1) total mass

(3) critical mass

(2) mass number

(4) mass defect

108 Which device is used to detect nuclear radiation?

(1) cyclotron
(2) Geiger counter
(3) linear accelerator
(4) Van de Graaff generator

109 When an atom of $^{238}_{92}\text{U}$ decays to an atom of $^{206}_{82}\text{Pb}$, the total number of alpha particles emitted is

(1) 5

(3) 8

(2) 6

(4) 14

110 A medical lab has a 16-gram sample of a radio-active isotope. After 6.0 hours, it is found that 12 grams of the sample have decayed. What is the half-life of the isotope?

(1) 6.0 hr

(3) 3.0 hr

(2) 2.0 hr

(4) 12.0 hr

111 The nuclear equation $^{30}_{15}\text{P} \rightarrow ^{30}_{14}\text{Si} + ^{0}_{+1}\text{e}$ represents

(1) alpha bombardment
(2) electron capture
(3) neutron emission
(4) positron emission

112 In a nuclear reactor, one of the primary functions of the coolant is to

(1) promote overheating in the reactor core
(2) transfer thermal energy to a heat exchanger
(3) adjust the number of neutrons
(4) protect the reactor operators from radiation

113 Protons and neutrons are composed of smaller particles called

(1) quarks

(3) alpha particles

(2) baryons

(4) bosons

114 The equation below represents a fission reaction in a nuclear reactor.

$$^{1}_{0}\text{n} + ^{235}_{92}\text{U} \rightarrow ^{141}_{56}\text{Ba} + ^{92}_{36}\text{Kr} + 3^{1}_{0}\text{n} + \text{energy}$$

Which product of this reaction must be absorbed by other $^{235}_{92}\text{U}$ nuclei to sustain a chain reaction?

(1) $^{141}_{56}\text{Ba}$

(3) $^{1}_{0}\text{n}$

(2) $^{92}_{36}\text{Kr}$

(4) energy

115 Which equation represents the process by which the Sun produces energy?

(1) $^{3}_{1}\text{H} + ^{1}_{1}\text{H} \rightarrow ^{4}_{2}\text{He} + Q$

(2) $^{235}_{92}\text{U} + ^{1}_{0}\text{n} \rightarrow ^{138}_{56}\text{Ba} + ^{95}_{36}\text{Kr} + 3^{1}_{0}\text{n} + Q$

(3) $^{14}_{6}\text{C} \rightarrow ^{14}_{7}\text{N} + ^{0}_{-1}\text{e} + Q$

(4) $^{40}_{19}\text{K} + ^{0}_{-1}\text{e} \rightarrow ^{40}_{18}\text{Ar} + Q$

Part III

You must answer *all* questions in this part. Record your answers in the spaces provided on the separate answer paper. Pen or pencil may be used. [15]

Base your answers to questions 116 through 119 on the information and diagram below, which is drawn to a scale of 1.0 centimeter = 30. meters.

A student on building *X* is located 240. meters from the launch site *B* of a rocket on building *Y*. The rocket reaches its maximum altitude at point *A*. The student's eyes are level with the launch site on building *Y*.

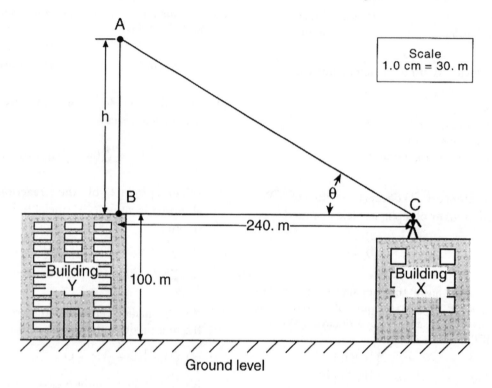

116 Using the scale diagram and a protractor, measure the angle of elevation, θ, of the rocket and record it to the *nearest degree*. [1]

117 Determine the height, *h*, of the rocket above the student's eye level. [1]

118 What is the total distance the rocket must fall from its maximum altitude to reach the ground? [1]

119 Determine how much time is required for the rocket to fall freely from point *A* back to ground level. [Show all calculations, including the equation and substitution with units.] [2]

120 A 0.65-meter-long pendulum consists of a 1.0-kilogram mass at the end of a string. The pendulum is released from rest at position *A*, 0.25 meter above its lowest point. The pendulum is timed at five positions, *A* through *E*.

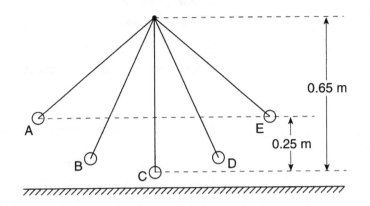

Data Table	
Position	Elapsed Time
A	0.00 s
B	0.20 s
C	0.40 s
D	0.60 s
E	0.80 s

Based on the information in the diagram and the data table, determine the period of the pendulum.   [1]

Base your answers to questions 121 through 123 on the information below.

A 680-newton student runs up a flight of stairs 3.5 meters high in 11.4 seconds. The student takes 8.5 seconds to run up the same flight of stairs during a second trial.

121 Determine the work done by the 680-newton student in climbing the stairs. [Show all calculations, including the equation and substitution with units.]   [2]

122 Determine the power developed by the student during the 11.4-second climb. [Show all calculations, including the equation and substitution with units.]   [2]

123 Using one or more complete sentences, compare the power developed by the student climbing the stairs in 11.4 seconds to the power developed during the 8.5-second trial.   [1]

Base your answers to questions 124 through 126 on the information below.

A 0.12-meter-long electromagnetic (radar) wave is emitted by a weather station and reflected from a nearby thunderstorm.

124 Determine the frequency of the radar wave. [Show all calculations, including the equation and substitution with units.]   [2]

125 Using one or more complete sentences, define the Doppler effect.   [1]

126 The thunderstorm is moving toward the weather station. Using one or more complete sentences, explain how the Doppler effect could have been used to determine the direction in which the storm is moving.   [1]

PHYSICS
JUNE 2001

ANSWER PAPER

Student . . . .

Teacher . . . .

School . . . .

Record all of your answers on this answer paper in accordance with the instructions on the front page of the test booklet.

Part I (65 credits)

#	1	2	3	4		#	1	2	3	4		#	1	2	3	4
1	1	2	3	4		21	1	2	3	4		41	1	2	3	4
2	1	2	3	4		22	1	2	3	4		42	1	2	3	4
3	1	2	3	4		23	1	2	3	4		43	1	2	3	4
4	1	2	3	4		24	1	2	3	4		44	1	2	3	4
5	1	2	3	4		25	1	2	3	4		45	1	2	3	4
6	1	2	3	4		26	1	2	3	4		46	1	2	3	4
7	1	2	3	4		27	1	2	3	4		47	1	2	3	4
8	1	2	3	4		28	1	2	3	4		48	1	2	3	4
9	1	2	3	4		29	1	2	3	4		49	1	2	3	4
10	1	2	3	4		30	1	2	3	4		50	1	2	3	4
11	1	2	3	4		31	1	2	3	4		51	1	2	3	4
12	1	2	3	4		32	1	2	3	4		52	1	2	3	4
13	1	2	3	4		33	1	2	3			53	1	2	3	
14	1	2	3	4		34	1	2	3	4		54	1	2	3	
15	1	2	3	4		35	1	2	3	4		55	1	2	3	
16	1	2	3	4		36	1	2	3	4						
17	1	2	3	4		37	1	2	3	4						
18	1	2	3	4		38	1	2	3	4						
19	1	2	3	4		39	1	2	3	4						
20	1	2	3	4		40	1	2	3	4						

FOR TEACHER USE ONLY

Part I Score (Use table below) . . . . . .

Part II Score . . . . . .

Part III Score . . . . . .

Total Score . . . . . .

Rater's Initials: . . . .

PART I CREDITS

Directions to Teacher:

In the table below, draw a circle around the number of right answers and the adjacent number of credits. Then write the number of credits (not the number right) in the space provided above.

No. Right	Credits		No. Right	Credits
55	65		27	45
54	64		26	44
53	64		25	43
52	63		24	43
51	62		23	42
50	61		22	41
49	61		21	41
48	60		20	40
47	59		19	39
46	59		18	38
45	58		17	38
44	57		16	37
43	56		15	36
42	56		14	36
41	55		13	35
40	54		12	32
39	54		11	30
38	53		10	27
37	52		9	24
36	51		8	22
35	51		7	19
34	50		6	16
33	49		5	13
32	48		4	11
31	48		3	8
30	47		2	5
29	46		1	3
28	46		0	0

No. right . . . .

Part II (20 credits)

Answer the questions in only two of the six groups in this part. Be sure to mark the answers to the groups of questions you choose in accordance with the instructions on the front page of the test booklet. Leave blank the four groups of questions you do not choose to answer.

Group 1
Motion in a Plane

56	1	2	3	4
57	1	2	3	4
58	1	2	3	4
59	1	2	3	4
60	1	2	3	4
61	1	2	3	4
62	1	2	3	4
63	1	2	3	4
64	1	2	3	4
65	1	2	3	4

Group 3
Electromagnetic Applications

76	1	2	3	4
77	1	2	3	
78	1	2	3	4
79	1	2	3	4
80	1	2	3	4
81	1	2	3	4
82	1	2	3	4
83	1	2	3	4
84	1	2	3	4
85	1	2	3	4

Group 5
Solid State

96	1	2	3	4
97	1	2	3	4
98	1	2	3	4
99	1	2	3	4
100	1	2	3	4
101	1	2	3	4
102	1	2	3	4
103	1	2	3	4
104	1	2	3	4
105	1	2	3	

Group 2
Internal Energy

66	1	2	3	
67	1	2	3	4
68	1	2	3	4
69	1	2	3	4
70	1	2	3	4
71	1	2	3	4
72	1	2	3	4
73	1	2	3	4
74	1	2	3	4
75	1	2	3	

Group 4
Geometric Optics

86	1	2	3	4
87	1	2	3	4
88	1	2	3	4
89	1	2	3	4
90	1	2	3	4
91	1	2	3	4
92	1	2	3	4
93	1	2	3	4
94	1	2	3	4
95	1	2	3	4

Group 6
Nuclear Energy

106	1	2	3	4
107	1	2	3	4
108	1	2	3	4
109	1	2	3	4
110	1	2	3	4
111	1	2	3	4
112	1	2	3	4
113	1	2	3	4
114	1	2	3	4
115	1	2	3	4

Part III (15 credits)

Answer <u>all</u> questions in this part.

116 _____

117 _____

118 _____

119

120 _____

121

122

123 _____

_____

_____

_____

_____

_____

_____

124

125

126

Physical Setting/PHYSICS

JUNE 2002

Part A

Answer all questions in this part.

Directions (1–35): For *each* statement or question, write on the separate answer sheet, the *number* of the word or expression that, of those given, best completes the statement or answers the question.

1 Which is a vector quantity?
(1) distance   (3) power
(2) speed   (4) force

2 The diagram below shows a granite block being slid at constant speed across a horizontal concrete floor by a force parallel to the floor.

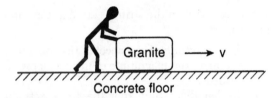

Which pair of quantities could be used to determine the coefficient of friction for the granite on the concrete?
(1) mass and speed of the block
(2) mass and normal force on the block
(3) frictional force and speed of the block
(4) frictional force and normal force on the block

3 An object with an initial speed of 4.0 meters per second accelerates uniformly at 2.0 meters per second² in the direction of its motion for a distance of 5.0 meters. What is the final speed of the object?
(1) 6.0 m/s   (3) 14 m/s
(2) 10. m/s   (4) 36 m/s

4 After a model rocket reached its maximum height, it then took 5.0 seconds to return to the launch site. What is the approximate maximum height reached by the rocket? [Neglect air resistance.]
(1) 49 m   (3) 120 m
(2) 98 m   (4) 250 m

5 The diagram below shows a student throwing a baseball horizontally at 25 meters per second from a cliff 45 meters above the level ground.

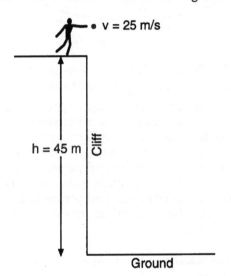

Approximately how far from the base of the cliff does the ball hit the ground? [Neglect air resistance.]
(1) 45 m   (3) 140 m
(2) 75 m   (4) 230 m

6 A projectile is fired from a gun near the surface of Earth. The initial velocity of the projectile has a vertical component of 98 meters per second and a horizontal component of 49 meters per second. How long will it take the projectile to reach the highest point in its path?
(1) 5.0 s   (3) 20. s
(2) 10. s   (4) 100. s

7 A 70.-kilogram astronaut has a weight of 560 newtons on the surface of planet Alpha. What is the acceleration due to gravity on planet Alpha?
(1) 0.0 m/s²   (3) 9.8 m/s²
(2) 8.0 m/s²   (4) 80. m/s²

Base your answers to questions 8 and 9 on the diagram and information below.

The diagram shows a student seated on a rotating circular platform, holding a 2.0-kilogram block with a spring scale. The block is 1.2 meters from the center of the platform. The block has a constant speed of 8.0 meters per second. [Frictional forces on the block are negligible.]

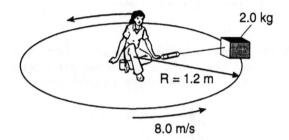

8 Which statement best describes the block's movement as the platform rotates?

   (1) Its velocity is directed tangent to the circular path, with an inward acceleration.

   (2) Its velocity is directed tangent to the circular path, with an outward acceleration.

   (3) Its velocity is directed perpendicular to the circular path, with an inward acceleration.

   (4) Its velocity is directed perpendicular to the circular path, with an outward acceleration.

9 The reading on the spring scale is approximately

   (1) 20. N   (3) 110 N
   (2) 53 N   (4) 130 N

10 The diagram below shows a horizontal 8.0-newton force applied to a 4.0-kilogram block on a frictionless table.

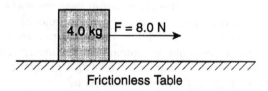

Frictionless Table

What is the magnitude of the block's acceleration?

   (1) 0.50 m/s²   (3) 9.8 m/s²
   (2) 2.0 m/s²   (4) 32 m/s²

11 A 0.10-kilogram model rocket's engine is designed to deliver an impulse of 6.0 newton-seconds. If the rocket engine burns for 0.75 second, what average force does it produce?

   (1) 4.5 N   (3) 45 N
   (2) 8.0 N   (4) 80. N

Base your answers to questions 12 and 13 on the information and diagram below.

The diagram shows a compressed spring between two carts initially at rest on a horizontal frictionless surface. Cart A has a mass of 2 kilograms and cart B has a mass of 1 kilogram. A string holds the carts together.

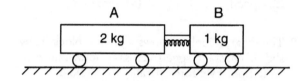

12 What occurs when the string is cut and the carts move apart?

   (1) The magnitude of the acceleration of cart A is one-half the magnitude of the acceleration of cart B.

   (2) The length of time that the force acts on cart A is twice the length of time the force acts on cart B.

   (3) The magnitude of the force exerted on cart A is one-half the magnitude of the force exerted on cart B.

   (4) The magnitude of the impulse applied to cart A is twice the magnitude of the impulse applied to cart B.

13 After the string is cut and the two carts move apart, the magnitude of which quantity is the same for both carts?

   (1) momentum   (3) inertia
   (2) velocity   (4) kinetic energy

14 An object moving at a constant speed of 25 meters per second possesses 450 joules of kinetic energy. What is the object's mass?

   (1) 0.72 kg   (3) 18 kg
   (2) 1.4 kg   (4) 36 kg

15 The diagram below shows a moving, 5.00-kilogram cart at the foot of a hill 10.0 meters high. For the cart to reach the top of the hill, what is the minimum kinetic energy of the cart in the position shown? [Neglect energy loss due to friction.]

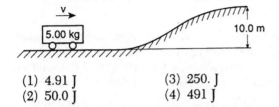

(1) 4.91 J
(2) 50.0 J
(3) 250. J
(4) 491 J

16 A constant force of 1900 newtons is required to keep an automobile having a mass of 1.0×10^3 kilograms moving at a constant speed of 20. meters per second. The work done in moving the automobile a distance of 2.0×10^3 meters is

(1) 2.0×10^4 J
(2) 3.8×10^4 J
(3) 2.0×10^6 J
(4) 3.8×10^6 J

17 The energy required to move one elementary charge through a potential difference of 5.0 volts is

(1) 8.0 J
(2) 5.0 J
(3) 8.0×10^{-19} J
(4) 1.6×10^{-19} J

18 The diagram below shows two identical metal spheres, A and B, on insulated stands. Each sphere possesses a net charge of -3×10^{-6} coulomb.

-3×10^{-6} C -3×10^{-6} C

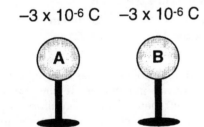

If the spheres are brought into contact with each other and then separated, the charge on sphere A will be

(1) 0 C
(2) $+3 \times 10^{-6}$ C
(3) -3×10^{-6} C
(4) -6×10^{-6} C

19 In a vacuum, light with a frequency of 5.0×10^{14} hertz has a wavelength of

(1) 6.0×10^{-21} m
(2) 6.0×10^{-7} m
(3) 1.7×10^6 m
(4) 1.5×10^{23} m

20 In the diagram below, 400. joules of work is done raising a 72-newton weight a vertical distance of 5.0 meters.

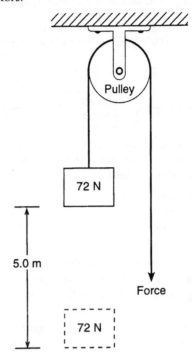

How much work is done to overcome friction as the weight is raised?

(1) 40. J
(2) 360 J
(3) 400. J
(4) 760 J

21 An incandescent light bulb is supplied with a constant potential diference of 120 volts. As the filament of the bulb heats up, its resistance

(1) increases and the current through it decreases
(2) increases and the current through it increases
(3) decreases and the current through it decreases
(4) decreases and the current through it increases

22 During a thunderstorm, a lightning strike transfers 12 coulombs of charge in 2.0×10^{-3} second. What is the average current produced in this strike?

(1) 1.7×10^{-4} A
(2) 2.4×10^{-2} A
(3) 6.0×10^3 A
(4) 9.6×10^3 A

Note that question 23 has only three choices.

23 A 30.-ohm resistor and a 60.-ohm resistor are connected in an electric circuit as shown below.

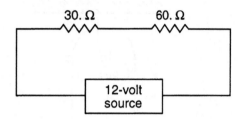

Compared to the electric current through the 30.-ohm resistor, the electric current through the 60.-ohm resistor is

(1) smaller
(2) larger
(3) the same

24 An operating electric heater draws a current of 10. amperes and has a resistance of 12 ohms. How much energy does the heater use in 60. seconds?

(1) 120 J   (3) 7200 J
(2) 1200 J   (4) 72,000 J

25 If the charge on each of two small charged metal spheres is doubled and the distance between the spheres remains fixed, the magnitude of the electric force between the spheres will be

(1) the same   (3) one-half as great
(2) two times as great (4) four times as great

26 The diagram below represents a periodic wave.

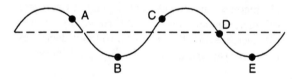

Which two points on the wave are in phase?

(1) A and C   (3) A and D
(2) B and D   (4) B and E

27 A beam of monochromatic light travels through flint glass, crown glass, Lucite, and water. The speed of the light beam is slowest in

(1) flint glass   (3) Lucite
(2) crown glass   (4) water

28 A standing wave pattern is produced when a guitar string is plucked. Which characteristic of the standing wave immediately begins to decrease?

(1) speed   (3) frequency
(2) wavelength   (4) amplitude

29 A source of sound waves approaches a stationary observer through a uniform medium. Compared to the frequency and wavelength of the emitted sound, the observer would detect waves with a

(1) higher frequency and shorter wavelength
(2) higher frequency and longer wavelength
(3) lower frequency and shorter wavelength
(4) lower frequency and longer wavelength

30 What is the smallest electric charge that can be put on an object?

(1) 9.11×10^{-31} C   (3) 9.00×10^{9} C
(2) 1.60×10^{-19} C   (4) 6.25×10^{18} C

31 Which characteristic of electromagnetic radiation is directly proportional to the energy of a photon?

(1) wavelength   (3) frequency
(2) period   (4) path

32 What is the maximum height to which a 1200-watt motor could lift an object weighing 200. newtons in 4.0 seconds?

(1) 0.67 m   (3) 6.0 m
(2) 1.5 m   (4) 24 m

33 A spring of negligible mass has a spring constant of 50. newtons per meter. If the spring is stretched 0.40 meter from its equilibrium position, how much potential energy is stored in the spring?

(1) 20. J   (3) 8.0 J
(2) 10. J   (4) 4.0 J

34 How much current flows through a 12-ohm flashlight bulb operating at 3.0 volts?

(1) 0.25 A   (3) 3.0 A
(2) 0.75 A   (4) 4.0 A

35 Which diagram below best represents the phenomenon of diffraction?

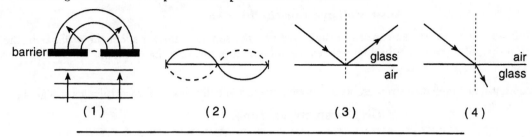

Part B–1

Answer all questions in this part.

Directions (36–45): For *each* statement or question, write on the separate answer sheet the *number* of the word or expression that, of those given, best completes the statement or answers the question.

36 The displacement-time graph below represents the motion of a cart initially moving forward along a straight line.

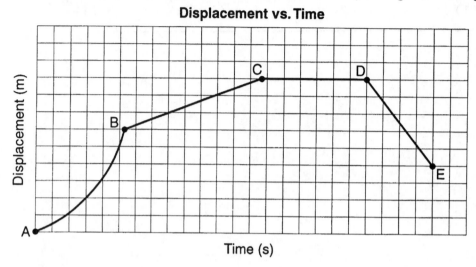

Displacement vs. Time

During which interval is the cart moving forward at constant speed?

(1) *AB*   (3) *CD*

(2) *BC*   (4) *DE*

37 The diagram below represents shallow water waves of wavelength λ passing through two small openings, *A* and *B*, in a barrier.

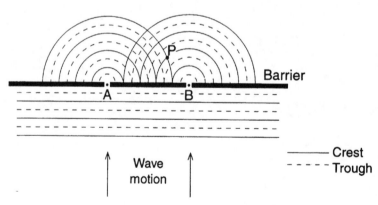

How much longer is the length of path *AP* than the length of path *BP*?

(1) 1λ   (3) 3λ

(2) 2λ   (4) 4λ

Note that question 38 has only three choices.

38 In the diagram below, lamps L_1 and L_2 are connected to a constant voltage power supply.

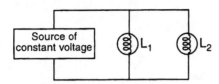

If lamp L_1 burns out, the brightness of L_2 will

(1) decrease
(2) increase
(3) remain the same

39 What is the approximate mass of a pencil?

(1) 5.0×10^{-3} kg   (3) 5.0×10^{0} kg
(2) 5.0×10^{-1} kg   (4) 5.0×10^{1} kg

40 What is the minimum energy needed to ionize a hydrogen atom in the n = 2 energy state?

(1) 13.6 eV   (3) 3.40 eV
(2) 10.2 eV   (4) 1.89 eV

41 The potential difference applied to a circuit element remains constant as the resistance of the element is varied. Which graph best represents the relationship between power (P) and resistance (R) of this element?

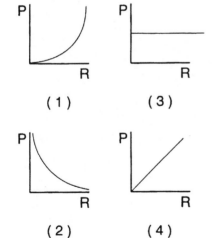

42 Which graph best represents the elastic potential energy stored in a spring (PE_s) as a function of its elongation, x?

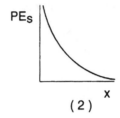
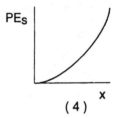

43 Which graph best represents the relationship between the gravitational potential energy of a freely falling object and the object's height above the ground near the surface of Earth?

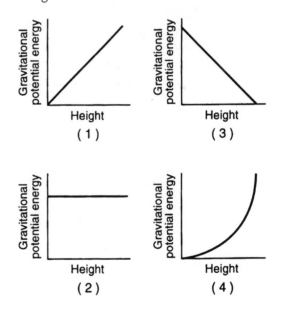

44 A force vector was resolved into two perpendicular components, F_1 and F_2, as shown in the diagram below.

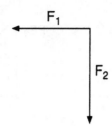

Which vector best represents the original force?

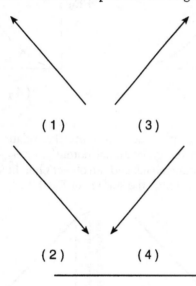

(1)   (3)

(2)   (4)

45 A beam of monochromatic light ($f = 5.09 \times 10^{14}$ hertz) passes through parallel sections of glycerol, medium X, and medium Y as shown in the diagram below.

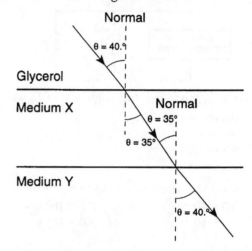

What could medium X and medium Y be?

(1) X could be flint glass and Y could be corn oil.
(2) X could be corn oil and Y could be flint glass.
(3) X could be water and Y could be glycerol.
(4) X could be glycerol and Y could be water.

Part B–2

Answer all questions in this part.

Directions (46–59): Record your answers in the spaces provided in your answer booklet.

46 The diagram below shows two compasses located near the ends of a bar magnet. The north pole of compass *X* points toward end *A* of the magnet.

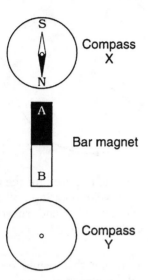

On the diagram provided *in your answer booklet*, draw the correct orientation of the needle of compass *Y* and label its polarity.   [1]

47 A ray of light traveling in air is incident on an air-water boundary as shown below.

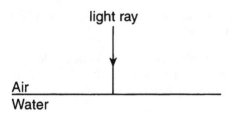

On the diagram provided *in your answer booklet*, draw the path of the ray in the water.   [1]

Base your answers to questions 48 and 49 on the information and diagram below.

A 160.-newton box sits on a 10.-meter-long frictionless plane inclined at an angle of 30.° to the horizontal as shown. Force (*F*) applied to a rope attached to the box causes the box to move with a constant speed up the incline.

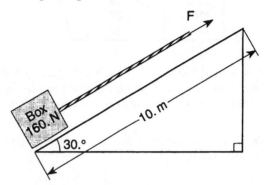

48 On the diagram *in your answer booklet*, construct a vector to represent the weight of the box. Use a metric ruler and a scale of 1.0 centimeter = 40. newtons. Begin the vector at point *B* and label its magnitude in newtons.   [2]

49 Calculate the amount of work done in moving the box from the bottom to the top of the inclined plane. [Show all work, including the equation and substitution with units.]   [2]

Base your answers to questions 50 through 53 on the information and table below.

The table lists the kinetic energy of a 4.0-kilogram mass as it travels in a straight line for 12.0 seconds.

Time (seconds)	Kinetic Energy (joules)
0.0	0.0
2.0	8.0
4.0	18
6.0	32
10.0	32
12.0	32

Directions (50–51): Using the information in the data table, construct a graph on the grid provided *in your answer booklet*, following the directions below.

50 Mark an appropriate scale on the axis labeled "Kinetic Energy (J)." [1]

51 Plot the data points for kinetic energy versus time. [1]

52 Calculate the speed of the mass at 10.0 seconds. [Show all work, including the equation and substitution with units.] [2]

53 Compare the speed of the mass at 6.0 seconds to the speed of the mass at 10.0 seconds. [1]

54 Using dimensional analysis, show that the expression v^2/d has the same units as acceleration. [Show all the steps used to arrive at your answer.] [2]

Base your answers to questions 55 through 57 on the information and diagram below.

A 1.50-kilogram cart travels in a horizontal circle of radius 2.40 meters at a constant speed of 4.00 meters per second.

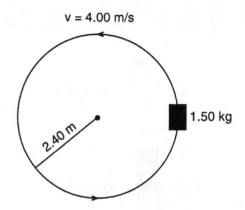

55 Calculate the time required for the cart to make one complete revolution. [Show all work, including the equation and substitution with units.] [2]

56 Describe a change that would quadruple the magnitude of the centripetal force. [1]

57 On the diagram *in your answer booklet*, draw an arrow to represent the direction of the acceleration of the cart in the position shown. Label the arrow *a*. [1]

Base your answers to questions 58 and 59 on the information below.

When an electron and its antiparticle (positron) combine, they annihilate each other and become energy in the form of gamma rays.

58 The positron has the same mass as the electron. Calculate how many joules of energy are released when they annihilate. [Show all work, including the equation and substitution with units.] [2]

59 What conservation law prevents this from happening with two electrons? [1]

Part C

Answer all questions in this part.

Directions (60–69): Record your answers in the spaces provided in your answer booklet.

Base your answers to questions 60 and 61 on the diagram below, which shows some energy levels for an atom of an unknown substance.

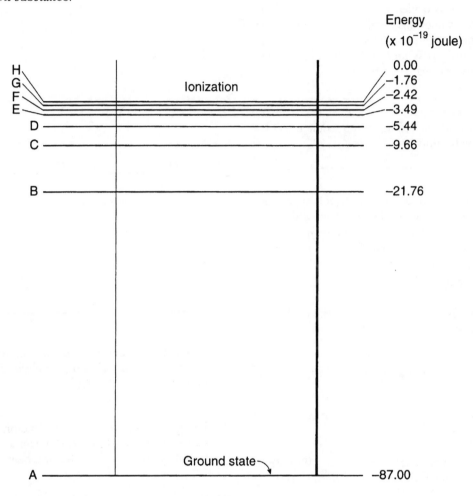

60 Determine the minimum energy necessary for an electron to change from the *B* energy level to the *F* energy level. [1]

61 Calculate the frequency of the photon emitted when an electron in this atom changes from the *F* energy level to the *B* energy level. [Show all work, including the equation and substitution with units.] [2]

Base your answers to questions 62 and 63 on the information below.

An electric circuit contains two 3.0-ohm resistors connected in parallel with a battery. The circuit also contains a voltmeter that reads the potential difference across one of the resistors.

62 In the space provided *in your answer booklet*, draw a diagram of this circuit, using the symbols from the *Reference Tables for Physical Setting/Physics*. [Assume availability of any number of wires of negligible resistance.]   [2]

63 Calculate the total resistance of the circuit. [Show all work, including the equation and substitution with units.]   [2]

---

64 Explain how to find the coefficient of kinetic friction between a wooden block of unknown mass and a tabletop in the laboratory. Include the following in your explanation:

- Measurements required   [1]
- Equipment needed   [1]
- Procedure   [1]
- Equation(s) needed to calculate the coefficient of friction   [1]

Base your answers to questions 65 and 66 on the information below.

A toaster having a power rating of 1050 watts is operated at 120. volts.

65 Calculate the resistance of the toaster. [Show all work, including the equation and substitution with units.]   [2]

66 The toaster is connected in a circuit protected by a 15-ampere fuse. (The fuse will shut down the circuit if it carries more than 15 amperes.) Is it possible to simultaneously operate the toaster and a microwave oven that requires a current of 10.0 amperes on this circuit? Justify your answer mathematically.   [2]

Base your answers to questions 67 through 69 on the information and diagram below. A monochromatic beam of yellow light, *AB*, is incident upon a Lucite block in air at an angle of 33°.

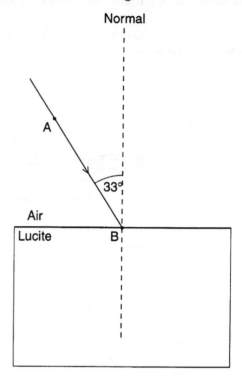

67 Calculate the angle of refraction for incident beam *AB*. [Show all work, including the equation and substitution with units.]   [2]

68 Using a straightedge, a protractor, and your answer from question 67, draw an arrow to represent the path of the refracted beam.   [2]

69 Compare the speed of the yellow light in air to the speed of the yellow light in Lucite.   [1]

Physical Setting/PHYSICS
June 2002

ANSWER SHEET

Student . . . . Grade . . . .

Teacher . . . . School . . . .

Record your answers to Part A and Part B–1 on this answer sheet.

Part A			Part B–1

Part A						Part B–1
1	13	25				36 . . . .
2	14	26				37 . . . .
3	15	27				38 . . . .
4	16	28				39 . . . .
5	17	29				40 . . . .
6	18	30				41 . . . .
7	19	31				42 . . . .
8	20	32				43 . . . .
9	21	33				44 . . . .
10	22	34				45 . . . .
11	23	35				
12	24					

Part A Score

Part B–1 Score

Write your answers to Part B–2 and Part C in your answer booklet.

Physical Setting/PHYSICS
June 2002

Part	Maximum Score	Student's Score
A	35	
B–1	10	
B–2	20	
C	20	

Total Written Test Score (Maximum Raw Score: 85)	
Final Score (from conversion chart)	

Raters' Initials:

Rater 1 . . . . Rater 2 . . . .

ANSWER BOOKLET

Student . . . .

Teacher . . . .

School . . . . Grade . . . .

Answer all questions in Part B–2 and Part C. Record your answers in this booklet.

Part B–2

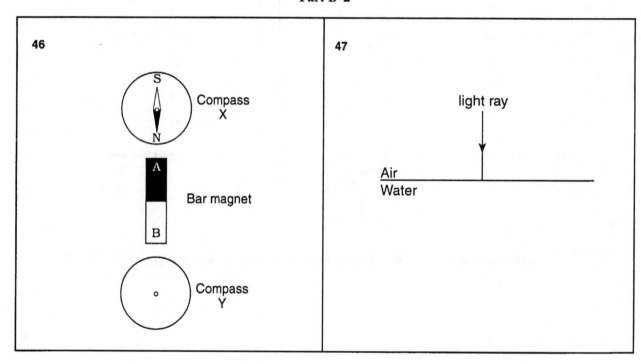

48

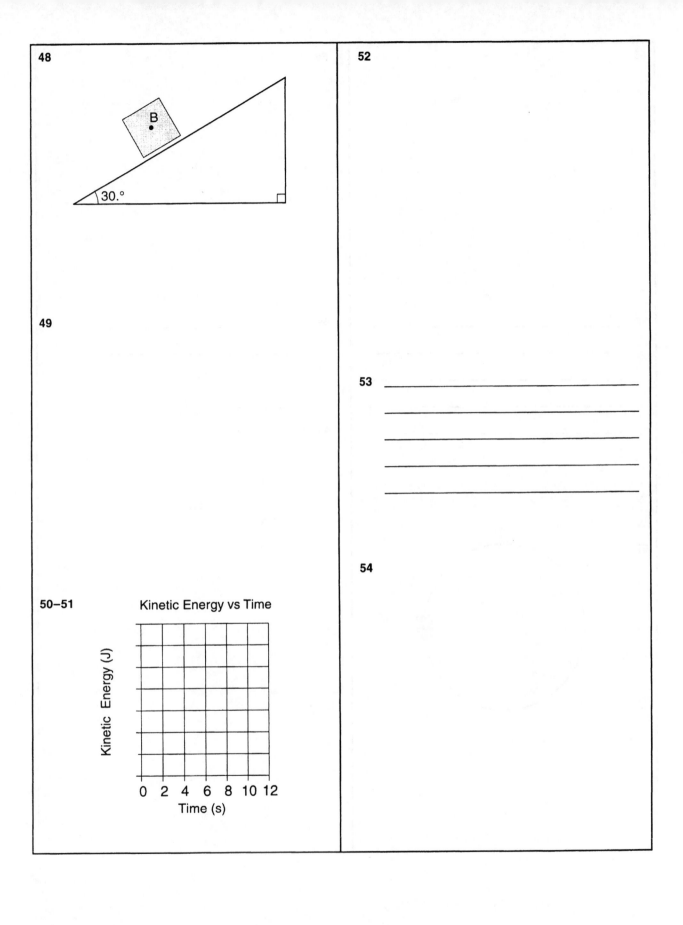

B

30.°

49

50–51

Kinetic Energy vs Time

Kinetic Energy (J)

0 2 4 6 8 10 12
Time (s)

52

53
_____
_____
_____
_____
_____

54

55

56 _____

_____

_____

_____

_____

57

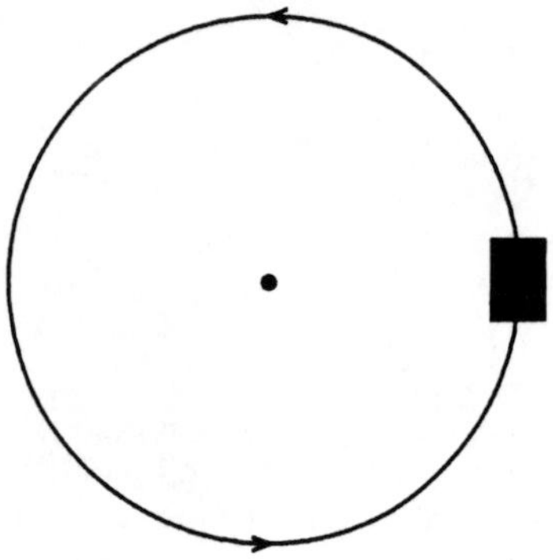

58

59 _____

_____

Part C

60 _____ J

61

62

63

64 _____

_____

_____

_____

_____

_____

_____

_____

_____

65

66 _____

67

68

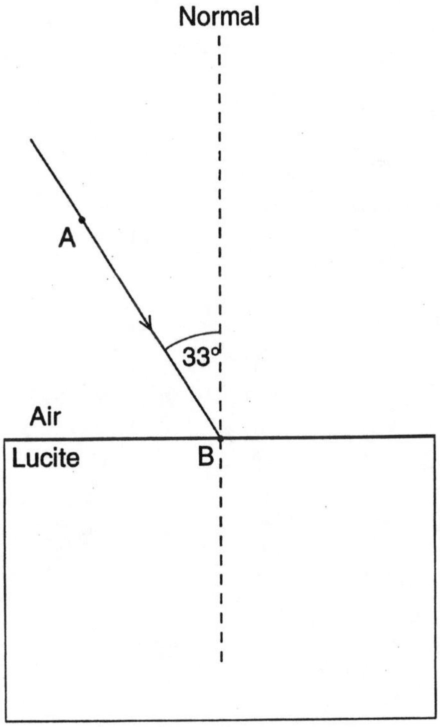

Normal

A

33°

Air

Lucite   B

69 _____

_____

_____

_____

Physical Setting/PHYSICS
AUGUST 2002

Directions (1–35): For *each* statement or question, write on the separate answer sheet, the *number* of the word or expression that, of those given, best completes the statement or answers the question.

1 A net force of 25 newtons is applied horizontally to a 10.-kilogram block resting on a table. What is the magnitude of the acceleration of the block?

(1) 0.0 m/s²   (3) 0.40 m/s²
(2) 0.26 m/s²   (4) 2.5 m/s²

2 The speed of a car is increased uniformly from 20. meters per second to 30. meters per second in 4.0 seconds. The magnitude of the car's average acceleration in this 4.0-second interval is

(1) 0.40 m/s²   (3) 10. m/s²
(2) 2.5 m/s²   (4) 13 m/s²

3 A roller coaster, traveling with an initial speed of 15 meters per second, decelerates uniformly at –7.0 meters per second² to a full stop. Approximately how far does the roller coaster travel during its deceleration?

(1) 1.0 m   (3) 16 m
(2) 2.0 m   (4) 32 m

4 The diagram below represents a 0.40-kilogram stone attached to a string. The stone is moving at a constant speed of 4.0 meters per second in a horizontal circle having a radius of 0.80 meter.

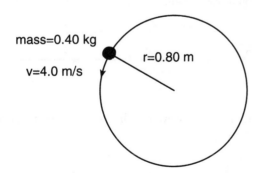

mass=0.40 kg
v=4.0 m/s
r=0.80 m

The magnitude of the centripetal acceleration of the stone is

(1) 0.0 m/s²   (3) 5.0 m/s²
(2) 2.0 m/s²   (4) 20. m/s²

5 In the diagram below, a box is at rest on an inclined plane.

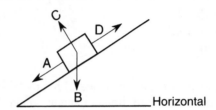

Which vector best represents the direction of the normal force acting on the box?

(1) A   (3) C
(2) B   (4) D

Note that question 6 has only three choices.

6 If the magnitude of the gravitational force of Earth on the Moon is *F*, the magnitude of the gravitational force of the Moon on Earth is

(1) smaller than *F*
(2) larger than *F*
(3) equal to *F*

7 Which term represents a scalar quantity?

(1) distance   (3) force
(2) displacement   (4) weight

8 A block weighing 15 newtons is pulled to the top of an incline that is 0.20 meter above the ground, as shown below.

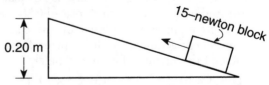

0.20 m
15–newton block

If 4.0 joules of work are needed to pull the block the full length of the incline, how much work is done against friction?

(1) 1.0 J   (3) 3.0 J
(2) 0.0 J   (4) 7.0 J

9 A 1.0-kilogram rubber ball traveling east at 4.0 meters per second hits a wall and bounces back toward the west at 2.0 meters per second. Compared to the kinetic energy of the ball before it hits the wall, the kinetic energy of the ball after it bounces off the wall is

(1) one-fourth as great   (3) the same
(2) one-half as great   (4) four times as great

Note that questions 10 and 11 have only three choices.

10 As a spring is stretched, its elastic potential energy

(1) decreases
(2) increases
(3) remains the same

11 An electroscope is a device with a metal knob, a metal stem, and freely hanging metal leaves used to detect charges. The diagram below shows a positively charged leaf electroscope.

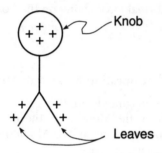

As a positively charged glass rod is brought near the knob of the electroscope, the separation of the electroscope leaves will

(1) decrease
(2) increase
(3) remain the same

12 A catapult with a spring constant of 1.0×10^4 newtons per meter is required to launch an airplane from the deck of an aircraft carrier. The plane is released when it has been displaced 0.50 meter from its equilibrium position by the catapult. The energy acquired by the airplane from the catapult during takeoff is approximately

(1) 1.3×10^3 J   (3) 2.5×10^3 J
(2) 2.0×10^4 J   (4) 1.0×10^4 J

13 A 10.-ohm resistor and a 20.-ohm resistor are connected in series to a voltage source. When the current through the 10.-ohm resistor is 2.0 amperes, what is the current through the 20.-ohm resistor?

(1) 1.0 A   (3) 0.50 A
(2) 2.0 A   (4) 4.0 A

14 In the circuit diagram below, what are the correct readings of voltmeters V_1 and V_2?

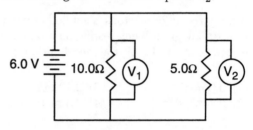

(1) V_1 reads 2.0 V and V_2 reads 4.0 V
(2) V_1 reads 4.0 V and V_2 reads 2.0 V
(3) V_1 reads 3.0 V and V_2 reads 3.0 V
(4) V_1 reads 6.0 V and V_2 reads 6.0 V

15 A physics student notices that 4.0 waves arrive at the beach every 20. seconds. The frequency of these waves is

(1) 0.20 Hz   (3) 16 Hz
(2) 5.0 Hz   (4) 80. Hz

16 An electric guitar is generating a sound of constant frequency. An increase in which sound wave characteristic would result in an increase in loudness?

(1) speed   (3) wavelength
(2) period   (4) amplitude

17 The diagram below shows two points, A and B, on a wave train.

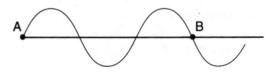

How many wavelengths separate point A and point B?

(1) 1.0   (3) 3.0
(2) 1.5   (4) 0.75

18 In a demonstration, a vibrating tuning fork causes a nearby second tuning fork to begin to vibrate with the same frequency. Which wave phenomenon is illustrated by this demonstration?

(1) the Doppler effect　(3) resonance
(2) nodes　(4) interference

19 The diagram below shows wave fronts spreading into the region behind a barrier.

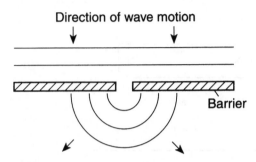

Which wave phenomenon is represented in the diagram?

(1) reflection　(3) diffraction
(2) refraction　(4) standing waves

20 The diagram below represents the wave pattern produced by two sources located at points A and B.

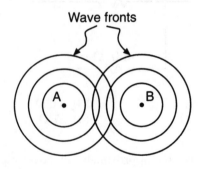

Which phenomenon occurs at the intersections of the circular wave fronts?

(1) diffraction　(3) refraction
(2) interference　(4) reflection

21 How much work is required to move a single electron through a potential difference of 100. volts?

(1) 1.6×10^{-21} J　(3) 1.6×10^{-17} J
(2) 1.6×10^{-19} J　(4) 1.0×10^{2} J

22 An object can *not* have a charge of

(1) 3.2×10^{-19} C　(3) 8.0×10^{-19} C
(2) 4.5×10^{-19} C　(4) 9.6×10^{-19} C

23 After electrons in hydrogen atoms are excited to the $n = 3$ energy state, how many different frequencies of radiation can be emitted as the electrons return to the ground state?

(1) 1　(3) 3
(2) 2　(4) 4

24 What type of nuclear force holds the protons and neutrons in an atom together?

(1) a strong force that acts over a short range
(2) a strong force that acts over a long range
(3) a weak force that acts over a short range
(4) a weak force that acts over a long range

25 Which is an acceptable unit for impulse?

(1) N•m　(3) J•s
(2) J/s　(4) kg•m/s

26 The centers of two 15.0-kilogram spheres are separated by 3.00 meters. The magnitude of the gravitational force between the two spheres is approximately

(1) 1.11×10^{-10} N　(3) 1.67×10^{-9} N
(2) 3.34×10^{-10} N　(4) 5.00×10^{-9} N

27 During a collision, an 84-kilogram driver of a car moving at 24 meters per second is brought to rest by an inflating air bag in 1.2 seconds. The magnitude of the force exerted on the driver by the air bag is approximately

(1) 7.0×10^{1} N　(3) 1.7×10^{3} N
(2) 8.2×10^{2} N　(4) 2.0×10^{3} N

28 An apple weighing 1 newton on the surface of Earth has a mass of approximately

(1) 1×10^{-1} kg　(3) 1×10^{1} kg
(2) 1×10^{0} kg　(4) 1×10^{2} kg

29 In raising an object vertically at a constant speed of 2.0 meters per second, 10. watts of power is developed. The weight of the object is

(1) 5.0 N　(3) 40. N
(2) 20. N　(4) 50. N

30 Which diagram best represents magnetic flux lines around a bar magnet?

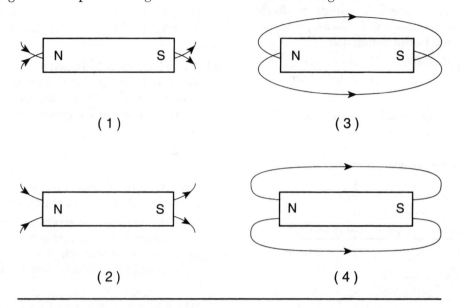

(1)

(3)

(2)

(4)

31 In which situation is the net force on the object equal to zero?

(1) a satellite moving at constant speed around Earth in a circular orbit
(2) an automobile braking to a stop
(3) a bicycle moving at constant speed on a straight, level road
(4) a pitched baseball being hit by a bat

Base your answers to questions 32 and 33 on the information below.

A 2.00×10^6-hertz radio signal is sent a distance of 7.30×10^{10} meters from Earth to a spaceship orbiting Mars.

32 Approximately how much time does it take the radio signal to travel from Earth to the spaceship?

(1) 4.11×10^{-3} s   (3) 2.19×10^8 s
(2) 2.43×10^2 s   (4) 1.46×10^{17} s

Note that question 33 has only three choices.

33 The spaceship is moving away from Earth when the radio signal is received. Compared to the frequency of the signal sent from Earth, the frequency of the signal received by the spaceship is

(1) lower
(2) higher
(3) the same

34 What is the total resistance of the circuit segment shown in the diagram below?

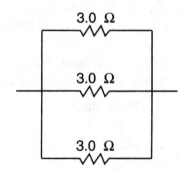

(1) 1.0 Ω   (3) 3.0 Ω
(2) 9.0 Ω   (4) 27 Ω

35 What is the approximate electrostatic force between two protons separated by a distance of 1.0×10^{-6} meter?

(1) 2.3×10^{-16} N and repulsive
(2) 2.3×10^{-16} N and attractive
(3) 9.0×10^{21} N and repulsive
(4) 9.0×10^{21} N and attractive

Part B–1

Answer all questions in this part.

Directions (36–47): For *each* statement or question, write on the separate answer sheet the *number* of the word or expression that, of those given, best completes the statement or answers the question.

36 The diagram below shows a 4.0-kilogram cart moving to the right and a 6.0-kilogram cart moving to the left on a horizontal frictionless surface.

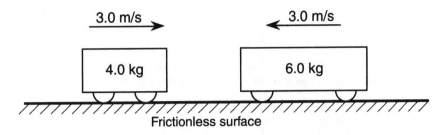

When the two carts collide they lock together. The magnitude of the total momentum of the two-cart system after the collision is

(1) 0.0 kg•m/s (3) 15 kg•m/s
(2) 6.0 kg•m/s (4) 30. kg•m/s

37 The diagram below shows a 10.0-kilogram mass held at rest on a frictionless 30.0° incline by force *F*.

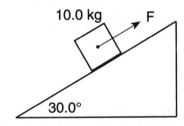

What is the approximate magnitude of force *F*?

(1) 9.81 N (3) 85.0 N
(2) 49.1 N (4) 98.1 N

38 An archer uses a bow to fire two similar arrows with the same string force. One arrow is fired at an angle of 60.° with the horizontal, and the other is fired at an angle of 45° with the horizontal. Compared to the arrow fired at 60.°, the arrow fired at 45° has a

(1) longer flight time and longer horizontal range
(2) longer flight time and shorter horizontal range
(3) shorter flight time and longer horizontal range
(4) shorter flight time and shorter horizontal range

39 The graph below shows the velocity of a race car moving along a straight line as a function of time.

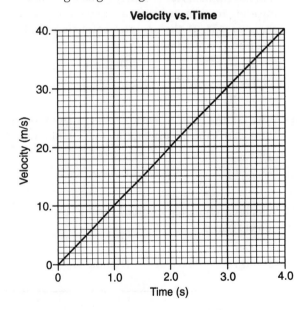

What is the magnitude of the displacement of the car from *t* = 2.0 seconds to *t* = 4.0 seconds?

(1) 20. m (3) 60. m
(2) 40. m (4) 80. m

40 Which vector diagram represents the greatest magnitude of displacement for an object?

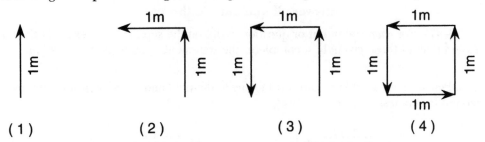

(1)   (2)   (3)   (4)

41 Which circuit diagram shows voltmeter V and ammeter A correctly positioned to measure the total potential difference of the circuit and the current through each resistor?

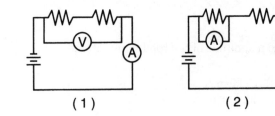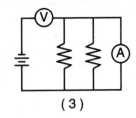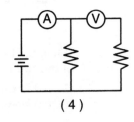

(1)   (2)   (3)   (4)

42 A monochromatic ray of light ($f = 5.09 \times 10^{14}$ hertz) traveling in air is incident upon medium A at an angle of 45°. If the angle of refraction is 29°, medium A could be

(1) water
(2) fused quartz
(3) Lucite
(4) flint glass

43 What is the total electrical energy used by a 1500-watt hair dryer operating for 6.0 minutes?

(1) 4.2 J
(2) 250 J
(3) 9.0×10^3 J
(4) 5.4×10^5 J

44 Which combination of quarks would produce a neutral baryon?

(1) uud
(2) udd
(3) $\bar{u}\bar{u}$d
(4) $\bar{u}$dd

45 A 12.0-meter length of copper wire has a resistance of 1.50 ohms. How long must an aluminum wire with the same cross-sectional area be to have the same resistance?

(1) 7.32 m
(2) 8.00 m
(3) 12.0 m
(4) 19.7 m

46 A 0.500-meter length of wire with a cross-sectional area of 3.14×10^{-6} meters squared is found to have a resistance of 2.53×10^{-3} ohms. According to the resistivity chart, the wire could be made of

(1) aluminum
(2) copper
(3) nichrome
(4) silver

Base your answer to question 47 on the cartoon below and your knowledge of physics.

47 In the cartoon, Einstein is contemplating the equation for the principle that
  (1) the fundamental source of all energy is the conversion of mass into energy
  (2) energy is emitted or absorbed in discrete packets called photons
  (3) mass always travels at the speed of light in a vacuum
  (4) the energy of a photon is proportional to its frequency

Part B–2

Answer all questions in this part.

Directions (48–60): Record your answers in the spaces provided in your answer booklet.

Base your answers to questions 48 through 52 on the information and data table below.

A variable resistor was connected to a battery. As the resistance was adjusted, the current and power in the circuit were determined. The data are recorded in the table below.

Current (amperes)	Power (watts)
0.75	2.27
1.25	3.72
2.25	6.75
3.00	9.05
4.00	11.9

48–49 Using the information in the data table, construct a line graph on the grid provided *in your answer booklet,* following the directions below. The grid below is provided for practice purposes only. Be sure your final answer appears *in your answer booklet.*

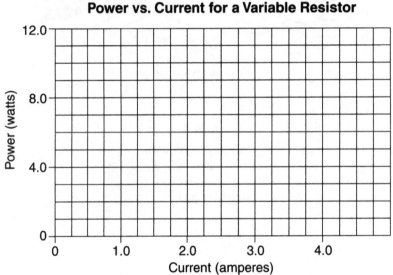

Power vs. Current for a Variable Resistor

48 Plot the data points for power versus current.   [1]

49 Draw the best-fit line.   [1]

50 Using your graph, determine the power delivered to the circuit at a current of 3.5 amperes.   [1]

51 Calculate the slope of the graph. [Show all calculations, including the equation and substitution with units.]   [2]

52 What is the physical significance of the slope of the graph?   [1]

Base your answers to questions 53 through 55 on the diagram below which shows a ray of monochromatic light ($f = 5.09 \times 10^{14}$ hertz) passing through a flint glass prism. [The same diagram appears in your answer booklet.]

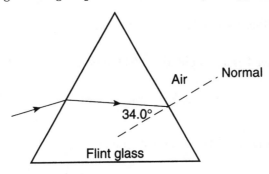

53 Calculate the angle of refraction (in degrees) of the light ray as it enters the air from the flint glass prism. [Show all calculations, including the equation and substitution with units.]   [2]

54 Using a protractor and a straightedge, construct the refracted light ray in the air on the diagram *in your answer booklet.*   [2]

55 What is the speed of the light ray in flint glass?
(1) 5.53×10^{-9} m/s
(2) 1.81×10^{8} m/s
(3) 3.00×10^{8} m/s
(4) 4.98×10^{8} m/s

Base your answers to questions 56 and 57 on the information and diagram below. The diagram shows the collision of an incident photon having a frequency of 2.00×10^{19} hertz with an electron initially at rest.

Before collision   **After collision**

Recoiling electron

Incident photon   Electron
at rest   Scattered photon

56 Calculate the initial energy of the photon. [Show all calculations, including the equation and substitution with units.] [2]

57 What is the total energy of the two-particle system after the collision? [1]

58 Determine the color of a ray of light with a wavelength of 6.21×10^{-7} meter.   [1]

Base your answers to questions 59 and 60 on the information below.

A periodic transverse wave has an amplitude of 0.20 meter and a wavelength of 3.0 meters.

59 On the grid provided *in your answer booklet,* draw at least one cycle of this periodic wave. [2]

60 If the frequency of this wave is 12 Hz, what is its speed?
  (1) 0.25 m/s
  (2) 12 m/s
  (3) 36 m/s
  (4) 4.0 m/s

Part C

Answer all questions in this part.

Directions (61–68): Record your answers in the spaces provided in your answer booklet.

Base your answers to questions 61 through 63 on the information and diagram below.

A child is flying a kite, *K*. A student at point *B*, located 100. meters away from point *A* (directly underneath the kite), measures the angle of elevation of the kite from the ground as 30.°.

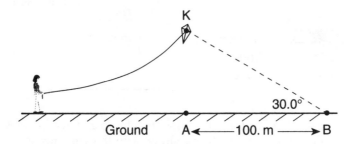

61 *In your answer booklet,* use a metric ruler and protractor to draw a triangle representing the positions of the kite, *K*, and point *A* relative to point *B* that is given. Label points *A* and *K*. Use a scale of 1.0 centimeter = 10. meters. [2]

62 Use a metric ruler and your scale diagram to determine the height, *AK*, of the kite. [1]

63 A small lead sphere is dropped from the kite. Calculate the amount of time required for the sphere to fall to the ground. [Show all calculations, including the equation and substitution with units. Neglect air resistance.] [2]

_____

Base your answers to questions 64 and 65 on the information given below.

Friction provides the centripetal force that allows a car to round a circular curve.

64 Find the minimum coefficient of friction needed between the tires and the road to allow a 1,600-kilogram car to round a curve of radius 80. meters at a speed of 20. meters per second. [Show all work, including formulas and substitutions with units.] [4]

65 If the mass of the car were increased, how would that affect the maximum speed at which it could round the curve? [1]

_____

Base your answers to questions 66 and 67 on the information below and on your knowledge of physics.

Using a spring toy like the one shown in the diagram, a physics teacher pushes on the toy, compressing the spring, causing the suction cup to stick to the base of the toy.

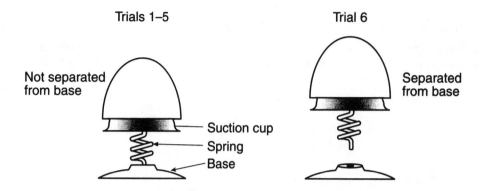

When the teacher removes her hand, the toy pops straight up and just brushes against the ceiling. She does this demonstration five times, always with the same result.

When the teacher repeats the demonstration for the sixth time the toy crashes against the ceiling with considerable force. The students notice that in this trial, the spring and toy separated from the base at the moment the spring released.

The teacher puts the toy back together, repeats the demonstration and the toy once again just brushes against the ceiling.

66 Describe the conversions that take place between pairs of the three forms of mechanical energy, beginning with the work done by the teacher on the toy and ending with the form(s) of energy possessed by the toy as it hits the ceiling. [Neglect friction.]   [3]

67 Explain, in terms of mass and energy, why the spring toy hits the ceiling in the sixth trial and not in the other trials.   [2]

68 Your school's physics laboratory has the following equipment available for conducting experiments:

accelerometers	lasers	stopwatches
ammeters	light bulbs	thermometers
bar magnets	meter sticks	voltmeters
batteries	power supplies	wires
electromagnets	spark timers	

Explain how you would find the resistance of an unknown resistor in the laboratory. Your explanation must include:

a Measurements required   [1]
b Equipment needed   [1]
c Complete circuit diagram   [2]
d Any equation(s) needed to calculate the resistance   [1]

Physical Setting/PHYSICS
August 2002

ANSWER SHEET

Student .... Grade ....

Teacher .... School ....

Record your answers to Part A and Part B–1 on this answer sheet.

Part A			Part B–1
1	13	25	36 ....
2	14	26	37 ....
3	15	27	38 ....
4	16	28	39 ....
5	17	29	40 ....
6	18	30	41 ....
7	19	31	42 ....
8	20	32	43 ....
9	21	33	44 ....
10	22	34	45 ....
11	23	35	46 ....
12	24		47 ....

Part A Score

Part B–1 Score

Write your answers to Part B–2 and Part C in your answer booklet.

Physical Setting/PHYSICS
August 2002

Part	Maximum Score	Student's Score
A	35	
B–1	12	
B–2	18	
C	20	

Total Written Test Score
(Maximum Raw Score: 85)

Final Score
(from conversion chart)

Raters' Initials:

Rater 1 . . . .   Rater 2 . . . .

ANSWER BOOKLET

Student . . . .

Teacher . . . .

School . . . .   Grade . . . .

Answer all questions in Part B–2 and Part C. Record your answers in this booklet.

Part B–2

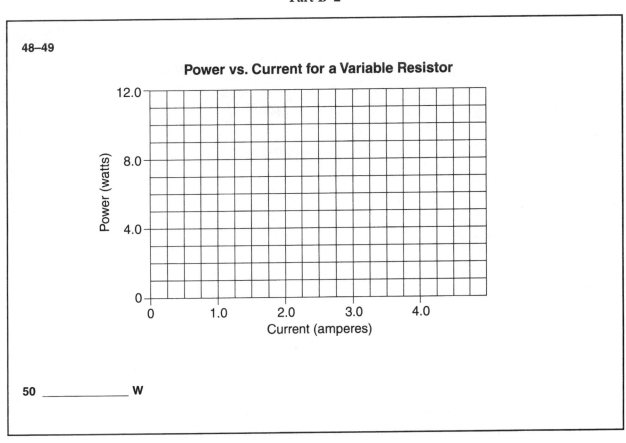

48–49

Power vs. Current for a Variable Resistor

Power (watts) vs. Current (amperes)

50 _____ W

51

52 _____

53

54

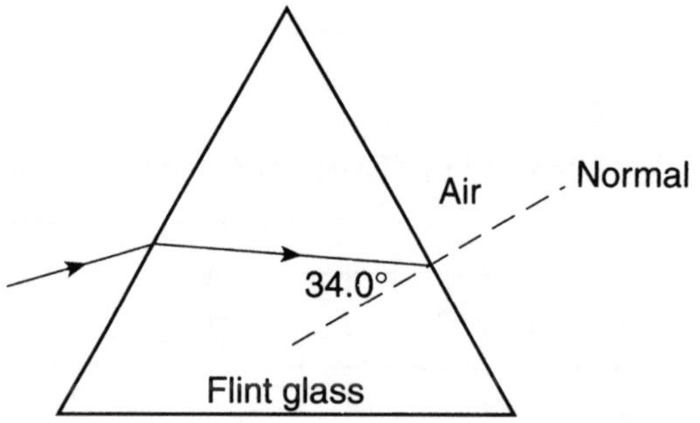

55 _____

56

57 _____

58 _____

59

```
0.20 m   ┬ - - - ┬ - - - ┬ - - - ┬ - - - ┬ - - - ┬ - - - ┬ - - - ┬
         |       |       |       |       |       |       |       |
0.10 m   ┼ - - - ┼ - - - ┼ - - - ┼ - - - ┼ - - - ┼ - - - ┼ - - - ┼
         |       |       |       |       |       |       |       |
0.00 m   ┼───────┼───────┼───────┼───────┼───────┼───────┼───────
         |   1.0 m   |   2.0 m   |   3.0 m   |   4.0 m
         |       |       |       |       |       |       |       |
-0.10 m  ┼ - - - ┼ - - - ┼ - - - ┼ - - - ┼ - - - ┼ - - - ┼ - - - ┼
         |       |       |       |       |       |       |       |
-0.20 m  ┴ - - - ┴ - - - ┴ - - - ┴ - - - ┴ - - - ┴ - - - ┴ - - - ┴
```

60 _____

Part C

61

> Scale
> 1.0 cm = 10. m

```
///////////////////////////////////////•///////
              Ground                    B
```

62 _____ m

63

64

65 _____

_____

_____

66 _____

_____

_____

_____

_____

_____

67 _____

_____

_____

68a _____

_____

_____

b _____

_____

_____

c

d _____

_____

_____

Physical Setting/PHYSICS
JANUARY 2003

Part A

Answer all questions in this part.

Directions (1–35): For *each* statement or question, write on the separate answer sheet, the *number* of the word or expression that, of those given, best completes the statement or answers the question.

1 The diagram below shows a worker using a rope to pull a cart.

The worker's pull on the handle of the cart can best be described as a force having

(1) magnitude, only
(2) direction, only
(3) both magnitude and direction
(4) neither magnitude nor direction

2 A car travels 90. meters due north in 15 seconds. Then the car turns around and travels 40. meters due south in 5.0 seconds. What is the magnitude of the average velocity of the car during this 20.-second interval?

(1) 2.5 m/s   (3) 6.5 m/s
(2) 5.0 m/s   (4) 7.0 m/s

3 How far will a brick starting from rest fall freely in 3.0 seconds?

(1) 15 m   (3) 44 m
(2) 29 m   (4) 88 m

4 If the sum of all the forces acting on a moving object is zero, the object will

(1) slow down and stop
(2) change the direction of its motion
(3) accelerate uniformly
(4) continue moving with constant velocity

5 A net force of 10. newtons accelerates an object at 5.0 meters per second². What net force would be required to accelerate the same object at 1.0 meter per second²?

(1) 1.0 N   (3) 5.0 N
(2) 2.0 N   (4) 50. N

6 The graph below represents the relationship between gravitational force and mass for objects near the surface of Earth.

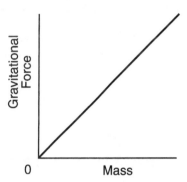

The slope of the graph represents the

(1) acceleration due to gravity
(2) universal gravitational constant
(3) momentum of objects
(4) weight of objects

7 A 1,200-kilogram car traveling at 10. meters per second hits a tree and is brought to rest in 0.10 second. What is the magnitude of the average force acting on the car to bring it to rest?

(1) 1.2×10^2 N   (3) 1.2×10^4 N
(2) 1.2×10^3 N   (4) 1.2×10^5 N

8 A spring scale reads 20. newtons as it pulls a 5.0-kilogram mass across a table. What is the magnitude of the force exerted by the mass on the spring scale?

(1) 49 N   (3) 5.0 N
(2) 20. N   (4) 4.0 N

Base your answers to questions 9 and 10 on the information below.

A 2.0×10^3-kilogram car travels at a constant speed of 12 meters per second around a circular curve of radius 30. meters.

9 What is the magnitude of the centripetal acceleration of the car as it goes around the curve?

(1) 0.40 m/s²   (3) 800 m/s²
(2) 4.8 m/s²   (4) 9,600 m/s²

10 As the car goes around the curve, the centripetal force is directed

(1) toward the center of the circular curve
(2) away from the center of the circular curve
(3) tangent to the curve in the direction of motion
(4) tangent to the curve opposite the direction of motion

───────────────

Note that question 11 has only three choices.

11 The diagram below shows a block sliding down a plane inclined at angle θ with the horizontal.

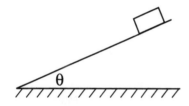

As angle θ is increased, the coefficient of kinetic friction between the bottom surface of the block and the surface of the incline will

(1) decrease
(2) increase
(3) remain the same

12 The amount of work done against friction to slide a box in a straight line across a uniform, horizontal floor depends most on the

(1) time taken to move the box
(2) distance the box is moved
(3) speed of the box
(4) direction of the box's motion

13 A 1.2-kilogram block and a 1.8-kilogram block are initially at rest on a frictionless, horizontal surface. When a compressed spring between the blocks is released, the 1.8-kilogram block moves to the right at 2.0 meters per second, as shown.

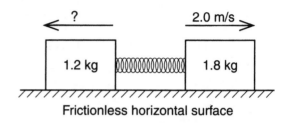

Frictionless horizontal surface

What is the speed of the 1.2-kilogram block after the spring is released?

(1) 1.4 m/s   (3) 3.0 m/s
(2) 2.0 m/s   (4) 3.6 m/s

14 An object weighs 100. newtons on Earth's surface. When it is moved to a point one Earth radius above Earth's surface, it will weigh

(1) 25.0 N   (3) 100. N
(2) 50.0 N   (4) 400. N

15 An object weighing 15 newtons is lifted from the ground to a height of 0.22 meter. The increase in the object's gravitational potential energy is approximately

(1) 310 J   (3) 3.3 J
(2) 32 J   (4) 0.34 J

Note that question 16 has only three choices.

16 As an object falls freely, the kinetic energy of the object

(1) decreases
(2) increases
(3) remains the same

17 Moving 2.5×10^{-6} coulomb of charge from point A to point B in an electric field requires 6.3×10^{-4} joule of work. The potential difference between points A and B is approximately

(1) 1.6×10^{-9} V   (3) 2.5×10^2 V
(2) 4.0×10^{-3} V   (4) 1.0×10^{14} V

18 A 3.0-kilogram block is initially at rest on a frictionless, horizontal surface. The block is moved 8.0 meters in 2.0 seconds by the application of a 12-newton horizontal force, as shown in the diagram below.

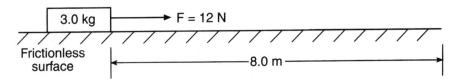

What is the average power developed while moving the block?

(1) 24 W

(2) 32 W

(3) 48 W

(4) 96 W

19 The diagram below shows three neutral metal spheres, x, y, and z, in contact and on insulating stands.

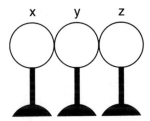

Which diagram best represents the charge distribution on the spheres when a positively charged rod is brought near sphere x, but does not touch it?

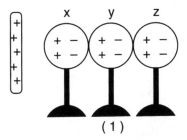

(1)

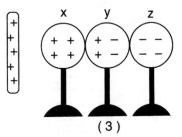

(3)

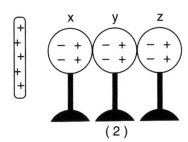

(2)

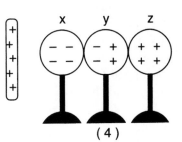

(4)

20 Which graph best represents the electrostatic force between an alpha particle with a charge of +2 elementary charges and a positively charged nucleus as a function of their distance of separation?

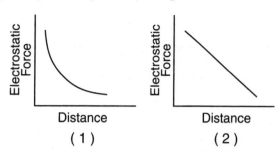

21 When a neutral metal sphere is charged by contact with a positively charged glass rod, the sphere

   (1) loses electrons   (3) loses protons
   (2) gains electrons   (4) gains protons

22 If 10. coulombs of charge are transferred through an electric circuit in 5.0 seconds, then the current in the circuit is

   (1) 0.50 A   (3) 15 A
   (2) 2.0 A   (4) 50. A

23 The diagram below represents a source of potential difference connected to two large, parallel metal plates separated by a distance of 4.0×10^{-3} meter.

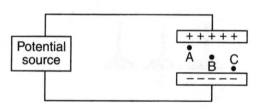

Which statement best describes the electric field strength between the plates?

   (1) It is zero at point *B*.
   (2) It is a maximum at point *B*.
   (3) It is a maximum at point *C*.
   (4) It is the same at points *A*, *B*, and *C*.

24 A periodic wave transfers

   (1) energy, only
   (2) mass, only
   (3) both energy and mass
   (4) neither energy nor mass

Note that question 25 has only three choices.

25 As the potential difference across a given resistor is increased, the power expended in moving charge through the resistor

   (1) decreases
   (2) increases
   (3) remains the same

26 An electric iron operating at 120 volts draws 10. amperes of current. How much heat energy is delivered by the iron in 30. seconds?

   (1) 3.0×10^2 J   (3) 3.6×10^3 J
   (2) 1.2×10^3 J   (4) 3.6×10^4 J

27 A motor is used to produce 4.0 waves each second in a string. What is the frequency of the waves?

   (1) 0.25 Hz   (3) 25 Hz
   (2) 15 Hz   (4) 4.0 Hz

28 The diagram below shows a periodic wave.

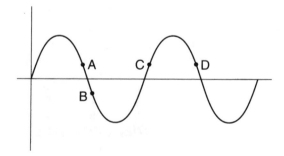

Which points are in phase with each other?

   (1) *A* and *C*   (3) *B* and *C*
   (2) *A* and *D*   (4) *C* and *D*

29 A surfacing whale in an aquarium produces water wave crests having an amplitude of 1.2 meters every 0.40 second. If the water wave travels at 4.5 meters per second, the wavelength of the wave is

(1) 1.8 m   (3) 3.0 m
(2) 2.4 m   (4) 11 m

30 In a certain material, a beam of monochromatic light ($f = 5.09 \times 10^{14}$ hertz) has a speed of 2.25×10^8 meters per second. The material could be

(1) crown glass   (3) glycerol
(2) flint glass   (4) water

31 Orange light has a frequency of 5.0×10^{14} hertz in a vacuum. What is the wavelength of this light?

(1) 1.5×10^{23} m   (3) 6.0×10^{-7} m
(2) 1.7×10^6 m   (4) 2.0×10^{-15} m

32 A radar gun can determine the speed of a moving automobile by measuring the difference in frequency between emitted and reflected radar waves. This process illustrates

(1) resonance   (3) diffraction
(2) the Doppler effect   (4) refraction

33 The diagram below shows a standing wave.

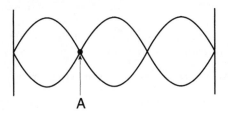

A

Point A on the standing wave is

(1) a node resulting from constructive interference
(2) a node resulting from destructive interference
(3) an antinode resulting from constructive interference
(4) an antinode resulting from destructive interference

34 An object possessing an excess of 6.0×10^6 electrons has a net charge of

(1) 2.7×10^{-26} C   (3) 3.8×10^{-13} C
(2) 5.5×10^{-24} C   (4) 9.6×10^{-13} C

35 One watt is equivalent to one

(1) N•m   (3) J•s
(2) N/m   (4) J/s

Part B–1

Answer all questions in this part.

Directions (36–50): For *each* statement or question, write on the separate answer sheet, the *number* of the word or expression that, of those given, best completes the statement or answers the question.

36 Which pair of forces acting concurrently on an object will produce the resultant of greatest magnitude?

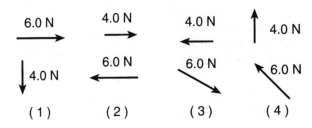

Note that question 37 has only three choices.

37 The diagram below shows a force of magnitude F applied to a mass at angle θ relative to a horizontal frictionless surface.

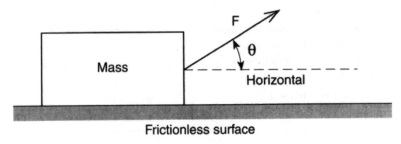

As angle θ is increased, the horizontal acceleration of the mass

(1) decreases
(2) increases
(3) remains the same

38 The mass of a high school football player is approximately

(1) 10^0 kg   (3) 10^2 kg
(2) 10^1 kg   (4) 10^3 kg

39 A constant force is used to keep a block sliding at constant velocity along a rough horizontal track. As the block slides, there could be an increase in its

(1) gravitational potential energy, only
(2) internal energy, only
(3) gravitational potential energy and kinetic energy
(4) internal energy and kinetic energy

40 A photon of which electromagnetic radiation has the most energy?

(1) ultraviolet   (3) infrared
(2) x ray   (4) microwave

41 The spring of a toy car is wound by pushing the car backward with an average force of 15 newtons through a distance of 0.50 meter. How much elastic potential energy is stored in the car's spring during this process?

(1) 1.9 J   (3) 30. J
(2) 7.5 J   (4) 56 J

42 The graph below shows the relationship between the potential difference across a metallic conductor and the electric current through the conductor at constant temperature T_1.

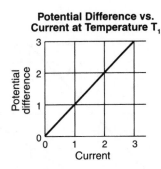

Which graph best represents the relationship between potential difference and current for the same conductor maintained at a higher constant temperature, T_2?

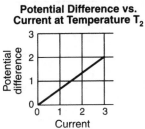
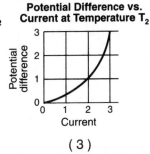
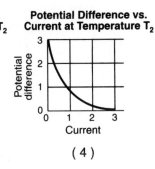

(1)   (2)   (3)   (4)

43 The diagram below shows a circuit with two resistors.

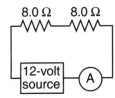

What is the reading on ammeter A?

(1) 1.3 A   (3) 3.0 A
(2) 1.5 A   (4) 0.75 A

44 The diagram below shows a bar magnet.

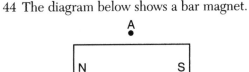

Which arrow best represents the direction of the needle of a compass placed at point A?

(1) ↑   (3) →
(2) ↓   (4) ←

45 Which graph best represents the motion of a block accelerating uniformly down an inclined plane?

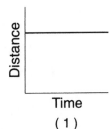
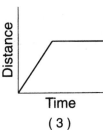
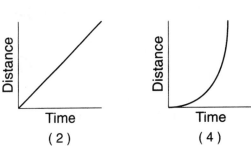

(1)

(3)

(2)

(4)

Note that question 46 has only three choices.

46 The graph below shows elongation as a function of the applied force for two springs, A and B.

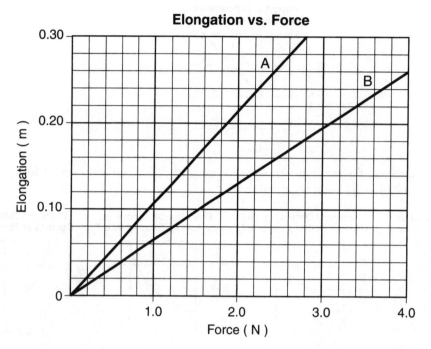

Elongation vs. Force

Compared to the spring constant for spring A, the spring constant for spring B is

(1) smaller
(2) larger
(3) the same

---

47 The diagram below represents currents in a segment of an electric circuit.

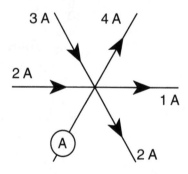

What is the reading of ammeter A?

(1) 1 A   (3) 3 A
(2) 2 A   (4) 4 A

Base your answers to questions 48 and 49 on the diagram below, which represents a light ray traveling from air to Lucite to medium Y and back into air.

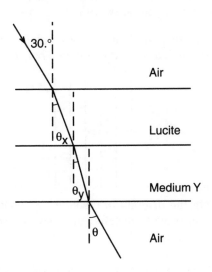

48 The sine of angle θ_x is

(1) 0.333   (3) 0.707
(2) 0.500   (4) 0.886

49 Light travels *slowest* in

(1) air, only
(2) Lucite, only
(3) medium Y, only
(4) air, Lucite, and medium Y

50 The diagram below shows two pulses traveling toward each other in a uniform medium.

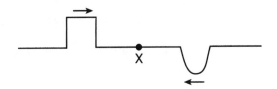

Which diagram best represents the medium when the pulses meet at point X?

(1)

(2)
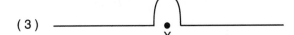

(3)

(4)
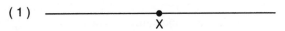

Part B-2

Answer all questions in this part.

Directions (51-62): Record your answers in the spaces provided in your answer booklet.

Base your answers to questions 51 and 52 on the information below.

An outfielder throws a baseball to the first baseman at a speed of 19.6 meters per second and an angle of 30.° above the horizontal.

51 Which pair represents the initial horizontal velocity (v_x) and initial vertical velocity (v_y) of the baseball?

(1) $v_x = 17.0$ m/s, $v_y = 9.80$ m/s
(2) $v_x = 9.80$ m/s, $v_y = 17.0$ m/s
(3) $v_x = 19.4$ m/s, $v_y = 5.90$ m/s
(4) $v_x = 19.6$ m/s, $v_y = 19.6$ m/s

52 If the ball is caught at the same height from which it was thrown, calculate the amount of time the ball was in the air. [Show all work, including the equation and substitution with units.] [2]

Base your answers to questions 53 and 54 on the circuit diagram below, which shows two resistors connected to a 24-volt source of potential difference.

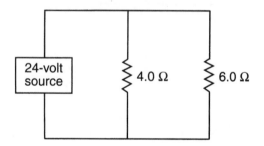

53 On the diagram *in your answer booklet,* use the appropriate circuit symbol to indicate a correct placement of a voltmeter to determine the potential difference across the circuit. [1]

54 What is the total resistance of the circuit?

(1) 0.42 Ω   (3) 5.0 Ω
(2) 2.4 Ω   (4) 10. Ω

55 The diagram below shows a plane wave passing through a small opening in a barrier.

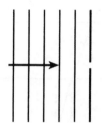

On the diagram *in your answer booklet,* sketch four wave fronts after they have passed through the barrier. [1]

56 What prevents the nucleus of a helium atom from flying apart? [1]

Base your answers to questions 57 and 58 on the information below.

A 1.00-meter length of nichrome wire with a cross-sectional area of 7.85×10^{-7} meter² is connected to a 1.50-volt battery.

57 Calculate the resistance of the wire. [Show all work, including the equation and substitution with units.] [2]

58 Determine the current in the wire. [1]

Base your answers to questions 59 through 62 on the information and table below.

In a laboratory exercise, a student kept the mass and amplitude of swing of a simple pendulum constant. The length of the pendulum was increased and the period of the pendulum was measured. The student recorded the data in the table below.

Length (meters)	Period (seconds)
0.05	0.30
0.20	0.90
0.40	1.30
0.60	1.60
0.80	1.80
1.00	2.00

Directions (59–61): Using the information in the table, construct a graph on the grid provided *in your answer booklet*, following the directions below.

59 Label each axis with the appropriate physical quantity and unit. Mark an appropriate scale on each axis. [2]

60 Plot the data points for period versus pendulum length. [1]

61 Draw the best-fit line or curve for the data graphed. [1]

_____

62 Using your graph, determine the period of a pendulum whose length is 0.25 meter. [1]

_____

Part C

Answer all questions in this part.

Directions (63–78): Record your answers in the spaces provided in your answer booklet.

Base your answers to questions 63 through 65 on the information and diagram below.

A mass, *M*, is hung from a spring and reaches equilibrium at position *B*. The mass is then raised to position *A* and released. The mass oscillates between positions *A* and *C*. [Neglect friction.]

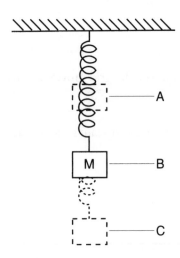

63 At which position, *A*, *B*, or *C*, is mass *M* located when the kinetic energy of the system is at a maximum? Explain your choice. [1]

64 At which position, *A*, *B*, or *C*, is mass *M* located when the gravitational potential energy of the system is at a maximum? Explain your choice. [1]

65 At which position, *A*, *B*, or *C*, is mass *M* located when the elastic potential energy of the system is at a maximum? Explain your choice. [1]

Base your answers to questions 66 through 69 on the information below.

A force of 6.0×10^{-15} newton due south and a force of 8.0×10^{-15} newton due east act concurrently on an electron, e^-.

66 On the diagram *in your answer booklet,* draw a force diagram to represent the *two* forces acting on the electron. (The electron is represented by a dot.) Use a metric ruler and the scale of 1.0 centimeter = 1.0×10^{-15} newton. Begin each vector at the dot representing the electron and label its magnitude in newtons. [2]

67 *In your answer booklet,* determine the resultant force on the electron, *graphically*. Label the resultant vector *R*. [1]

68 Determine the magnitude of the resultant vector *R*. [1]

69 Determine the angle between the resultant and the 6.0×10^{-15}-newton vector. [1]

Base your answers to questions 70 through 74 on the information below.

A force of 10. newtons toward the right is exerted on a wooden crate initially moving to the right on a horizontal wooden floor. The crate weighs 25 newtons.

70 Calculate the magnitude of the force of friction between the crate and the floor. [Show all work, including the equation and substitution with units.]   [2]

71 On the diagram *in your answer booklet,* draw and label all vertical forces acting on the crate. [1]

72 On the diagram *in your answer booklet,* draw and label all horizontal forces acting on the crate. [1]

73 What is the magnitude of the net force acting on the crate?   [1]

74 Is the crate accelerating? Explain your answer. [1]

Base your answers to questions 75 through 78 on the information below.

An electron in a hydrogen atom drops from the $n = 3$ energy level to the $n = 2$ energy level.

75 What is the energy, in electronvolts, of the emitted photon?   [1]

76 What is the energy, in joules, of the emitted photon?   [1]

77 Calculate the frequency of the emitted radiation. [Show all work, including the equation and substitution with units.]   [2]

78 Calculate the wavelength of the emitted radiation. [Show all work, including the equation and substitution with units.]   [2]

Physical Setting/PHYSICS
January 2003

ANSWER SHEET

Student .... Grade ....

Teacher .... School ....

Record your answers to Part A and Part B–1 on this answer sheet.

Part A			Part B–1	
1	13	25	36	44 ....
2	14	26	37	45 ....
3	15	27	38	46 ....
4	16	28	39	47 ....
5	17	29	40	48 ....
6	18	30	41	49 ....
7	19	31	42	50 ....
8	20	32	43	**Part B–1 Score**
9	21	33		
10	22	34		
11	23	35		
12	24	**Part A Score**		

Write your answers to Part B–2 and Part C in your answer booklet.

Physical Setting/PHYSICS
January 2003

Part	Maximum Score	Student's Score
A	35	
B–1	15	
B–2	15	
C	20	

Total Written Test Score
(Maximum Raw Score: 85)

Final Score
(From Conversion Chart)

ANSWER BOOKLET

Student . . . .

Teacher . . . .

School . . . . Grade . . . .

Answer all questions in Part B–2 and Part C. Record your answers in this booklet.

Raters' Initials:

Rater 1 . . . . Rater 2 . . . .

Part B–2

51 _____

52

53

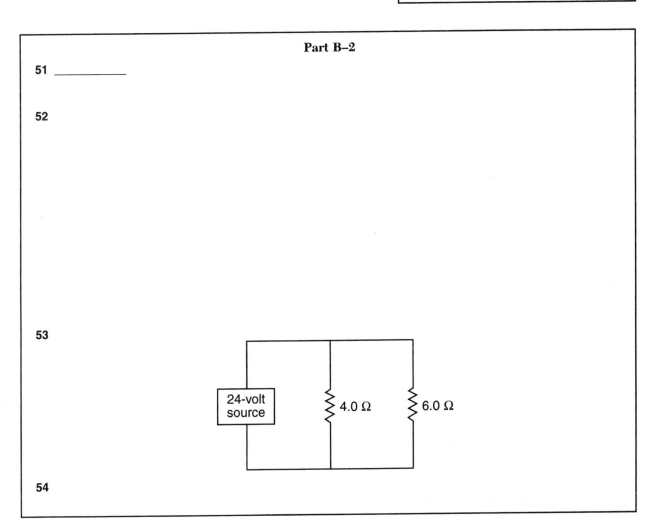

54

55

56 _____

_____

57

58 _____ **A**

Period vs. Length of Pendulum

62 _____ s

Part C

63 _____

_____

64 _____

_____

65 _____

_____

66–67

e⁻
•

N
W ← → E
S

68 _____ **N**

69 _____ °

70

71–72

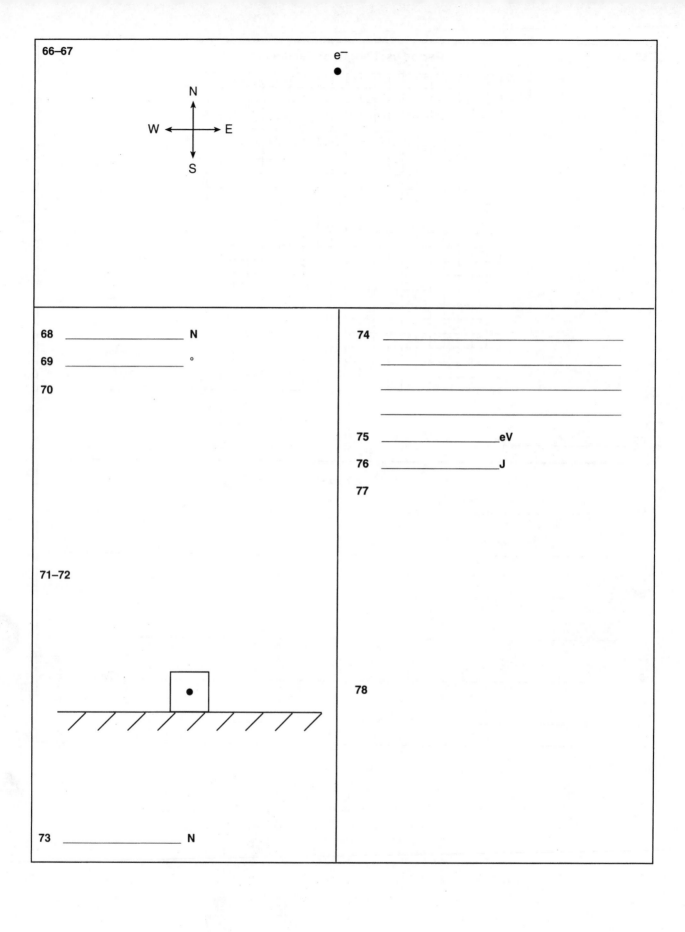

73 _____ **N**

74 _____
_____
_____
_____

75 _____ **eV**

76 _____ **J**

77

78